GCSE MATHS

The AQA Modular Course

Foundation/Intermediate Edition

David Bowles
Senior Team Leader with AQA

Paul Metcalf
Principal Moderator with AQA

Text © David Bowles and Paul Metcalf 1997, 2000, 2002
Original illustrations © Nelson Thornes Ltd 1997, 2000, 2002

First published in 1997 by:
Stanley Thornes (Publishers) Ltd
Second edition 2000

Third edition published in 2002 by:
Nelson Thornes Ltd
Delta Place
27 Bath Road
CHELTENHAM
GL53 7TH
United Kingdom

05 06 / 19 18 17 16 15 14 13

A catalogue record for this book is available from the British Library

ISBN 0 7487 6680 4

Illustrations by Peters & Zabransky and Bill Piggins
Page make-up by Tech Set Ltd

Printed and bound in Italy by Canale

CONTENTS

A message from the examiners

The AQA GCSE mathematics course (Specification B) offers a modular approach to GCSE mathematics and can be taken as a one year or two year course. The GCSE is split into five modules, three of which are assessed by a written exam and two of which are assessed by submitting a coursework task. Modules 1–4 can be taken in any order. Examinations and marking of coursework are offered three times a year; in November, March and June and the module results are reported at the end of each module so that you can see how well you are doing.

THE MODULES

	Title Method of assessment	Weighting
Module 1	**Handling data (statistics)** One 50 minute written paper Section A (25 minutes) with a calculator Section B (25 minutes) without a calculator	11%
Module 2	**Handling data task** One coursework task (handling data is covered in module 1)	10%
Module 3	**Number** One 80 minute written paper Section A (40 minutes) with a calculator Section B (40 minutes) without a calculator	19%
Module 4	**Investigative task** One coursework task on Number, Algebra or Shape, Space and Measures	10%
Module 5	**Terminal Module** Two 75 minute papers (60 minute at the Foundation tier) Paper 1 without a calculator Paper 2 with a calculator	50%

GRADING

Each module has three tiers of entry and it is possible to enter different modules at different tiers

Expected grades	Tier of entry	Available grades
E, F & G	Foundation tier	D, E, F & G
C & D	Intermediate tier	B, C, D & E
A★, A & B	Higher tier	A★, A, B & C

Your final GCSE grade is awarded after you sit module 5. You can sit different modules at different tiers but remember that half your marks come from the terminal tier so that is quite important.

If you are not happy with your GCSE grade, you can decline your GCSE and resit modules to get a better grade. Each module can be re-sat once and your best grade will count. You don't need to resit the module at the same level that you originally sat it and there is no time limit on when you can resit the module.

For modules 1 and 3 the calculator paper (Section A) is issued first. When the time is up for this paper you will be asked to put your calculator under your seat and you will be given the non-calculator paper (Section B). For module 5 the calculator and non-calculator papers are done in different sittings.

You are expected to have the following equipment:

- pens
- sharp pencil
- pencil sharpener
- eraser
- ruler
- protractor
- compasses
- a scientific calculator (for calculator paper)

The written papers will also include a formula sheet. It is helpful to familiarise yourself with these formulae before the exam, although you will not need to learn them.

The following hints should help you when undertaking the written papers:

- read the question carefully
- if you get stuck, miss out the question and come back to it later
- show your working and write down any calculations you do
- make sure your answer is reasonable and sensible
- when you correct an answer don't cross anything out until you have a better answer
- when you have finished, go back and check you have answered all of the questions

You can prepare for the written papers by attempting the sample papers in Chapters 4, 9 and 16. Practice papers are also available from the exam board (see the end of the Introduction). Remember practice makes perfect!

COURSEWORK

You are required to complete two coursework tasks (modules 2 and 4) as part of the GCSE mathematics course. Both coursework tasks can be set and marked by your tutor, set and marked by the board or you can do one tutor-marked and one board-marked task.

Coursework allows you to be tested on your ability to think statistically (module 2) and mathematically (module 4). There is no time limit specified by the examination board although your own centre may wish to set its own deadline. Coursework from other subject areas (for example, statistics, geography, design and technology, etc.) is acceptable, although, such coursework will need to be matched to the given assessment criteria.

Marks for the data handling task (module 2) are awarded for each of the following areas:

- specifying the problem and planning
- collecting, processing and representing data
- interpreting and discussing the results.

Further information on the handling data coursework task can be found in Chapter 5.

Marks for the investigative task (module 4) are awarded in each of the following areas:

- making and monitoring decisions to solve problems
- communicating mathematically
- developing skills of mathematical reasoning.

Further information on the investigative task coursework can be found in Chapter 10.

INFORMATION

For further information about the content of the modules (the specification), example material and past papers, contact the board at:

> Publications
> Assessment and Qualifications Alliance
> Aldon House
> 39 Heald Grove
> Rusholme
> Manchester
> M14 4NA

by email at publications@aqa.org.uk or visit their website at www.aqa.org.uk.

HOW TO USE THIS BOOK

The book is divided into four sections:

Section 1 Handling data (module 1) including handling data coursework (module 2)

Section 2 Number (module 3) including investigative coursework (module 4)

Section 3 Algebra (module 5)

Section 4 Shape, space and measures (module 5)

Each section is divided into a number of chapters and each chapter is further divided into a series of topics. The first topic in most chapters is called **Recap** and covers material from the Foundation tier, which you need to know before you can start the chapter. The rest of the chapter will allow you to get a grade B or C at Intermediate tier.

Each topic includes a number of **practice** questions which you should try to complete before moving on to further work. These practice questions are designed to consolidate work as well as to give you a flavour of examination-type questions. In some chapters, the questions are split into calculator and non-calculator questions to allow you to practise for the written papers. **Answers** to the practice questions, along with brief explanations where neessary, can be found at the back of the book. When you have completed a **section** and are happy that you can do the practice questions, you can then have a go at **the sample exam paper** for this module, which can be found at the end of the section (the module 5 paper is at the end of section 4). Answers and the mark scheme are provided at the end of each paper.

Each chapter concludes with a **Summary**. This is included to summarise the work of the chapter and highlights areas that you need to know. You can use the summary to remind yourself of the work of the chapter or to identify areas for further consideration if you have decided that you do not need to study the whole chapter. You can also use the summary for quick revision before the exam.

Remember that there is no substitute for practice so try and do as many past papers as you can before the exam.

GOOD LUCK!

Acknowledgements

The publishers would like to thank the following for permission to reproduce copyright material:

Cover photo: Pyramid Entrance to The Musée du Louvre, Nik Wheeler, Corbis

Page 374: Simon Burt\Apex

Page 443: Digital Vision (NT)

SECTION ONE
Handling data (Module 1)

CONTENTS

CHAPTER 1

Collecting and representing data

In this chapter you will need to:
▸ know the difference between quantitative and qualitative data
▸ know the difference between discrete and continuous data

Quantitative and qualitative data

Quantitative data is data that has numerical values and measures quantities.
Some examples of quantitative data are; length, weight, capacity,….

Qualitative data is data that does not have numerical values but measures qualities.
Some examples of qualitative data are; colour, brightness, taste,….

Discrete and continuous data

Discrete data is data that can only take particular values such as whole numbers.
Some examples of discrete data are; the number of students in the class, the number of cars passing a point during 20 minutes, etc.…

Continuous data is data that can take all values within a given range.
Some examples of continuous data are; the heights of students in the class, the length of cars passing a point during 20 minutes, etc.…

To help you to tell the difference between discrete and continuous it might be helpful to consider that:

● people's shoe sizes are discrete but the lengths of people's feet are continuous and the costs of sending parcels are discrete but the weights of parcels are continuous.

PRACTICE 1.1.1

1 For each of the following, state whether they are quantitative or qualitative:
   a the height of people in a class,
   b the colour of cars in a car park,
   c the sweetness of different orange juices,
   d the lengths of pencils in a pencil case,
   e the number of students in different classes,
   f the number of leaves on different types of trees,
   g the brightness of light bulbs in six rooms,
   h the age of people in a youth club,
   i the musical ability of students in a class.

2   For each of the following, state whether they are continuous or discrete:
   a   the height of people in a class,
   b   the time taken by runners to complete a race,
   c   the number of matches in a sample of matchboxes,
   d   the lengths of pencils in a pencil case,
   e   the number of students in different classes,
   f   the number of leaves on different trees,
   g   the shoe sizes of people at a party,
   h   the age of people in a youth club.

Primary and secondary data

When we collect data for a statistical study or investigation it is either **primary** or **secondary data.** Primary data is 'first hand' data – that which you collect yourself. It has the advantage that it is collected exactly for your needs but the disadvantage is that it may take a long time to collect and/or be expensive. Secondary data is 'second hand' data – that which has already been collected as part of another statistical investigation from which you are going to **extract,** or take, the bits you need. Official government statistics are a good example of secondary data. The advantage is that the data has already been collected and is therefore easy and cheap to obtain but a disadvantage is that you may not know how the information was collected and it may affect the results of your study, making it **biased** (See Topic 1.2).

Useful sources of secondary data are to be found in government departments, professional institutes, businesses and in market research organisations.

Population

We have looked at data. Now we look at where the data comes from. As an example, imagine a family owning three cars; a red Toyota Corolla, a white Toyota Avensis and a green Ford Orion. Each of those cars belong to many different **populations**. A population is a group of objects or people which may be studied.

All three cars are members of the population **'all cars'**. We could also say all three are members of the population **'all powered vehicles'** and this population would include motorbikes and planes etc. Two of the cars are members of the population **'Toyota cars'**. A different two are members of the population **'Red cars'**. One car is a member of the population **'Ford cars'** or **'Ford Orion cars'** or **'Toyota Corolla cars'** or **'Toyota Avensis cars'**.

Samples

When we want to study a population we may not be able to investigate every member of it. A population can be **finite**, for example, all occupants of a particular street, so you could study all of them, or it can be **infinite**, i.e. one where it is impossible to know every single member of it, for example, the total number of stars in the universe. We can only guess at the exact number. If we need to study a large or an **infinite** population we have to study a **sample** of items drawn from this population.

The advantages of **sampling** are that it is cheaper and quicker than studying every member of the population. Sometimes sampling would be destructive, i.e. it would destroy the population, for example, tasting apples to measure sweetness or seeing how long a light bulb will last. In cases like these we HAVE to sample.

We must be careful, though, that the size of our sample is:

a a good indicator of the population as a whole and is truly representative,
b large enough so that the results we get from our investigation can be reasonably assumed to be true to the whole population,
c properly collected.

The following methods of sampling are explained below.

- random sampling,
- systematic sampling,
- stratified sampling,
- quota sampling,
- convenience sampling.

Random sampling

In **random sampling**, each member of the population has an equal chance of being selected. The simplest way to do this would be to give every member of the population a number and then choose the numbers randomly using random number tables or a computer. The NationaL Lottery is an example of random sampling.

Systematic sampling

Systematic sampling is the same as random sampling except that there is some system involved in choosing the member of the population to be sampled. Such a system might include numbering each member of the population and then choosing every tenth number to form the sample.

Stratified sampling

In **stratified sampling**, each member of the population is divided into some particular group or category. Within each group, a random sample is selected so that the sample size is proportional to the size of that group or category in the population as a whole.

For example, in a college where 55% of the students are female and 45% are male, then a representative sample of the students in the college should also include 55% females and 45% males.

Quota sampling

In **quota sampling**, a certain number of the population are chosen with specific characteristics which are fixed beforehand. Quota sampling is very popular in **market research** where the interviewers are given clear instructions about the people to be interviewed. Such instructions might include the requirement that there are as many men as women or twice as many adults as children or that the sample should include 15 shoppers and 12 commuters, etc.

Convenience sampling

Convenience sampling or **opportunity sampling** is a sampling method which involves choosing the first people that come along. Such a method is far from random and this fact should be highlighted in any such work undertaken for coursework purposes.

Bias

If data for a statistical study is not collected properly the results of the survey would be **biased**. Bias comes when any data we collect gives the wrong influence on our survey and stops the results truly representing the population. We can get biased data by:

a collecting a **non-random sample**. We can never be sure that we have a truly random sample but we do our best to make it as random as possible. For example we may pick 13 cards 'at random' from a full pack but if the pack is not shuffled first the sample will be non-random.

b **not sampling from the complete population**. For example, choosing a sample from the telephone directory for an area means that those who do not own a telephone are not included in the population. It would not provide good data for a study of incomes because usually those without telephones are not as well off as those who have telephones.

c being **'subjective'** in collecting our data. We must never let personal preference influence data collection. For example, talking only to young people, because we do not like older people, in a survey of eating habits would produce biased data.

d **non-response** to a questionnaire. Usually only people who have a particular interest in the study would reply. For example, a postal questionnaire sent to people who have travelled with a particular train company. Those replying are usually those who have had only very good or very bad experiences while travelling with that company.

e using **alternative data**. For example, in a survey when the sampling method chosen specifically needs the responses from someone between 40 and 50, talking to a 20 year old person because someone of the right age is not available at the time would bias the results.

Designing and carrying out a handling data coursework study

Before you carry out a piece of statistical research you must plan it very carefully.

1 Decide exactly what your study is about. This is not as easy as it sounds. It must:
   a be about something that you have some knowledge of and interest in,
   b give you the opportunity to show your statistical skills,
   c not be too complicated to allow you to finish it in time.

2 Decide on the exact title, or question asked. For example, it could be something like 'What effect has the movement of the school on to a combined site had on students?' or 'Is there any correlation between the marks obtained by your own class in Mathematics and English?'

3 Decide exactly who, or what, the population is for your investigation. You cannot think about methods of collecting data until you know where it is coming from.

4 Make a note of any special factors that may affect your investigation. These might be:
   a What sort of investigation do I need to carry out? Should it be:
      i whole population or sample? What sort of sample method would be best? What sample size?
      ii direct observation?
      iii a questionnaire? How do I deal with non-response?
      iv a controlled experiment?
      v data logging?
   b What sort of data do I need to collect? Should it be:
      i taken from completely primary observations?
      ii taken from completely secondary observations? From which?
      iii a mixture of both?
      iv discrete or continuous, qualitative or quantitative?
      v ungrouped, grouped or grouped frequency? (See Topic 1.4)

c How easy is it to collect my data?

d When is the best time to collect data?

e How can my collected data solve my problem? What analysis is needed? Do I need:

   i measures of central tendency i.e. means, modes, medians?

   ii measures of spread – i.e. range, interquartile range, standard deviation?

   iii correlation?

   iv time series and moving averages?

f What accuracy do I need in my data? Nearest unit, grouped class intervals?

g Are there any special or exceptional cases which need to be accounted for?

h What assumptions can I make, or not, from the data when I have analysed it?

i How can I avoid bias in my data?

5 When you have designed the study you must collect and process the data. This will include designing data collection sheets (see example below), representing the data in the most suitable diagrammatic forms (see Topic 1.5).

6 When you have done this you must analyse the data, form conclusions and draw conclusions to the original problem stated (see Chapter 2).

Sample data collection sheet

NOTE
The marks in the last nine columns are *tally marks*. See page 12 for more information about these.

Data recording sheet											
Numbers and colours of cars passing my home											
DATE	DAY	TIME INTERVAL	BLACK	BLUE	GOLD	GREEN	RED	SILVER	WHITE	YELLOW	OTHER
25 Jan	Thur	0900 1000	II	卌 卌 卌 II	III	卌 卌 I	卌 卌 卌 IIII	IIII	卌 卌 卌 III	III	卌
		1000 1100	I	卌 卌 卌 卌 II	IIII	卌 卌 卌 I	卌 卌 卌 卌 I	IIII	卌 卌 卌 卌	卌 II	卌 II
		1100 1200	III	卌 卌 卌 卌 II	III	卌 卌 卌 IIII	卌 卌 卌 卌 卌 卌 III	卌	卌 卌 卌 卌 卌 III	卌 I	卌 III
		1200 1300									

PRACTICE 1.2.1

1 A college wishes to undertake a survey on the part-time employment of its students. Explain how you would take:
 a a random sample of 100 students,
 b a stratified sample of 100 students.

2 Explain how you would use the electoral roll to obtain a simple random sample.

3 Explain why each of the following might not produce a truly representative sample:
 a selecting people at random outside a food store,
 b selecting every tenth name from the electoral register starting with M,
 c selecting names from the telephone directory.

4 In a telephone poll conducted one morning, 25 people were asked whether they regularly used the bus to get to work. Give three reasons why this sample might not be truly representative.

5 In an opinion poll, 500 men in Cambridge were asked how they intended to vote in the General Election.
 a Give three reasons why this is an unreliable way of predicting the outcome of the General Election.
 b Give three ways in which the opinion poll might be improved.

6 The populations of three villages are given below:

Little Whitton	840
Marchwoode	240
Newtonabbey	720

The local councillor wishes to undertake a survey and chooses 100 people from each village.
 a Explain why this might not be the most appropriate sampling method.
 b How could the councillor select a more representative sample of 300 people from the three villages?

The following survey methods are explained:

- observation,
- interviewing,
- questionnaires.

Observation

This method involves collecting information by observation. It might include **participant observation** where the observer participates in the activity, or **systematic observation** where observation is undertaken without the participants knowing.

Interviewing

Interviewing involves a conversation between two or more people where the interviewing can be **formal** or **informal**. In formal interviews, the questions asked will follow a strict form whereas in informal interviews, the questions asked follow some general form with opportunities to change the order or the way in which the questions are presented.

Questionnaires

The use of a questionnaire is by far the most common survey method and is usually undertaken as a postal questionnaire. The advantage of a postal questionnaire is that it is relatively cheap to distribute and can involve large numbers of people. The disadvantage of postal questionnaires is the poor response rate and the inability to follow up questions set.

In designing a good questionnaire, it is important that it should be:

- simple, short, clear and precise,
- attractively laid out and quick to complete.

The questions should:

- be free from bias and not personal or offensive,
- be written in a sensible language for the respondent,
- be related to the work being investigated,
- give clear instructions on how to respond.

Worked Examples

The following examples illustrate poor question design:

Given that drinking is bad for you, how much do you drink in a day?

The question is biased as it expresses the questioner's own opinion and it does not explain what is meant by drinking – drinking water is not bad for you!

> **NOTE**
>
> The use of telephone interviewing is becoming increasingly common although this method is not very successful as people are generally wary about such interviewing techniques. Recent developments also allow you to complete questionnaires on the internet although many of these can be time consuming and response rates are low.

How often do you have a wash?

The question is clearly personal and almost certainly offensive to some people. Answers received would also be suspect as people are unlikely to answer the question truthfully.

How many hours of television do you watch?

The question is difficult to answer as it does not say over what period of time and might therefore provide a variety of answers.

Do you or do you not listen to the radio?

The question is badly composed and does not really make any sense.

Pilot survey

Before carrying out any questionnaire or survey, it is important that you are completely satisfied with the way it has been written. It is often useful to undertake a small scale *dummy run* to find any likely problems and highlight areas needing further clarification. This dummy run is called a **pilot survey** and an analysis of the data received should be used to improve the questionnaire or survey before it is undertaken properly.

PRACTICE 1.3.1

1 Name two different types of questions which should be avoided when designing a questionnaire.

2 Give two advantages of undertaking a pilot survey.

3 The following three questions about television viewing habits are included on a questionnaire:
 a How many hours have you watched the television during the past two months?
 b How much money do you earn in a year?
 c Do you or do you not watch the news programmes?
 Criticise each of these questions.

4 Criticise each of the following questions and suggest alternatives to find out the information.
 a What do you think about our new improved fruit juice?
 b How much do you earn?

   c Do you or do you not agree with a new bypass?
   d Given that smoking is bad for you, how many cigarettes do you smoke a day?
   e Would you prefer not to sit in a non-smoking area?
   f How often do you have a shower?

5 The following appears on a questionnaire for students at a college:

How much money do you earn?

Less than £10	☐
Between £11 and £20	☐
More than £20	☐

Write down three criticisms of this question.

6 A group of students are considering the possibility of producing a school magazine. Design a questionnaire which might be useful in helping them to decide whether to go ahead with the project.

1.4 TABULATING DATA

Raw data

Raw data is any information which has been collected by some method but has not been organised in any way.

Tally chart

A tally chart is a useful way of collecting or collating information. A tally chart consists of a series of tallies which are grouped into fives as follows:

$$
\begin{aligned}
\text{llll} \quad &= 4 \\
\text{ЖН} \quad &= 5 \\
\text{ЖН l} \quad &= 6 \\
\text{ЖН ЖН} &= 10, \text{ etc.}
\end{aligned}
$$

> **NOTE**
> The word *frequency* is used to denote the number of times an event happens or occurs.

Frequency distribution

A **frequency distribution** can be constructed from a tally chart by totalling the tallies and adding a further column for these totals or frequencies.

Worked Example

Construct a frequency distribution for the following raw data which shows the number of breakfasts served in a restaurant during the month of May.

15   19   18   16   16   19   20   16
17   16   15   20   19   18   15   13
20   15   16   19   21   20   19   21
12   17   13   16   18   23   17

The frequency distribution for this information will look like this:

Breakfasts	Tallies	Frequency
12	I	1
13	II	2
14		0
15	IIII	4
16	IIII I	6
17	III	3
18	III	3
19	IIII	5
20	IIII	4
21	II	2
22		0
23	I	1
		31

The total frequency serves as a useful check.

NOTE
After collating the results we usually write the frequency distribution without the tallies.

Breakfasts	Frequency
12	1
13	2
14	0
15	4
16	6
17	3
18	3
19	5
20	4
21	2
22	0
23	1

or else

Breakfasts	12	13	14	15	16	17	18	19	20	21	22	23
Frequency	1	2	0	4	6	3	3	5	4	2	0	1

PRACTICE 1.4.1

1   The following information gives the marks obtained in a test for 30 pupils in a class. Use tally marks to draw up a frequency table of this information.

8	7	6	8	9	10	7	5	4	10
6	8	7	9	9	4	8	9	7	6
10	9	5	6	7	5	9	8	8	7

2   The following information shows how 50 people paid for their goods at a certain store. Use tally marks to draw up a frequency table of this information.

cheque	visa	switch	storecard	cash	cash
switch	cheque	visa	cash	cash	cash
cheque	storecard	storecard	cash	cheque	cash
visa	cheque	cash	cash	visa	cheque
switch	cash	cheque	switch	visa	cash
storecard	cash	cheque	cash	cash	visa
cash	cheque	switch	cheque	cash	visa
switch	cash	cheque	storecard	cash	cheque
visa	switch				

3   The following information shows the colours of cars in a car park one lunchtime. Use tally marks to draw up a frequency table of this information.

red	yellow	red	red	blue	blue	green	red
green	red	blue	blue	white	blue	white	yellow
green	blue	blue	red	red	white	green	blue
blue	yellow	white	white	red	blue	blue	white
green	yellow	red	red	white	blue	green	blue

4   The following information shows how 60 people travel to college each day. Use tally marks to draw up a frequency table of this information.

bus	train	walk	cycle	walk	walk
bus	train	train	car	walk	cycle
walk	bus	train	walk	cycle	train
walk	bus	train	bus	train	car
walk	cycle	walk	train	train	walk
bus	train	train	car	walk	bus
walk	walk	walk	car	cycle	bus
train	car	walk	train	bus	walk
walk	bus	cycle	walk	cycle	bus
train	walk	walk	cycle	cycle	train

Grouped frequency distribution

Sometimes it is easier to put the data into a series of groups or classes. The groups or classes into which the data are arranged are called **class intervals**.

Worked Example

For the previous example we might group the data in a number of ways as shown:

Breakfasts	Frequency
12 – 13	3
14 – 15	4
16 – 17	9
18 – 19	8
20 – 21	6
22 – 23	1

or else

Breakfasts	Frequency
12 – 14	3
15 – 17	13
18 – 20	12
21 – 23	3

or else

Breakfasts	Frequency
12 – 15	7
16 – 19	17
20 – 23	7

Notice that, as the number of groups or classes decrease, so the information about the distribution of frequencies becomes more and more lost. Unfortunately, the more the classes, the more the work required to analyse the information, so it is important to strike a balance.

In general, it is helpful to divide the data into approximately 6 to 10 groups or classes as shown in the following worked example.

Worked Example

The following information gives the lengths of 50 leaves measured to the nearest millimetre. Using suitable class intervals, construct a frequency distribution for this information.

41	30	39	31	13	21	42	35	26	34
36	33	31	11	30	32	16	17	41	36
25	35	24	21	26	14	34	47	22	40
29	33	18	27	18	38	20	39	30	33
28	43	37	28	23	38	32	20	31	25

From the figures we can see that the smallest length is 11 mm and the largest length is 47 mm giving us a range of 36 mm.

If we have 10 classes then each class interval would be $\frac{36}{10} = 3.6$ mm, with 8 classes then each class interval would be $\frac{36}{8} = 4.5$ mm and with 6 classes then each class interval would be $\frac{36}{6} = 6$ mm.

Common sense suggests that class sizes should be whole numbers so we should choose easily identifiable class intervals such as:

10–14, 15–19, 20–24,…

or   11–15, 16–20, 21–25,…
or   10–15, 16–20, 21–25,…
or   11–16, 17–22, 23–28,…
or   10–16, 17–23, 24–30,…
or   11–17, 18–24, 25–31,…

Any of these series of class intervals can be used although the 11–15, 16–20, 21–25, 26–30, 31–35,… class intervals would be easier to work with. Constructing a frequency distribution for this information:

Length (mm)	Tally	Frequency
11–15	III	3
16–20	IIII I	6
21–25	IIII II	7
26–30	IIII IIII	9
31–35	IIII IIII II	12
36–40	IIII III	8
41–45	IIII	4
46–50	I	1
		50

The total frequency, again, serves as a useful check.

Remember the following terms:

Class interval

Class interval is used to refer to the groups or classes into which the data is split. The class interval is chosen by considering the range of the whole data and dividing this into convenient class intervals.

Class limits

The class limits are the values given in each class interval. In the class interval 11–15, the class limits are 11 and 15. We usually say that the lower class limit is 11 and the upper class limit is 15. For the class interval 16–20, the lower class limit is 16 and the upper class limit is 20.

Class boundaries

In the previous distribution, the first class interval (11–15) will have leaves with lengths ranging from 10.5 to 15.5 mm since the lengths are given to the nearest millimetre. Similarly, the second class interval (16–20) will have leaves with lengths 15.5 to 20.5 mm.

The boundaries of the classes are 10.5 mm, 15.5 mm, 20.5 mm, etc. The first class interval has class boundaries of 10.5 mm and 15.5 mm. The lower class boundary is 10.5 mm and 15.5 mm is the upper class boundary.

For the second class interval the lower class boundary is 15.5 mm and the upper class boundary is 20.5 mm. The upper class boundary of one class interval is the same as the lower class boundary of the next class interval.

NOTE

The class width is sometimes referred to as the class length or the class size.

Class width

The class width is the **difference** between the upper and lower class boundaries. For the data in the previous distribution all of the class widths are the same and the class width equals $15.5 - 10.5 = 5$ mm (or $20.5 - 15.5 = 5$ mm, …etc.).

PRACTICE 1.4.2

1 Draw up a grouped frequency table for the information which shows the number of calls made. Use class intervals of 0–4, 5–9, 10–14, 15–19, etc.

10	5	3	8	9	4	12	25	12
13	18	7	14	18	22	11	5	9
20	20	26	17	15	6	3	22	19

2 Draw up a grouped frequency table for the following information which shows approximations to the value of π. Use class intervals of width 0.05 starting at 3.00.

3.08	3.12	3.16	3.18	3.15	3.14	3.13	3.22	3.01	3.06	3.21
3.17	3.13	3.10	3.09	3.12	3.07	3.14	3.12	3.09	3.15	3.16

3 Copy and complete the frequency table for the following information which shows the annual wages for 50 jobs advertised in a newspaper one weekend.

£26 850	£34 500	£33 000	£44 500	£32 750	£38 850
£38 650	£42 000	£55 000	£32 000	£33 850	£44 500
£36 500	£31 500	£26 500	£35 000	£46 500	£44 000
£35 500	£43 000	£26 000	£28 000	£54 000	£33 500
£52 600	£49 500	£47 500	£36 500	£45 000	£26 500
£38 500	£36 250	£41 600	£50 000	£37 950	£45 000
£32 200	£25 500	£49 000	£41 500	£52 000	£33 500
£38 000	£31 500	£37 950	£37 500	£38 700	£40 000
£37 200	£26 600				

Wages	Tally	Frequency
£25 000–£29 999		
£30 000–£34 999		
£35 000–£39 999		
£40 000–£44 999		
£45 000–£49 999		
£50 000–£54 999		
£55 000–£59 999		

4 Copy and complete the frequency table for the following information which shows the length of time (measured in minutes to the nearest minute) it takes for 40 workers to travel to work one morning.

```
23   14   16   33   44   25   36   38   22   24
33   41   28   24   48   16   37   32   30   42
25   20   45   36   39   26   18   22   14   23
29   25   22   38   36   20   24   26   41   29
```

Time (mins)	Tally	Frequency
$10 \leqslant t < 15$		
$15 \leqslant t < 20$		
$20 \leqslant t < 25$		
$25 \leqslant t < 30$		
$30 \leqslant t < 35$		
$35 \leqslant t < 40$		
$40 \leqslant t < 45$		
$45 \leqslant t < 50$		

1.5 PICTORIAL REPRESENTATIONS

NOTE
Cumulative Frequency Diagrams are fully discussed in Topic 2.4 'Measures of spread'.

It is often a good idea to show data pictorially or in a diagram. There are a variety of ways to do this but you should make sure that the ones you use are appropriate to the type of data being represented.

The following displays will be considered:

- pictograms,
- bar charts,
- stem and leaf diagrams,
- line graphs,
- pie charts,
- frequency polygons,
- scatter graphs.

Pictograms

A **pictogram** is a simple way of showing data by using pictures (or some other diagram) to show the data. A pictogram must have a **key** to tell the reader what individual pictures stand for.

The advantage of the pictogram is that it is easy to draw and has a strong visual impact. A disadvantage is that it can only be used to show a few variables.

Worked Example

The following distribution shows the number of people entering an exhibition on different days of the week. Show this information as a pictogram.

Day	Number
Thursday	22
Friday	27
Saturday	33
Sunday	21

The information can be shown as a pictogram:

	Number of people at an exhibition
Thursday	𝄃𝄃𝄃𝄃𝄃𝄃𝄃𝄃𝄃𝄃𝄃𝄃𝄃𝄃𝄃𝄃𝄃𝄃𝄃𝄃𝄃𝄃
Friday	𝄃𝄃𝄃𝄃𝄃𝄃𝄃𝄃𝄃𝄃𝄃𝄃𝄃𝄃𝄃𝄃𝄃𝄃𝄃𝄃𝄃𝄃𝄃𝄃𝄃𝄃𝄃
Saturday	𝄃𝄃𝄃𝄃𝄃𝄃𝄃𝄃𝄃𝄃𝄃𝄃𝄃𝄃𝄃𝄃𝄃𝄃𝄃𝄃𝄃𝄃𝄃𝄃𝄃𝄃𝄃𝄃𝄃𝄃𝄃𝄃𝄃
Sunday	𝄃𝄃𝄃𝄃𝄃𝄃𝄃𝄃𝄃𝄃𝄃𝄃𝄃𝄃𝄃𝄃𝄃𝄃𝄃𝄃𝄃

Key ⚲ = 1 person

or else allowing ⚲ = 2 people, then:

	Number of people at an exhibition
Thursday	(11 figures)
Friday	(13 + half figures)
Saturday	(16 + half figures)
Sunday	(10 + half figures)

In this pictogram,

⌇ = 1 person and

⚲ = 2 people

or else allowing ⚲ = 4 people, then:

	Number of people at an exhibition
Thursday	(5 + half figures)
Friday	(7 figures)
Saturday	(8 + half figures)
Sunday	(5 + half figures)

In this pictogram,

⌇ = 1 person

⌇ = 2 people

⌇ = 3 people and

⚲ = 4 people

PRACTICE 1.5.1

1 The following distribution shows the number of people queuing at a local post office at different times during the same day. Show this information as a pictogram.

Time	Number
9.30 am	4
11.30 am	1
1.30 pm	9
3.30 pm	4
5.30 pm	2

2 The following distribution shows the number of people in the local library at midday on different days of the week. Show this information as a pictogram.

Day	Number
Monday	19
Tuesday	13
Wednesday	17
Thursday	27
Friday	33
Saturday	41

3 The following distribution shows the sales of different flavoured ice creams at a park one day. Show this information as a pictogram.

Flavour	Frequency
Strawberry	51
Vanilla	77
Chocolate	38
Other	14

4 Draw a pictogram to illustrate the frequency distribution found in question 3 of Practice 1.4.1 on page 14.

5 Draw a pictogram to illustrate the frequency distribution found in question 4 of Practice 1.4.1 on page 14.

Bar charts

Bar charts are a very common way of showing data. They use bars (horizontal or vertical) to represent the number or frequency of the data. Both axes of the bar chart should be labelled to help the reader interpret the chart.

The advantage of the bar chart is that it makes visual comparison easy but a disadvantage is that only simple information can be shown.

Worked Examples

1   The following bar chart shows the average price of a house in different areas.

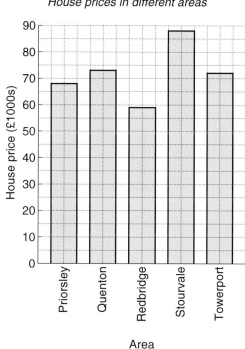

House prices in different areas

a   What was the average price of a house in Quenton?
b   What was the cheapest average house price?
c   Where is the most expensive average house price to be found?
d   Where was the average house price £68 000?
e   Which two areas had average house prices which were roughly the same?

Using the chart:
a   The average price of a house in Quenton was £73 000.
b   The cheapest average house price was £59 000.
c   The most expensive average house price can be found in Stourvale.
d   The average house price was £68 000 in Priorsley.
e   The two areas which had average house prices roughly the same were Quenton and Towerport.

2   The following grouped frequency table shows the heights of 30 rosemary plants to the nearest centimetre.

Height (cm)	11–15	16–20	21–25	26–30	31–35
Frequency	4	7	11	6	2

Draw a bar chart to illustrate this information.

In the case of continuous data it is important to make sure that the bars are drawn at the class boundaries, hence, in this example, the bars are drawn at 10.5–15.5, 15.5–20.5, 20.5–25.5,… etc. as follows

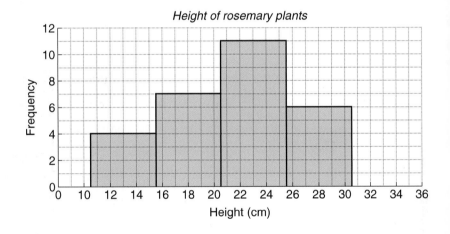

Compound bar charts

The compound bar chart is similar to the bar chart except that the bars are replaced by a series of different bars representing different aspects of the data.

The advantage of the compound bar chart is that it allows information to be compared in a variety of ways. A disadvantage is that only a few items can be included.

Worked Example

The following chart shows the sales of new and second-hand cars during the first week of March over a period of 4 years.

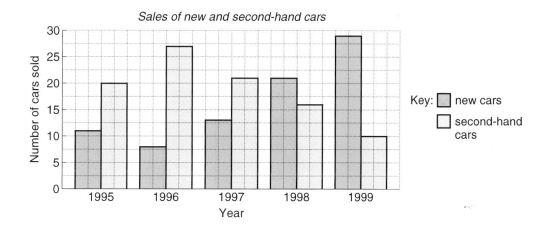

a In what year were the most new cars sold?

b In what year were the most second-hand cars sold?

c How many new cars were sold in 1998?

d How many second-hand cars were sold in 1996?

e How many cars were sold altogether in 1997?

Using the chart:

a The most new cars were sold in 1999.

b The most second-hand cars were sold in 1996.

c 21 new cars were sold in 1998.

d 27 second-hand cars were sold in 1996.

e 34 cars (13 new and 21 second-hand) were sold altogether in 1997.

Component bar charts

NOTE

Component bar charts are also sometimes called *composite* bar charts or *sectional* bar charts.

The component bar chart is used to show how an individual item can be split into a series of components. The advantage of the component bar chart is that it allows you to see how an item is divided into its constituent parts. A disadvantage is that only a few items can be included.

Worked Example

The component bar chart represents the number of different airline tickets sold for a flight from London to Manchester on different days of the same week.

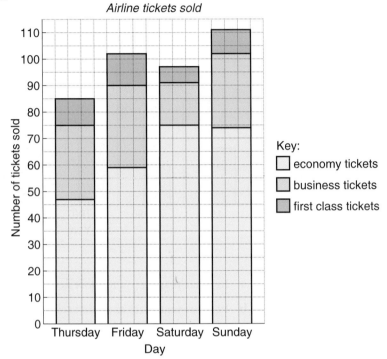

Airline tickets sold

a   Calculate the total number of each type of ticket sold over the four days.
b   Express this information as a **percentage component bar chart**.

a   The number of economy tickets $= 47 + 59 + 75 + 74 = 255$
    The number of business tickets $= 28 + 31 + 16 + 28 = 103$
    The number of first tickets $= 10 + 12 + 6 + 9 = 37$

b   Writing this information as a percentage component bar chart we need to work out the percentage of economy, business and first class tickets for each day.

Total number of tickets for Thursday $= 47 + 28 + 10 = 85$

Percentage of economy tickets $= \frac{47}{85} \times 100$ $= 55.3\%$

Percentage of business tickets $= \frac{28}{85} \times 100$ $= 32.9\%$

Percentage of first class tickets $= \frac{10}{85} \times 100$ $= 11.8\%$

Total number of tickets for Friday $= 59 + 31 + 12 = 102$

Percentage of economy tickets $= \frac{59}{102} \times 100$ $= 57.8\%$

Percentage of business tickets $= \frac{31}{102} \times 100$ $= 30.4\%$

Percentage of first class tickets $= \frac{12}{102} \times 100$ $= 11.8\%$

Total number of tickets for Saturday $= 75 + 16 + 6 = 97$

Percentage of economy tickets $= \frac{75}{97} \times 100 \quad = 77.3\%$

Percentage of business tickets $= \frac{16}{97} \times 100 \quad = 16.5\%$

Percentage of first class tickets $= \frac{6}{97} \times 100 \quad = 6.2\%$

Total number of tickets for Sunday $= 74 + 28 + 9 = 111$

Percentage of economy tickets $= \frac{74}{111} \times 100 \quad = 66.7\%$

Percentage of business tickets $= \frac{28}{111} \times 100 \quad = 25.2\%$

Percentage of first class tickets $= \frac{9}{111} \times 100 \quad = 8.1\%$

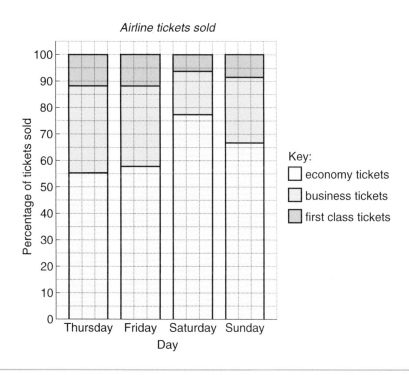

PRACTICE 1.5.2

1   The following information shows the number of flights from a regional airport on one day of the week made by different airlines.

Airline	No. of flights
Eagle Air	6
Air European	7
Falconair	3
Europa Airlines	2

Draw a bar chart to illustrate this information.

2 Five coins were tossed 100 times and the number of heads showing uppermost was recorded as shown in the table.

Number	Frequency
0	2
1	17
2	29
3	34
4	15
5	3

Draw a bar chart to illustrate this frequency distribution.

3 Draw a bar chart to illustrate the frequency distribution given in question 2 of Practice 1.5.1 on page 20.

4 Draw a bar chart to illustrate the frequency distribution given in question 3 of Practice 1.5.1 on page 20.

5 The following information shows the length of time it takes for a group of people to complete a sponsored walk. The times are given in hours to the nearest hour.

Time	Frequency
1–2	3
2–3	17
3–4	26
4–5	8
5–6	1

Draw a bar chart to illustrate this grouped frequency distribution.

6 The following frequency distribution shows the weight of 40 animals in a zoo given to the nearest stone.

Weight	1–5	6–10	11–15	16–20	21–25
Frequency	9	16	9	4	2

Draw a bar chart to illustrate this distribution.

7 Draw a bar chart to illustrate the distribution found in question 4 of Practice 1.4.2 on page 18.

8 The following information shows the number of people in a department store on different days of the week.

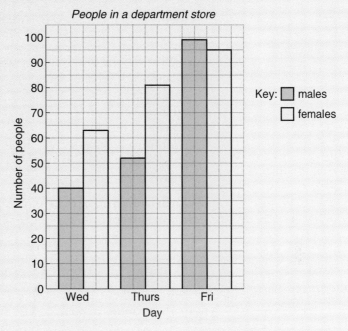

People in a department store

Use the information from this compound bar chart to create a component bar chart.

9 The following information shows the favourite subjects of students at a college.

Favourite subject	Girls	Boys
Mathematics	9	18
Science	11	14
Languages	20	11
Humanities	10	8
Arts	23	18

Illustrate this information as:
a a compound bar chart,
b a component bar chart.

10 The following information shows the revenue (in thousands of £) spent on advertising over three consecutive years.

Year	Papers	Radio	Television
1999	45	26	39
2000	38	46	32
2001	40	53	27

Illustrate this information as:
a a compound bar chart,
b a component bar chart.

11 The number of vehicles passing a certain point over a period of 5 hours on two consecutive days is shown in the diagram below.

Use the diagram to answer the following questions.

a What was the total number of vehicles for each day?

b How many lorries were there on the first day?

c How many buses were there on the second day?

Use the information from the diagram to create a percentage component bar chart.

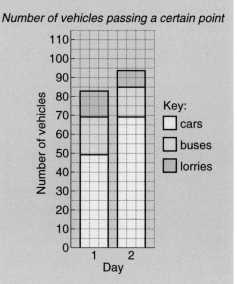

Number of vehicles passing a certain point

Key:
☐ cars
☐ buses
☐ lorries

Stem and leaf diagrams

A different way to show data is to use a **stem and leaf diagram**.

Worked Example

The ages of the 25 players in the squad of a local rugby team are:

17   23   26   30   33   19   24   21   32   34
27   18   28   28   24   30   33   17   21   29
24   26   30   28   23

Show this data using a stem and leaf diagram.

A stem and leaf diagram to represent these numbers would look like this:

Squad ages	**2 | 6** means 26

Stem ──────────► **1** │ 7 7 8 9 ◄──────────── Leaves

2 │ 1 1 3 3 4 4 4 6 6 7 8 8 8 9

3 │ 0 0 0 2 3 3 4

The diagram has been created by splitting the players' ages into two sections.

The stem consists of the digits 1, 2 and 3 representing the 10s digits in the players' ages i.e. 10, 20 and 30. The leaves are the units digits.

It is a little like a grouped frequency distribution but its great advantage is that it retains all the original data. We usually write the stems and leaves in numerical order.

A stem and leaf diagram can be used to compare two sets of related figures by making the leaves go to the left and right. The following example shows this.

Worked Example

There are 40 people in a choir; 24 females and 16 males. Their heights, to the nearest centimetre, are given below. Show this data using a stem and leaf diagram.

Females: 166 173 149 158 172 164 167 169 178 172
           168 152 161 182 166 175 181 173 169 159
           164 171 163 177 166
Males: 186 178 175 169 162 172 189 174 164 172
           169 191 183 175 167 183

A stem and leaf diagram to represent these numbers would look like this:

Choir heights   **18** | 2 means 182   7 | **16** means 167

Females		Males
	19	1
2 1	**18**	3 3 6 9
8 7 5 3 3 2 2 1	**17**	2 2 4 5 5 8
9 9 8 7 6 6 6 4 4 3 1	**16**	2 4 7 9 9
9 8 2	**15**	
9	**14**	

The diagram above does not give us exact answers but it is easy to see from it that the average height of the males is higher than that of the females. We could not have seen this so easily from the original figures.

PRACTICE 1.5.3

1   The average hours of sunshine per day at Upholland for one month were as follows:

3.6	5.4	2.9	6.8	7.2	6.1	4.3
4.6	7.2	3.3	4.8	6.8	4.2	2.9
2.4	6.7	8.1	6.8	5.1	2.9	5.0
7.8	2.5	4.7	6.6	7.2	3.5	7.6
6.6	3.9	7.5	6.7	7.9	6.8	3.5

Show this data using a stem and leaf diagram.

2   The number of accidents on a stretch of road over a year was as follows:

Jan	Feb	Mar	Apr	May	Jun	Jul	Aug	Sep	Oct	Nov	Dec
27	24	22	19	16	13	13	15	19	22	23	29

Show this data using a stem and leaf diagram.

3   The list below shows the average gestation times, to the nearest day, of some creatures. Show this data using a suitable stem and leaf diagram. (Source: Diagram book of Comparisons; *Penguin Books, 1980*)

Common Opossum	13	Falcon	29	Swan	30
Marine Turtle	55	Hawk	44	Alligator	61
Grass Lizard	42	Spiny Lizard	63	Royal Albatross	79
Emperor Penguin	63	Python	61	Australian Skink	30
House Mouse	19	Pheasant	22	Ostrich	42
Dog	63	Wren	16	Thrush	14
Finch	12				

4   The following data shows the playing time (minutes and seconds) of the tracks on some CDs. Show this data using a stem and leaf diagram.

3.21 2.29 2.25 2.49 2.57 3.30 3.19 2.25 3.34 2.45 2.44 3.34
3.19 3.30 2.10 3.00 2.44 2.25 2.54 3.43 2.22 2.54 2.55 2.24
3.35 2.10 3.55 3.07 2.54 2.08 3.22 3.33 2.43 3.50 2.22 2.57

Line graphs

Line graphs are drawn by plotting points and then joining them, in order, with a series of straight lines.

The advantage of the line graph is that it makes visual comparison easy. A disadvantage is that only simple information can be shown and readings between the points might not be meaningful.

Worked Example

The following information shows the temperatures of a patient over a period of 6 hours.

Time	10 00	11 00	12 00	13 00	14 00	15 00
Temp. (°C)	38.5	39.6	40.0	39.1	38.5	37.9

a Draw a line graph to represent this data.
b What was the maximum temperature recorded?
c Use your line graph to estimate the patient's temperature at 1130.
d After 1300, the patient's temperature began to fall at a constant rate until it reached 37 °C. Use your line graph to estimate the time at which the temperature reached 37 °C.

a

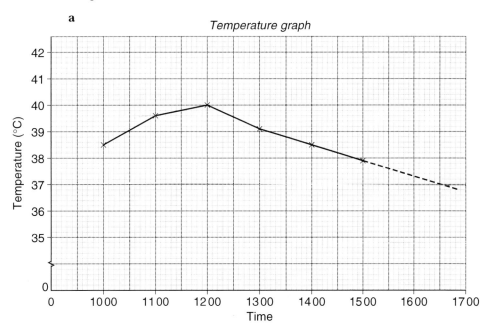

b The maximum temperature recorded was 40 °C at 12 00.

(Although this is the maximum recorded temperature it is not necessarily the maximum temperature as the temperature could have gone above 40 °C just before or just after 12 00.)

c   To find the patient's temperature at 11 30 we read off the value at 11 30. The patient's temperature at 11 30 is 39.8 °C.

(This value is only approximate as we do not know exactly how the temperature changed between 11 00 and 12 00.)

d   To estimate the time at which the temperature reached 37 °C we need to continue the graph as shown by the dotted line and read off the time when the temperature equals 37 °C.

The temperature reached 37 °C at 16 30.

PRACTICE 1.5.4

1   The number of microwaves sold at an electrical shop is shown in the table below:

Month	Oct	Nov	Dec	Jan	Feb
Sales	20	46	102	42	16

Draw a line graph to illustrate this information.

2   The number of hours of sunshine at a certain holiday resort is shown in the table below:

Month	May	Jun	Jul	Aug	Sep	Oct
Hrs of sunshine	15	$16\frac{1}{2}$	$16\frac{1}{2}$	14	$12\frac{1}{2}$	$10\frac{1}{2}$

Draw a line graph to illustrate this information.

3   The weight of a child is recorded at birth and at the end of each month as follows:

Age (months)	0	1	2	3	4	5	6
Weight (kg)	3.5	4.2	5.3	6.5	7.1	7.5	8.2

Draw a line graph to represent this information.

4 The temperature in a lecture theatre is taken at hourly intervals as shown:

Time	08 00	09 00	10 00	11 00	12 00	13 00	14 00	15 00	16 00
Temp. (°C)	15.5	16.0	16.5	18.0	19.5	20.5	20.5	20.0	18.5

Draw a line graph to represent this information.

Use your graph to estimate:

a the time at which the temperature rose above 20 °C,

b the temperature at 14 30 hours.

Explain why these answers are only estimates.

5 The number of students in the common room was counted at hourly intervals and the results recorded on a line graph.

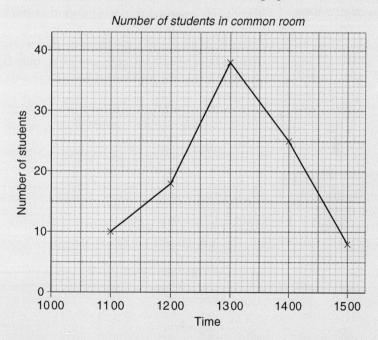

Number of students in common room

a How many students were in the common room at 11 00?
b How many students were in the common room at 13 00?
c How many students were in the common room at 14 30?
d Why is your answer to **c** only an approximation?
e What is the maximum number of students recorded in the common room?

Other graphs

Time Series

Time series use line graphs in a very useful way. The method, worked examples and Practice exercise are found in Topic 2.3.

Cumulative frequency diagrams

Cumulative frequency diagrams are another very good way of displaying (and analysing) data. The method, worked examples and Practice exercise are found in Topic 2.4

Pie charts

A pie chart (or circular diagram) is a circle divided into sectors (or slices) whose angles (or areas) are used to represent the data.

The advantages of a pie chart are that it has a strong visual impact and easily shows how the whole thing is divided into its constituent parts and what size these parts are in relation to one another and to the whole.

The disadvantages of a pie chart are that it requires some difficult calculations to find the respective angles and it can only be used for a few variables. Also, the drawing of the pie chart is not easy as it involves having to use a protractor accurately.

The following worked examples are given to show the construction of a pie chart.

Worked Examples

1   In a survey, 180 people were asked which was their favourite soap opera. Their responses were as follows:

Coronation Street	59
Brookside	19
Eastenders	48
Hollyoaks	25
Other	22
None	7

Calculate the angles for a pie chart and construct the pie chart to show the different categories.

The pie chart needs to be drawn to represent 180 people. There are 360° in a full circle so each person will get $\frac{360°}{180} = 2°$ of the pie chart as follows:

Soap opera	Number	Angle
Coronation Street	59	$59 \times 2° = 118°$
Brookside	19	$19 \times 2° = 38°$
Eastenders	48	$48 \times 2° = 96°$
Hollyoaks	25	$25 \times 2° = 50°$
Other	22	$22 \times 2° = 44°$
None	7	$7 \times 2° = 14°$
		Total 360°

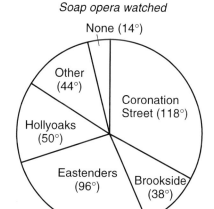

Soap opera watched

2   500 students at a college are surveyed regarding which GNVQ courses they are following. The responses were as follows:

Travel & tourism   225

Business   126

Health & social care   83

Performing arts   51

Engineering   15

Calculate the angles and construct the pie chart to show the different categories.

The pie chart needs to be drawn to represent 500 people so each person will get $\frac{360}{500}$ of the pie chart as follows:

Course	Number	Angle
Travel & tourism	225	$225 \times \frac{360}{500} = 162°$
Business	126	$126 \times \frac{360}{500} = 90.7°$
Health & social care	83	$83 \times \frac{360}{500} = 59.8°$
Performing arts	51	$51 \times \frac{360}{500} = 36.7°$
Engineering	15	$15 \times \frac{360}{500} = 10.8°$
		Total 360°

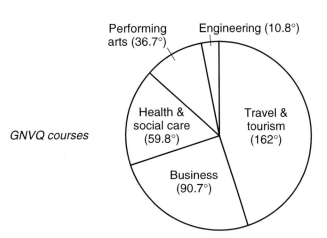

GNVQ courses

3   The following pie chart shows how a sample of students come to college in the morning.

How students travel to college

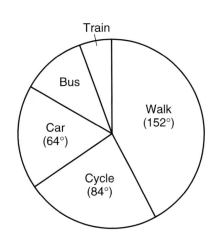

21 students cycle to college in the morning.

a How many students walk?
b How many students come by car?

Twice as many students come by bus as come by train.

c How many students come by bus?
d How many students come by train?
e How many students were there altogether in the sample?

From the diagram we can see that the number of students who cycle to the college is represented by an angle of 84°.

$$84° \text{ represents } 21 \text{ people}$$

so $1°$ represents $\frac{21}{84} = \frac{1}{4}$ person (or 1 person is represented by $4°$)

a The number of students who walk is represented by 152°.

So the number who walk is $152 \times \frac{1}{4} = 38$ students.

b The number of students who come by car is represented by 64°.

So the number who walk is $64 \times \frac{1}{4} = 16$ students.

We are told that twice as many students come by bus as come by train. The angles for these two sectors add up to 60°. We can find this out by adding all of the given angles and subtracting them from 360°.

Dividing 60° in the ratio 2 : 1, so that the angle for the bus is twice as much as that for the train, we get:

Bus   40°   Train   20°

c The number of students who come by bus is represented by 40°.

So the number who come by bus is $40 \times \frac{1}{4} = 10$ students.

d The number of students who come by train is represented by 20°.

So the number who come by train is $20 \times \frac{1}{4} = 5$ students.

e To find out how many students there were in the sample we can add up all of the figures above or else appreciate that the total number of students is represented by the angle of 360°.

So the number in the sample is $360 \times \frac{1}{4} = 90$ students.

PRACTICE 1.5.5a   Try these questions without a calculator

1 A survey of favourite pets produced the following information.

Pet	cat	dog	rabbit	bird	fish
Frequency	10	13	6	3	4

Draw a pie chart to represent this information.

2   Katie keeps a note of all the first class tickets that she sells on the Eurostar service to Paris as follows. Draw a pie chart to represent this information.

Ticket	Frequency
Business	92
Leisure first	35
Child	17
Senior	24
Pass holder	12

3   Draw a pie chart to illustrate the frequency distribution given in question 3 of Practice 1.5.1 on page 20.

4   Draw a pie chart to illustrate the frequency distribution given in question 1 of Practice 1.5.2 on page 25.

5   Draw a pie chart to illustrate the frequency distribution given in question 2 of Practice 1.5.2 on page 26.

PRACTICE 1.5.5b   Try these questions with a calculator

1   The following information shows the types of properties advertised in an estate agent's window. Draw a pie chart to represent this information.

Type	Frequency
Bungalow	11
Semi detached	17
Detached	14
Terraced	18
Flat	20

2   Draw a pie chart to illustrate the frequency distribution found in question 2 of Practice 1.4.1 on page 14.

3   Draw a pie chart to illustrate the frequency distribution given in question 2 of Practice 1.5.1 on page 20.

4   The incomplete pie chart shows the outcomes of 30 different football matches where the outcome is either a win, draw or lose.

Football match outcomes

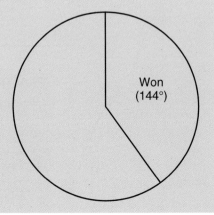

a Calculate the number of matches won.

Seven matches were lost altogether.
b Calculate the angle needed for this on the pie chart.
c Complete the pie chart for the information given.

5   The pie chart shows how 200 students travelled to college one day in winter.

How students travel to college in winter

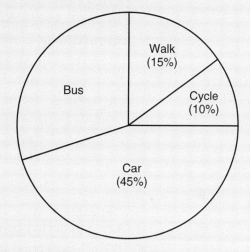

a Which method of transport was most popular in winter?
b What percentage of the students travelled by bus?
c Calculate the number of students who travelled by bus.

In a similar survey the following summer, the following pie chart was obtained:

How students travel to college in summer

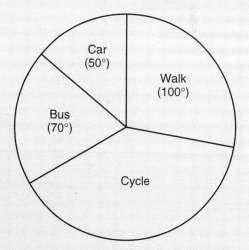

d Which method of transport was most popular in summer?

During the summer 50 people walked to the college.

e How many students were there altogether in the summer?
f How many students cycle to the college?

Frequency polygons

A frequency polygon can be obtained from a bar chart by joining up the mid-points of the top of each bar with straight lines to form a polygon. In the case of the first and last class intervals, the lines are extended to the base line so that the area under the frequency polygon is the same as the area under the bar chart.

Worked Example

The following frequency distribution shows the length of 50 leaves measured to the nearest millimetre.

Length	Frequency
11–15	3
16–20	6
21–25	7
26–30	9
31–35	12
36–40	8
41–45	4
46–50	1

Draw a frequency polygon to represent this information.

The length is a continuous variable and a bar chart of the information can be drawn as follows:

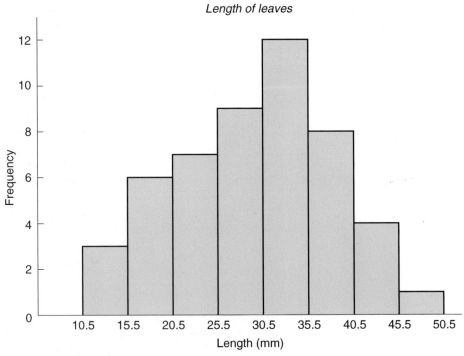

Length of leaves

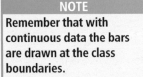

NOTE
Remember that with continuous data the bars are drawn at the class boundaries.

The frequency polygon can be obtained from the bar chart by joining up the mid-points of the top of each bar with straight lines to form a polygon as shown by the dotted lines on the following diagram.

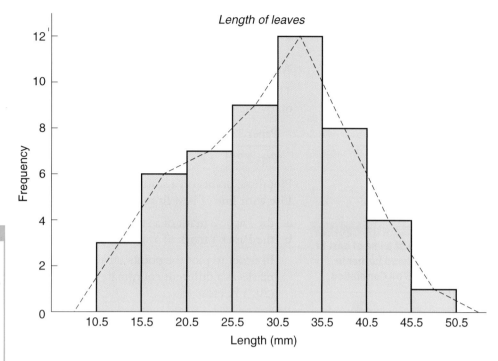

NOTE

The class interval before the 11–15 class would be 6–10 with a mid-point of 8. The class interval after the 46–50 class would be 51–55 with a mid-point of 53. The lines of the frequency polygon are extended to the base line at the mid-points 8 and 53 so that the area under the polygon is the same as the area under the bar chart.

The frequency polygon can be more quickly drawn without the bar chart by plotting the frequencies at the mid-points of each interval. The mid-point of the interval is exactly halfway between the lower class boundary and the upper class boundary.

PRACTICE 1.5.6

1   The diameters of 100 cylinders are measured as follows.

Dia. (mm)	2.91-2.93	2.94-2.96	2.97-2.99	3.00-3.02	3.03-3.05	3.06-3.08	3.09-3.11
Frequency	1	3	17	53	20	4	2

Draw a frequency polygon to represent this information.
2   Draw a frequency polygon to illustrate the frequency distribution given in question 4 of Practice 1.4.2 on page 18.
3   Draw a frequency polygon to illustrate the frequency distribution given in question 5 of Practice 1.5.2 on page 26.
4   Draw a frequency polygon to show the frequency distribution given in question 6 of Practice 1.5.2 on page 26.

Scatter graphs

Scatter graphs are useful when the data collected links two or more variables and you want to find out if there is any link or **correlation** between the two variables. In a scatter graph each of the two sets of data is assigned to a different axis and the information collected can be represented as different coordinates.

Where there is a link or correlation between the two variables you can draw a **line of best fit** as shown in the following worked example.

Worked Example

The following information shows the marks awarded to 11 different students on two science examination papers.

Paper 1	56	44	20	75	36	50	66	62	42	62	30
Paper 2	44	34	13	61	26	41	56	47	29	53	22

Plot these points on a scatter graph and draw the line of best fit.
Use your line of best fit to estimate:

a the Paper 2 mark of a student who gained 65 marks on Paper 1,

b the Paper 1 mark of a student who gained 38 marks on Paper 2.

NOTE
The idea of a line of best fit is considered further in Topic 2.5 on Correlation.

In order to plot the points on a graph we need to consider each pair of marks as a different coordinate so we plot the points (56, 44), (44, 34), (20, 13), etc.

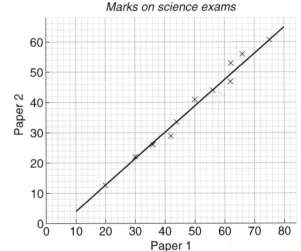

We now draw the line which best fits all of the data provided.

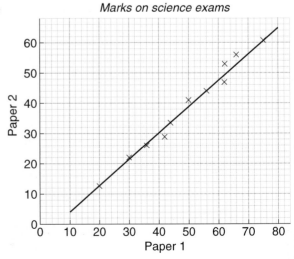

We can now use this line of best fit to estimate the required marks as follows:

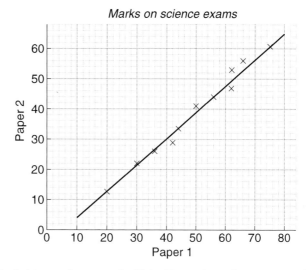

a To find this mark we read off the Paper 2 mark corresponding to 65 marks on Paper 1.

An estimate for the Paper 2 mark would be 52.

b To find this mark we read off the Paper 1 mark corresponding to 38 marks on Paper 2.

An estimate for the Paper 1 mark would be 49.

Further work on scatter graphs can be found in Topic 2.5 on Correlation.

PRACTICE 1.5.7

1 The following information shows the marks awarded to 10 different students on examination papers in maths and music.

Maths	68	28	81	85	86	50	58	38	63	99
Music	80	45	87	89	90	62	68	51	62	100

Plot these points on a graph and draw the line of best fit.

2 The following information shows the height (in cm) and the weight (in kg) of 8 people.

Height (cm)	135	105	60	101	85	74	120	130
Weight (kg)	80	45	87	89	90	62	68	51

Plot these points on a graph and draw the line of best fit.

3 The following information shows the relationship between engine size and the distance (in miles) travelled on one gallon of petrol by eight different cars.

Engine size (litres)	2.6	1.5	3.0	2.0	1.3	1.0	1.1	1.5
Distance (miles)	24.5	30.0	15.0	27.5	34.0	36.5	33.0	32.5

Plot these points on a graph and draw the line of best fit.

Use your line of best fit to estimate the distance travelled on one gallon of petrol by a car with an engine size of:

a 2.2 litres,
b 3.5 litres.

Explain why the second estimate is not so reliable as the first one.

1.6 SUMMARY

Quantitative and qualitative data

Quantitative data is data that takes numerical values and measures quantities. Qualitative data is data that does not take numerical values but measures qualities.

Discrete and continuous data

Discrete data is data that can only take particular values such as whole numbers. Continuous data is data that can take all values within any given range.

Bias

Bias is likely to occur if:
- an incorrect sampling method is used,
- the sample is unrepresentative,
- the questions are unclear,
- the questions are biased.

Primary and secondary data

Primary (first-hand) data is data that is collected as part of a statistical investigation and secondary data (second-hand data) is data that is already available.

Sampling and data capture

Sampling methods considered include:

Random sampling

In random sampling, each member of the population has an equally likely chance of being selected.

Systematic sampling

Systematic sampling is the same as random sampling except that there is some system involved in choosing the member of the population to be sampled.

Stratified sampling

In stratified sampling, each member of the population is divided into some particular group or category (strata). Within each strata, a random sample or systematic sample is selected so that the sample size is proportional to the size of the group or category in the population as a whole.

Quota sampling

In quota sampling, a certain number of the population are chosen with specific characteristics which are decided beforehand.

Questionnaires and surveys

A good questionnaire should be:
- simple, short, clear and precise,
- attractively laid out,
- quick to complete,

and the questions should:
- be free from bias and not personal or offensive,
- be written in a sensible language for the respondent,
- be related to the work being investigated,
- give clear instructions on how to respond.

Raw data

Raw data is any information which has been collected by some method but has not been organised in any way.

Tally chart

A tally chart consists of a series of tallies which are grouped into fives as follows:

$$
\begin{array}{ll}
\text{||||} & = 4 \\
\text{||||} & = 5 \\
\text{|||| |} & = 6 \\
\text{|||| ||||} & = 10, \text{ etc.}
\end{array}
$$

Frequency distribution

A frequency distribution can be constructed from a tally chart by totalling the tallies.

Grouped frequency distribution

A grouped frequency distribution is where the data are classified into a series of groups or classes.

Pictograms

A pictogram (or pictograph or ideograph) is a simple way of representing data by using pictures (or some other representation).

Bar charts

Bar charts are a very common way of representing data and use bars (horizontal or vertical) to represent the number or frequency of the data.

Stem and leaf diagrams

Stem and leaf diagrams are useful ways of representing information given a stem and associated leaf (e.g. tens and units or minutes and seconds).

Compound bar charts

The compound (or multiple) bar chart is similar to the bar chart except that the bars are replaced by a series of different bars representing different aspects of the data.

Component bar charts

The component bar chart (or composite or sectional bar chart) is used to show how an individual item can be split into a series of components.

Line graphs

Line graphs are drawn by plotting points and then joining the points, in order, with a series of straight lines.

Pie charts

A pie chart (or circular diagram) is a circle divided into sectors (or slices) whose angles (or areas) are used to represent the data.

Frequency polygons

A frequency polygon can be obtained from a bar chart by joining up the mid-points of the top of each bar with straight lines to form a polygon.

Scatter graphs

In a scatter graph each of two sets of data is assigned to a different axis and the information collected can be represented as different coordinates.

CHAPTER 2
Analysing and interpreting data

In this chapter you will need to:
▸ know how to construct and use a tally chart
▸ appreciate the various pictorial representations used in statistics
▸ use the statistical functions on a calculator

Tally chart

We saw in Topic 1.4 **Tabulating data** that a tally chart consists of a series of tallies which are grouped into fives as follows:

$$\text{IIII} \quad = 4$$
$$\text{IIII} \quad = 5$$
$$\text{IIII I} \quad = 6$$
$$\text{IIII IIII} = 10, \text{ etc.}$$

The tally chart is a useful way of organising raw data and finding frequencies.

Pictorial representations

The following representations were considered in Topic 1.5 on **Pictorial representations**:

- pictograms,
- bar charts,
- stem and leaf diagrams,
- line graphs,
- pie charts,
- frequency polygons,
- scatter diagrams.

Using a calculator

Our calculator can be used to help us with our statistical calculations but remember to set the calculator to statistics mode before starting.

You should read the user manual accompanying your calculator for further information on how this can be done as well as how individual data items can be input into the calculator.

NOTE
You can see more on how to make the most of your calculator in Topic 7.4 Using a calculator.

Function	Explanation
MODE	Sets the mode for normal calculations, statistical calculations, etc.
n	Displays the number of data items which have been input into the calculator.
Σx	Calculates the sum of the numerical data which have been input into the calculator.
Σx^2	Calculates the sum of the squares of the numerical data which have been input into the calculator.
$\bar{x}$	Calculates the mean of the numerical data which have been input into the calculator.
σn or σx	Calculates the standard deviation of the numerical data which have been input into the calculator.

2.2 MEASURES OF CENTRAL TENDENCY

A frequent statistical calculation is the measurement of **central tendency or average**. There are several different types of average including the mode, median and arithmetic mean.

Mode

The **mode** is the value that occurs the most frequently.

Worked Examples

1 The following numbers were recorded when a single dice was thrown 15 times. What is the modal value?

   2, 5, 5, 6, 1, 6, 4, 2, 4, 6, 1, 1, 5, 2, 1

   The number 1 was thrown 4 times
   The number 2 was thrown 3 times
   The number 3 was thrown 0 times
   The number 4 was thrown 2 times
   The number 5 was thrown 3 times
   The number 6 was thrown 3 times

   The number 1 occurs the most frequently so we say that the mode is 1.

2 The dice was thrown one more time giving a 5. What is the modal value now?

   2, 5, 5, 6, 1, 6, 4, 2, 4, 6, 1, 1, 5, 2, 1, 5

The number 1 was thrown 4 times
The number 2 was thrown 3 times
The number 3 was thrown 0 times
The number 4 was thrown 2 times
The number 5 was thrown 4 times
The number 6 was thrown 3 times

The numbers 1 and 5 occur the most frequently so we say that the mode is 1 and 5.

One of the advantages of the mode is that it is easy to obtain from pictorial representations as shown in the following worked examples.

Worked Examples

Find the mode of the following pictorial representations:

a   *Number of bedrooms in 20 houses*

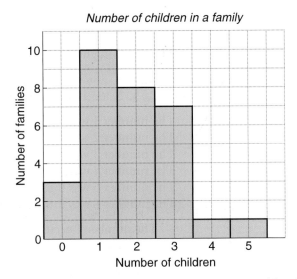

The mode is 3 bedrooms. It is easy to find the mode from a pictogram.

b

The mode is 1 child. The mode will always be represented by the tallest (or longest) bar.

c

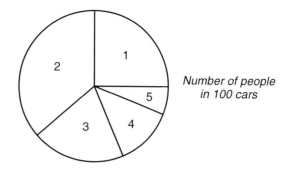

Number of people in 100 cars

The mode is 2 people. The mode will always be represented by the sector with the largest angle (or area) in the pie chart.

Mode of frequency distribution

The mode of a frequency distribution is easily found by noting which value has the highest frequency.

Worked Example

Find the mode of the following frequency distribution:

Value	Frequency
10	12
11	23
12	35
13	**42** ← the value with the highest frequency
14	21

The mode or modal value of the frequency distribution is 13.

> **NOTE**
> Make sure that you write down the value and not the frequency of the value when giving the mode or modal value.

Mode of a grouped frequency distribution

The mode of a grouped frequency distribution has no meaning. However, it is possible to find the modal group. This is the group that occurs the most frequently.

Worked Example

Find the modal group of the following grouped frequency distribution:

Weight (g)	Frequency
25–35	14
35–45	**19** ← the group with the highest frequency
45–55	17
55–65	11

The modal group of the grouped frequency distribution is 35–45 g.

PRACTICE 2.2.1

1 Find the mode of the following data:
   a 4, 5, 5, 6, 6, 6, 7, 7, 8
   b 2, 3, 4, 5, 2, 3, 4, 2, 3, 2
   c 33, 36, 37, 33, 35, 35, 38, 39
   d 12.2, 13.5, 12.6, 12.3, 13.5, 12.4, 12.5, 12.3, 13.6
   e −3, −2, −2, −1, −1, −1, 0, 1, 2, 3

2 Salima is undertaking a survey of the colour of cars in the staff car park.
   She draws up a tally chart as follows:

     Red   卌 卌 |||
     Blue   卌 卌 |
     Green 卌 |||
     White 卌 卌 卌 ||

   What is the modal colour?

3 Find the mode for each of the following representations.

   a

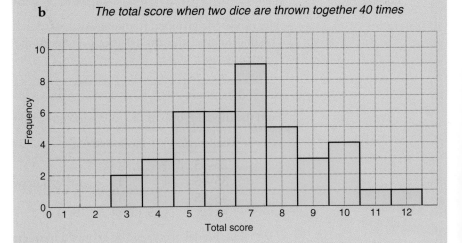

              Number of items in a shopping basket of 25 people

     1 item

     2 items

     3 items

     4 items

     5 items

     5+ items

                  Key: 1 shopping basket

   b   *The total score when two dice are thrown together 40 times*

c

Pie chart to show the number of credit cards held by 50 people

4   Find the mode of the following frequency distribution:

Value	Frequency
20	8
21	11
22	10
23	6

5   Find the mode of the following frequency distribution:

Value	$6\frac{1}{2}$	7	$7\frac{1}{2}$	8	$8\frac{1}{2}$	9
Frequency	11	17	13	15	9	6

6   Find the modal group of the following grouped frequency distribution:

Weight (kg)	Frequency
0.5–1.5	12
1.5–2.5	15
2.5–3.5	22
3.5–4.5	17
4.5–5.5	10

Median

The **median** is the middle value when all of the values are arranged in numerical order.

Worked Examples

1   Find the median of the following numbers:

12, 5, 3, 6, 10, 9, 2, 8, 9

First the numbers must be arranged in order:

2, 3, 5, 6, (**8,**) 9, 9, 10, 12

The middle value is the 5th number so the median is 8.

2 Find the median of the following numbers:

2, 12, 5, 3, 6, 10, 9, 2, 8, 9

First the numbers must be arranged in order:

2, 2, 3, 5, (6, 8,) 9, 9, 10, 12

In this case there is no middle number as there are an even number of values. To overcome this problem, we take the two middle numbers and find their mean.

The middle values are the 5th and 6th numbers so the median is

$$\frac{6 + 8}{2} = 7.$$

Median of a frequency distribution

The following example shows how to find the median of a frequency distribution.

Worked Examples

1 Find the median of the following frequency distribution which shows the number of goals scored in a series of football matches:

Number of goals	Frequency
0	2
1	3
2	5
3	2
4	1
	13

One way to find the median would be to write out the number of goals as before:

0, 0, 1, 1, 1, 2, 2, 2, 2, 2, 3, 3, 4

As there are 13 numbers then the middle value will be the $\frac{13 + 1}{2}$ = 7th number.

0, 0, 1, 1, 1, 2, (2,) 2, 2, 2, 3, 3, 4

The median number of goals is 2.

2 Find the median of the following frequency distribution which shows the number of matches in 24 different matchboxes:

Number of matches	Frequency
48	2
49	5
50	14
51	2
52	1
	24

As there are 24 numbers then the middle value will be the $\dfrac{24+1}{2} = 12\frac{1}{2}$th number (i.e. between the 12th and 13th number).

We can see this more clearly by looking at the cumulative frequencies (giving an accumulated total for the frequencies):

Number of matches	Frequency	Cumulative frequency
48	2	2
49	5	7
50	14	21 ← the $12\frac{1}{2}$th value will
51	2	: occur here
52	1	:

The median number of matches is 50.

Median of a grouped frequency distribution

A cumulative frequency diagram is the best way to find the median of a **grouped frequency distribution**. Cumulative frequency diagrams are explained in Topic 2.4 in **Measures of spread**.

PRACTICE 2.2.2

1 Find the median of the following data:
   a 2, 3, 4, 6, 8, 11, 15
   b 4, 4, 4, 4, 5, 5, 5, 6, 7
   c 4, 5, 6, 7
   d 103, 102, 101, 100
   e 3, 6, 8, 2, 6, 9, 10, 2, 5
   f 4, 7, 12, 4, 11, 10, 3, 5
   g 4, 6, 8, −3, −5, −7, 0, −2, −4

2 Find the median of the following frequency distribution which shows the size of trainers sold at a sports shop:

Number	Frequency
5	10
$5\frac{1}{2}$	15
6	9
$6\frac{1}{2}$	3
7	2

3 Find the median of the following frequency distribution:

Number	Frequency
16	4
17	8
18	11
19	6
20	10
21	15
22	6

Arithmetic mean

The **arithmetic mean** or **mean** is the most common average and is found by adding up the values and dividing by the number of values.

NOTE
You should practice this work without a calculator.

Worked Example

The lengths of four petals are measured as 56 mm, 48 mm, 49 mm and 61 mm. What is the mean length of the petals?

Total length $= 56 + 48 + 49 + 61$

$= 214$ mm

Number of petals $= 4$

Mean length $= \dfrac{\text{total length}}{\text{number of petals}}$

$= \dfrac{214}{4}$

$= 53.5$ mm

PRACTICE 2.2.3   Try these questions without a calculator

1   Find the mean of the following data:
   a   4, 6, 11
   b   3, 7, 8, 4, 8
   c   8, 9, 10, 11, 12
   d   8, 9, 10, 11, 12, 13
   e   18, 19, 20, 21, 22, 23
   f   28, 29, 30, 31, 32, 33
   g   2.8, 2.9, 3.0, 3.1, 3.2, 3.3
   h   280, 290, 300, 310, 320, 330
   i   −280, −290, −300, −310, −320, −330

Sigma notation

Sigma notation (Σ) is a useful shorthand used in statistics to mean *the sum of*.

Σx means the *sum of the x values* so that in the following worked example,

Σf means *the sum of the frequencies* and Σfx means *the sum of all the (frequency × marks) values*.

Mean of a frequency distribution

The following example illustrates how to find the mean of a frequency distribution.

Worked Example

Find the mean of the following frequency distribution.

Mark x	Frequency f
6	3
7	5
8	7
9	3
10	2
	$\Sigma f = 20$

One way to find the mean would be to write out the marks as before:

   6, 6, 6, 7, 7, 7, 7, 7, 8, 8, 8, 8, 8, 8, 8, 9, 9, 9, 10, 10

The mean of these 20 numbers can be found as follows:

$$\text{Mean} = \frac{6+6+6+7+7+7+7+7+8+8+8+8+8+8+8+9+9+9+10+10}{20}$$

$$= \frac{156}{20}$$

$$= 7.8$$

A quicker way to work out the mean is to appreciate that the mean of the marks can be worked out as:

$$\frac{(3 \text{ lots of } 6) + (5 \text{ lots of } 7) + (7 \text{ lots of } 8) + (3 \text{ lots of } 9) + (2 \text{ lots of } 10)}{20}$$

$$= \frac{(3 \times 6) + (5 \times 7) + (7 \times 8) + (3 \times 9) + (2 \times 10)}{20}$$

$$= \frac{156}{20}$$

$$= 7.8 \quad \text{as before}$$

Using the original table we need to work out the frequency × mark and total these as follows:

Mark x	Frequency f	Frequency × mark fx
6	3	$3 \times 6 = 18$
7	5	$5 \times 7 = 35$
8	7	$7 \times 8 = 56$
9	3	$3 \times 9 = 27$
10	2	$2 \times 10 = 20$
	$\Sigma f = 20$	$\Sigma fx = 156$

For the frequency distribution   Mean $= \dfrac{\Sigma fx}{\Sigma f}$

$$= \frac{156}{20}$$

$$= 7.8 \quad \text{as before}$$

PRACTICE 2.2.4   Try these questions without a calculator

1 Find the mean of the following data:

Mark x	Frequency f
3	7
4	9
5	4
6	3
7	1

2 A customer purchases 5 apples at 12 p, 3 bananas at 14 p, 6 oranges at 15 p and 1 pineapple at 48 p. What is the mean cost per item of the purchases?

3 The following information shows the scores of 80 people in a quiz.
What is the average score?

Score	13	14	15	16	17	18	19	20
Frequency	2	0	7	11	13	19	16	12

4 Find the mean of the following data:

Age (years)	16	17	18	19	20	21
Frequency	8	4	12	4	0	2

Mean of a grouped frequency distribution

When we have data arranged in groups we use the mid point of the interval to
represent the group. In this case the mean will not be exact but should be a
good estimate of the mean.

Worked Examples

1 The following information shows the speed of 60 vehicles passing a
motorway bridge one evening in August. Calculate an estimate of the
mean speed of the vehicles.

Speed (mph)	20-30	30-40	40-50	50-60	60-70	70-80
Frequency	3	10	16	18	11	2

Speed (mph)	Mid-interval value x	Frequency f	Frequency × mid-interval value fx
20–30	25	3	$3 \times 25 = 75$
30–40	35	10	$10 \times 35 = 350$
40–50	45	16	$16 \times 45 = 720$
50–60	55	18	$18 \times 55 = 990$
60–70	65	11	$11 \times 65 = 715$
70–80	75	2	$2 \times 75 = 150$
		$\Sigma f = 60$	$\Sigma fx = 3000$

For the frequency distribution   Mean $= \dfrac{\Sigma fx}{\Sigma f}$

$$= \frac{3000}{60}$$

$$= 50 \, \text{mph}$$

2 The following information shows the duration of telephone calls (to the nearest minute) monitored by the switchboard in a large office block. Calculate an estimate of the mean length of the telephone calls. Give your answer to an appropriate degree of accuracy.

Time (minutes)	Frequency
3–5	67
6–8	43
9–12	28
13–16	13
17–20	7
21–25	4
26–30	3
31–40	2

As the data is grouped, we need to use mid-interval values to calculate an estimate of the mean length of the telephone calls.

Time (minutes)	Mid-interval value x	Frequency f	Frequency × mid-interval value fx
3–5	4	67	268
6–8	7	43	301
9–12	10.5	28	294
13–16	14.5	13	188.5
17–20	18.5	7	129.5
21–25	23	4	92
26–30	28	3	84
31–40	35.5	2	71
		$\Sigma f = 167$	$\Sigma fx = 1428$

For the frequency distribution Mean $= \dfrac{\Sigma fx}{\Sigma f}$

$$= \dfrac{1428}{167}$$

$$= 8.550\,898\,2\ldots$$

$$= 9 \text{ minutes}$$
(to the nearest minute)

NOTE

Giving the answer to the most sensible degree of accuracy would indicate an answer of 9 minutes (to the nearest minute) bearing in mind that the time in the question was given *to the nearest minute.* Also, further inaccuracies will have resulted from the use of the mid-interval value to represent the given class interval.

PRACTICE 2.2.5   Try these questions with a calculator

1 Calculate an estimate of the mean for the following distribution.

Length (mm)	0–10	10–20	20–30	30–40	40–50
Frequency	6	7	10	6	3

2 Students in a college were asked how much money they spent on entertainment each week. The following frequency distribution shows the results.

Amount (£)	Frequency
0 and less than 10	6
10 and less than 20	14
20 and less than 30	21
30 and less than 40	17
40 and less than 50	10
50 and less than 60	4
60 and less than 70	2
70 and less than 80	1

Use the frequency table to calculate an estimate of the mean.

3 The length of each telephone call received by a switchboard is shown in the table.

Length of call (minutes)	Frequency
0 and less than 1	65
1 and less than 2	123
2 and less than 3	72
3 and less than 4	47
4 and less than 5	23
5 and less than 6	7

Calculate an estimate of the mean length of the telephone calls.

4 The following table shows the weights of 75 teenagers. Calculate an estimate of the mean weight giving your answer to a sensible degree of accuracy.

Weight (kg)	45–	55–	65–	75–	85–95
Frequency	14	37	18	4	2

5 The following data show the times taken to service cars at a garage with all times given to the nearest minute.

Time (mins)	5–25	26–45	46–60	61–90	91–120	121–140
Frequency	24	15	10	6	2	1

Calculate an estimate of the mean length of the time taken to service cars.

Advantages and disadvantages of the mode, median and mean

Advantages of the mode:	Represents an actual value i.e. the most frequently occurring Easy to see from pictorial representations (diagrams)
Disadvantages of the mode:	Does not take account of all values There may be no mode or many modes
Advantages of the median:	Often represents an actual value Is not affected by values at the ends of the range
Disadvantages of the median:	Not widely used Not representative for a small group
Advantages of the mean:	Widely used and makes use of all the data Mathematically produced
Disadvantages of the mean:	May not correspond to an actual value Affected by values at the ends of the range

PRACTICE 2.2.6   Try these questions without a calculator

1 Find the mode, median and arithmetic mean of the following data:

   a 1, 2, 2, 3, 3, 3, 4, 4, 4, 4
   b 2, 3, 3, 4, 5, 6, 6, 6, 7, 8
   c 4, 4, 2, 2, 2, 7, 7, 7, 1, 8, 7, 3, 3, 6
   d 1, 2, 6, 5, 2, 2, 5, 9
   e 1, 2, 3, 4, 5, 6, 7, 8, 9, 10
   f 11, 12, 13, 14, 15, 16, 17, 18, 19, 20
   g 3, −3, −3, 2, −2, 1, −1, −1, 0, 0, 1, −1, 2, −1, −2, 3

2 Debbie asks some of the people in her church how many brothers and sisters they have. She puts the information in a table.

Number of brothers		0	1	2	3	4	5
	5		1				
	4	0	2				
	3	2	2	1			
	2	4	3	3	1		
	1	5	3	2	1	1	
	0	5	6	2	1		1

Number of sisters

a How many people have no sisters?

b How many people have only one brother?

c How many people have equal numbers of brothers and sisters?

d How many people did Debbie survey altogether?

e What is the modal number of sisters?

f Calculate the mean number of brothers.

3 A teacher records the marks of 10 pupils in her record book as follows:

  28   27   32   17   23   28   28   20   27   29

  a Calculate:
   i the mean mark,
   ii the median mark,
   iii the modal mark.

  The teacher realises that the mark recorded as 32 should have been 35.

  b What effect will this have on:
   i the mean mark,
   ii the median mark,
   iii the modal mark?

4 The prices of eight three-bedroomed houses are as follows:

| £63 000 | £67 500 | £59 950 | £67 500 |
| £58 500 | £66 950 | £119 500 | £61 000 |

  Which of the averages, mode, median or mean, gives the best measure for the *average* price of a three-bedroom house? Give a reason to justify your answer.

Look at the following figures. They show the fuel bill for Victor and Margaret's house for each quarter over three years.

	Year 1	Year 2	Year 3
January 1st to March 31st	£200	£220	£250
April 1st to June 30th	£150	£160	£180
July 1st to September 30th	£140	£120	£150
October 1st to December 31st	£170	£180	£210

If we plotted a graph to show these figures we would get the diagram below: Because each of the figures represent a period of time, they are plotted at the mid-point of the periods they represent – i.e. Mid February, Mid May, Mid August and Mid November.

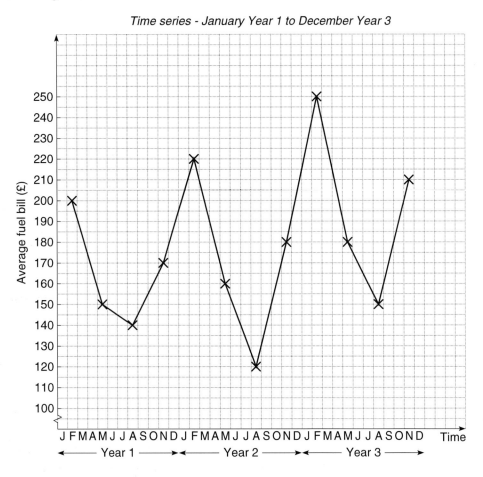

Time series - January Year 1 to December Year 3

This sort of graph is called a **Time Series**.

As we can see the shape is rather jagged! This is because Victor and Margaret do not use so much fuel at times when the weather is hotter.

Now take **every set of four readings** in turn and find their arithmetic means, as shown below:

Jan (Year 1)–Dec (Year 1) $\dfrac{200 + 150 + 140 + 170}{4} = 165$

Apr (Year 1)–Mar (Year 2) $\dfrac{150 + 140 + 170 + 220}{4} = 170$

Jul (Year 1)–Jun (Year 2) $\dfrac{140 + 170 + 220 + 160}{4} = 172.5$

Oct (Year 1)–Sep (Year 2) $\dfrac{170 + 220 + 160 + 120}{4} = 167.5$

Jan (Year 2)–Dec (Year 2) $\dfrac{220 + 160 + 120 + 180}{4} = 170$

Apr (Year 2)–Mar (Year 3) $\dfrac{160 + 120 + 180 + 250}{4} = 177.5$

Jul (Year 2)–Jun (Year 3) $\dfrac{120 + 180 + 250 + 180}{4} = 182.5$

Oct (Year 2)–Sep (Year 3) $\dfrac{180 + 250 + 180 + 150}{4} = 190$

Jan (Year 3)–Dec (Year 3) $\dfrac{250 + 180 + 150 + 210}{4} = 197.5$

If we plot these points on top of the original graph we can see that the new graph has 'smoothed out' the jaggedness of the original.

Again, because each of the figures represent a period of time, they are plotted at the midpoint of the periods they represent, i.e. End of June, End of Sep, End of Dec and End of Mar.

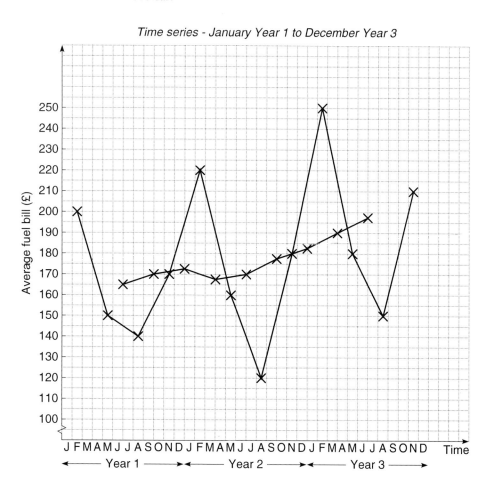

Time series - January Year 1 to December Year 3

These are called **Moving Averages** and, because we took every possible set of **four** readings, this one is a **four point moving average.** Calculating moving averages is a very good way of 'smoothing out' the 'jagged edges' of a time graph. From the resulting graph it is much easier to view how the figures are doing and to see the **trends** over a period of time. You can, of course, take two point moving averages, three point moving averages or any particular point that suits your problem. Shops could take a six point moving average for sales over days of the week (assuming they are closed on Sundays). This would 'smooth out' their sales where some days of the week are usually busier than others. The moving average graph may not be exactly straight, but it should be much smoother than the original time series. Firms could have a six point moving average (showing half year trends) or a 12 point moving average (showing full yearly trends, thus removing the effect of the most busy and the least busy seasons).

Simplifying the working

Calculating moving averages can be very time consuming. Fortunately there is a way we can speed them up.

a Calculate the first 'set' of moving averages. For example, from the figures above:

Jan (Year 1)–Dec (Year 1) $\dfrac{200 + 150 + 140 + 170}{4} = 165$

b The next average can be found by the formula :
Next average

$$= \text{Previous average} + \frac{\text{Next reading} - \text{first reading of above set}}{\text{Number in each set of moving averages}}$$

i. e. Next average $= 165 + \dfrac{220 - 200}{4} = 165 + 5 = 170$

As you can see this is the same answer as we got originally!

PRACTICE 2.3.1

1 a Calculate the three point moving averages for the following set of figures:

   2   4   5   2   3   6   8   4

   b Calculate the four point moving averages for the following set of figures:

   203   215   206   190   195   210   202   182   190   200

   c Calculate the five point moving averages for the following set of figures:

   55   57   62   60   58   57   60   70   66   63   60   64   71   68   65

2 Ian Brainbox has kept a record of his last 12 mathematics test results. Plot a three point moving average and comment on the trend.

Test	1	2	3	4	5	6	7	8	9	10	11	12
%	55	52	56	49	44	47	46	48	51	49	50	55

3 'BROLLIES R US' have issued their sales figures for the past 2 years. Draw a graph of these figures and superimpose on them

   a six point and
   b 12 point moving average graphs. (Figures are to the nearest £000.)

	Jan	Feb	Mar	Apr	May	Jun	Jul	Aug	Sep	Oct	Nov	Dec
Y1	210	204	165	144	126	96	72	51	153	155	178	195
Y2	200	190	158	140	130	110	104	76	150	162	183	199

What conclusions do you draw from the graphs for the periods:
i Jan–Apr in Year 2,   **ii** Jun–Aug in Year 2?

4 The local cinema records the number of customers watching its films over a four week period. Plot a suitable moving average graph and comment on its trends.

Week	Mon	Tues	Wed	Thurs	Fri	Sat
1	248	253	305	241	356	422
2	209	233	277	220	326	397
3	225	247	298	234	342	412
4	266	278	321	288	389	440

2.4 MEASURES OF SPREAD

We cannot always compare data just by looking at their averages. Doing that does not always give a true picture of the situation. For example, consider the mean value of the following two sets of numbers:

   5, 5, 5, 5, 5, 5, 5, 5, 5, 5
   1, 9, 1, 1, 9, 1, 9, 9, 9, 1

The mean of each set of data is the same (5) although the data is clearly very different.

If each of the sets of figures above represented a different student's test marks then what would you say about the performance of the two students?

We might say that the marks of the first student are more consistent than those of the second student or that the second student's marks are more spread out (or dispersed).

In this topic we will look at the following ways to measure spread or dispersion:

   range
   interquartile range

Range

The **range** of a distribution is found by working out the difference between the highest value and the lowest value.

Worked Example

The following data give the wages of six people working in a restaurant:

£225   £245   £205   £400   £260   £225

a   Calculate:
   i the mean,
   ii the range.

b   Why isn't the range a good measure of spread in this case?

a   i   The mean $= \dfrac{£225 + £245 + £205 + £400 + £260 + £225}{6}$

$= \dfrac{£1560}{6}$

$= £260$

ii The highest value $= £400$
    The lowest value $= £205$

Range = highest value − lowest value
$= £400 - £205$
$= £195$

b   The range is not a good measure of spread here because it is affected by an extreme value. The value of £400 distorts the mean value and considerably increases the range.

PRACTICE 2.4.1   Try these questions without a calculator

1   Find the range of the following sets of data:
   a   2, 4, 5, 7, 11, 18
   b   12, 6, 14, 15, 19, 22
   c   8 cm, 11 cm, 6 cm, 15 cm, 6 cm, 4 cm, 13 cm
   d   2.4 km, 6.1 km, 2.5 km, 4.7 km, 9.3 km, 5.7 km
   e   5, −2, 4, 11, −3, −4, 12, 8
   f   −0.6, −2.4, 0.8, 6.5, 5.7, 3.4, 2.1
   g $\frac{1}{4}, \frac{2}{3}, \frac{3}{5}, \frac{7}{8}, \frac{3}{20}, \frac{1}{10}, \frac{3}{7}$

Cumulative frequency diagram

Another very useful tool in statistics is provided through the use of the **cumulative frequency diagram** (which is also called a cumulative frequency curve or an ogive). The cumulative frequency diagram is found by plotting the *cumulative frequencies* and joining them with a **smooth curve**.

Worked Example

The following information gives the waiting time for patients at Miss Thornton's dental practice. Draw the cumulative diagram for the information and use your diagram to find:

a   how many patients waited less than 4 minutes,

b   how many patients waited more than 10 minutes.

Waiting time (mins)	Frequency
0–3	9
3–6	17
6–9	12
9–12	6
12–15	2
15–18	1

NOTE
You should be able to work out the cumulative frequencies without using a calculator.

In order to draw the cumulative diagram, we need to work out the cumulative frequencies by totalling (or accumulating) the frequencies in the table.

Waiting time (mins)	Frequency	Cumulative frequencies	
0–3	9	9	
3–6	17	26	$9 + 17 = 26$
6–9	12	38	$26 + 12 = 38$
9–12	6	44	$38 + 6 = 44$
12–15	2	46	$44 + 2 = 46$
15–18	1	47	$46 + 1 = 47$

NOTE
It is useful to check that the *final* cumulative frequency is the same as the *total* of the frequency column.

To find how many patients waited less than 4 minutes and how many patients waited more than 10 minutes we read off the corresponding cumulative frequencies on the cumulative frequency axis as follows:

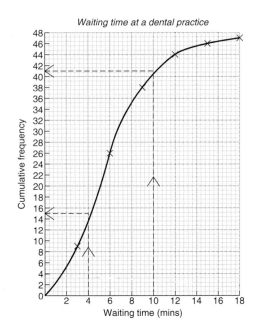

Waiting time at a dental practice

a From the diagram, we can see that 15 patients waited less than 4 minutes.

b From the diagram, we can see that 6 $(47 - 41)$ patients waited more than 10 minutes.

In part **b** the cumulative frequency curve tells us how many patients waited less than 10 minutes. All the remaining patients must have waited more than 10 minutes so we subtract the answer from 47 as there were 47 patients altogether.

Median

We have already seen that the median is the **middle value** when all of the values are arranged in numerical order. The cumulative frequency diagram can also be used to find the median by reading off the middle value, i.e. the $\frac{1}{2}(n + 1)$th value, on the cumulative frequency axis.

Worked Example

Find the median waiting time for the previous worked example.

The middle value is the $\frac{1}{2}(47 + 1)$th value, i.e. the 24th value on the cumulative frequency axis. The median is found by finding the corresponding time on the time axis as follows:

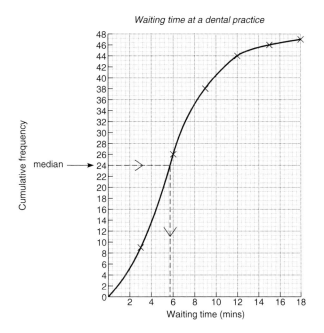

The median time is 5.8 minutes.

Quartiles

The **median** divides the distribution into two equal parts. The **quartiles** divide the distribution into four equal parts.

The Lower Quartile or first quartile (written LQ or Q_1) is the $\frac{1}{4}(n + 1)$th value.

The Upper Quartile or third quartile (written UQ or Q_3) is the $\frac{3}{4}(n + 1)$th value.

Worked Example

Find the lower quartile and the upper quartile of the waiting time in the previous worked example.

The lower quartile is the $\frac{1}{4}(47 + 1)$th value, i.e. the 12th value on the cumulative frequency axis and the upper quartile is the $\frac{3}{4}(47 + 1)$th value, i.e. the 36th value on the cumulative frequency axis. The values for the lower quartile and the upper quartile are found from the corresponding time on the time axis as follows:

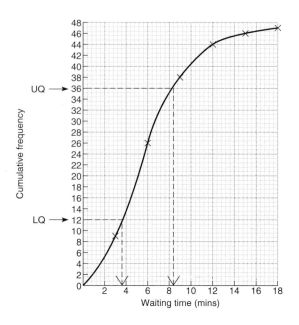

Interquartile range

The **interquartile range**, like the range discussed earlier, also measures spread. However, unlike the range, the interquartile range only considers the middle 50% of the distribution and is therefore unaffected by extreme values.

The interquartile range is calculated as follows:

Interquartile range = upper quartile − lower quartile

Worked Example

Find the interquartile range for the waiting time in the previous worked example.

From the previous worked example we found that:

upper quartile = 8.4
lower quartile = 3.6

Interquartile range = upper quartile − lower quartile
= 8.4 − 3.6
= 4.8

| NOTE |
Another distribution with a smaller interquartile range is likely to have a smaller range and therefore be less spread out. A distribution with a bigger interquartile range is likely to have a larger range and therefore be more spread out.

Although cumulative frequency diagrams are usually used to find the interquartile range we can find the interquartile range from original data as shown in the following worked examples.

Worked Examples

1   The following information shows the weekly earnings of 11 people employed in a call centre. Find the range and interquartile range and comment upon your findings.

£200, £200, £200, £200, £200, £200, £240, £240, £240, £265, £680

The range of the earnings are £680 − £200 = £480.

The value of the range is distorted by the figure of £680 which is an extreme value compared to the earnings of the other ten people.

To find the interquartile range we need to find the value of the upper and lower quartiles. The lower quartile is the $\frac{1}{4}(11 + 1)$th value, i.e. the 3rd value and the upper quartile is the $\frac{3}{4}(11 + 1)$th value, i.e. the 9th value. This information can be seen on the original data which are already written in numerical order.

£200, £200, £200, £200, £200, £200, £240, £240, £240, £265, £680

↑   ↑   ↑

lower quartile   median   upper quartile

Interquartile range   = upper quartile − lower quartile
= £240 − £200
= £40

This is a better measure of the spread of the data since it only considers the central 50% of the distribution and is unaffected by extreme values.

2   Find the range and interquartile range for the following set of data:

34   29   38   25   22   23   32   25   30   51   37   27   42

The range of the data is 51 − 22 = 29.

To find the interquartile range we need to find the value of the upper and lower quartiles. The lower quartile is the $\frac{1}{4}(13 + 1)$th = $3\frac{1}{2}$th value, i.e. half way between the 3rd and 4th value. The upper quartile is the $\frac{3}{4}(13 + 1)$th = $10\frac{1}{2}$th value i.e. half way between the 10th and 11th value.

Arranging the data into numerical order:

22   23   25   25   27   29   30   32   34   37   38   42   51

The lower quartile lies half way between the 3rd and 4th value so equals 25.
The upper quartile lies half way between the 10th and 11th value i.e. between 37 and 38 = 37.5.

Interquartile range   = upper quartile − lower quartile
= 37.5 − 25
= 12.5

PRACTICE 2.4.2

1 The table below shows the lifetime of 200 light bulbs given to the
nearest hour.

Lifetime (hours)	Frequency
1000–1499	35
1500–1999	92
2000–2499	49
2500–2999	17
3000–3499	5
3500–3999	2

Draw a cumulative frequency curve to illustrate this information and
use your graph to find:

a how many light bulbs lasted less than 2250 hours,
b how many light bulbs lasted more than 2250 hours,
c how many light bulbs lasted more than 3250 hours,
d the median,
e the interquartile range.

2 The wages of workers at a factory are shown as follows:

Income (£)	100–	150–	200–	250–	300–	350–400
Frequency	6	15	28	37	11	3

Draw a cumulative frequency curve to illustrate this information and
use your graph to find:

a the median,
b the interquartile range.

3 The following table shows the number of words per sentence in a local
newspaper.

Number of words per sentence	Number of sentences
1–10	15
11–20	58
21–30	92
31–40	30
41–50	5

Draw a cumulative frequency curve to illustrate this information and use your graph to estimate:

a the median,

b the percentage of sentences over 25 words in length.

4 A zoologist times how long it takes her chimps to complete an exercise as follows:

Time (minutes)	Frequency
0 and less than 9.5	6
9.5 and less than 19.5	12
19.5 and less than 29.5	10
29.5 and less than 39.5	5
39.5 and less than 49.5	2

a Draw a cumulative frequency curve to illustrate this information and use your graph to find the median and the interquartile range of the time taken.

b The interquartile range for a different set of chimps is 20 minutes. What can you conclude about the times for the two groups of chimps?

5 The frequency distribution for the time taken to travel across the channel on the seacat is shown for 30 journeys.

Time, t (minutes)	Frequency
$25 \leqslant t < 30$	2
$30 \leqslant t < 35$	6
$35 \leqslant t < 40$	9
$40 \leqslant t < 45$	5
$45 \leqslant t < 50$	4
$50 \leqslant t < 55$	3
$55 \leqslant t < 60$	1

Draw a cumulative frequency curve to show this information and use your curve to find an estimate of the median and the interquartile range.

Box plots

We can use our calculations of the range and quartiles of a distribution of numbers to draw an interesting diagram. This is known as a **Box Plot** or a **Box and Whisker Diagram**. It is drawn as the following worked examples show.

Worked Examples

1 Draw the box plot representing the following data:

$$1 \quad 3 \quad 5 \quad 6 \quad 8 \quad 10 \quad 11 \quad 12 \quad 14 \quad 15 \quad 15$$

The smallest observation = 1 and the largest observation   = 15

There are 11 observations so:

The First Quartile (Q_1) is the $\dfrac{(11 + 1)^{th}}{4}$ observation –
i.e. the 3rd observation   = 5

The Second Quartile (Q_2) (Median) is the $\dfrac{(11 + 1)^{th}}{2}$ observation –
i.e. the 6th observation   = 10

The Third Quartile (Q_3) is the $3\dfrac{(11 + 1)^{th}}{4}$ observation –
i.c. the 9th observation   = 14

The box plot is drawn as shown:

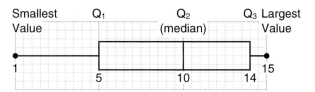

2 Draw the box plot representing the data found in the worked example on waiting times at Miss Thornton's Dental Surgery on page 69:

Since this is a grouped distribution we assume the smallest observation to be 0 and the largest observation to be 18.

There are 47 observations so, using data already calculated:

The First Quartile (Q_1) is the $\dfrac{(47 + 1)^{th}}{4}$ observation –
i.e. the 12th observation   = 3.6

The Second Quartile (Q_2) (Median) is the $\dfrac{(47 + 1)^{th}}{2}$ observation –
i.e. the 24th observation   = 5.8

The Third Quartile (Q_3) is the $3\dfrac{(47 + 1)^{th}}{4}$ observation –
i.e. the 36th observation   = 8.4

The box plot is drawn as shown:

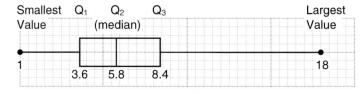

Box plot diagrams show several interesting facts about the distribution:

a Q_1 to Q_3 contains from 25% to 75% of the distribution. Therefore the box itself shows where the middle 50% of the distribution lies.

b The position of the median line inside the box shows whether the median is symmetrical compared to the two other quartiles or whether it is closer to one or the other. Distributions like this are called **skewed** distributions.

c The position of the box compared to the line joining the smallest and largest values shows whether there are any 'extreme' values in the distribution.

PRACTICE 2.4.3   Try these questions without a calculator

1 a Find the range, quartiles and interquartile range of the following sets of data. Draw box plots to illustrate the data.

    i Question 1c of Practice 2.4.1 on page 68.
    ii Question 1f of Practice 2.4.1 on page 68.

  b Draw box plots to illustrate the data in the worked examples on page 73.

2 to 6 Find the range, quartiles and interquartile range of the sets of data found in Practice 2.4.2 on page 74. Draw box plots to illustrate the data.

Scatter graphs

2.5 CORRELATION

The idea of a scatter graph was first introduced in Topic 1.5 **Pictorial representations**. The idea is now developed further to see how they can be used to find relationships between two sets of data.

The distribution of points on a scatter graph can be used to show the relationship or **correlation** between two sets of data. This is illustrated in the following diagrams:

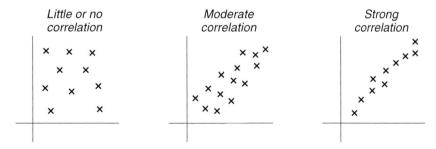

Little or no correlation   Moderate correlation   Strong correlation

In the first graph, the points are scattered randomly over the graph. This shows little or no correlation between the two sets of data. We call this **zero correlation**.

In the second graph, the points lie close to a straight line. This shows **moderate correlation** between the two sets of data. The closer the points are to a straight line then the stronger the correlation is between the two sets of data.

In the third graph, the points are scattered along a straight line. This shows a **strong correlation** between the two sets of data.

Positive, negative and zero correlation

Where an increase in one variable is matched with an increase in the other variable then the correlation is said to be **positive** (or direct).

Where an increase in one variable is matched with a decrease in the other variable then the correlation is said to be **negative** (or inverse).

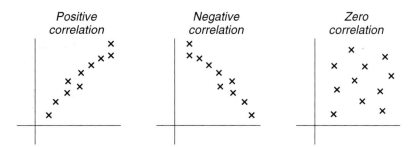

Zero correlation

In the above diagram showing zero correlation the points are scattered randomly on the graph. This usually means that there is no relationship between the two variables. This is not always the case, however. Look at the following data:

Values of x	1	2	3	4	5
Values of y	1	4	9	16	25

There is a very clear relationship between the two sets of data; the y value is the x value squared! A graph drawn of these figures would show a marked quadratic curve (see Topic 11.5).

It would not be sensible to draw a line of best fit on this graph and it would have zero correlation. But there is a relationship.

Zero correlation does not, therefore, mean **no** correlation – it means **no linear** (straight line) **correlation**.

PRACTICE 2.5.1

1   For each of the following scatter graphs, say whether there is any correlation between the two variables.

2 For each of the following sets of data, draw a scatter graph and say whether there is any correlation between the two variables.

a

x	6	3	18	30	15
y	12	10	22	32	19

b

x	0.5	2.2	1.5	1.4	0.7
y	0.5	0.6	2.2	1.4	2.8

c

x	90	200	150	120	260	240
y	50	120	130	90	160	140

d

x	5	20	15	9	26	18
y	22	9	13	16	5	10

Correlation between two sets of data does not always prove that there is a connection between them. For example, the following scatter graph shows the relationship between the number of cars on the road and the sales of refrigerators over a period of time.

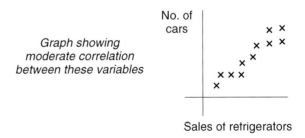

Graph showing
moderate correlation
between these variables

No. of
cars

Sales of refrigerators

Clearly, there is no direct relationship between the number of cars on the road and the sales of refrigerators; the relationship between them is an example of a **spurious correlation**.

Line of best fit

Where the points on a scatter graph show moderate or strong correlation, it is possible to imagine a line around which the points lie and this line is called the **line of best fit** (or regression line). The line of best fit can be used to predict possible values for the data. This is shown in the following worked example.

2 The following information shows the petrol consumption of a car and
   the distance travelled.

Petrol consumption (gallons)	1	2	0.5	1.5	2	1.75
Distance travelled (miles)	25	50	18	38	60	44

   a Draw a scatter graph and comment on the relationship betwen the
      two measurements.

   b Draw a line of best fit and use it to estimate the following:
      i the petrol consumption of a car travelling 30 miles,
      ii the distance travelled by a car whose petrol consumption was
         1.25 gallons.

3 The following scatter graph shows the relationship between the
   distance jumped in the long jump trials and leg length.

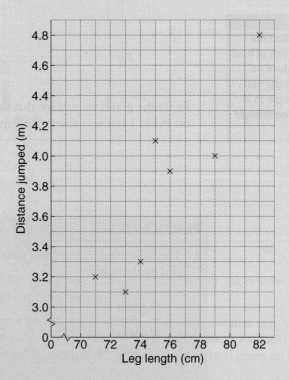

   a Use the line of best fit to estimate:
      i the leg length of someone who jumped a distance of 3.5 m,
      ii the distance jumped by someone with a leg length of 82 cm.

   b Explain why one of these estimates is more reliable than the other.

Standard deviation

Standard deviation is NOT in the specification for the GCSE Intermediate examination. However, it can be very useful to candidates who might use it for their Handling Data coursework. For this reason it is included here.

Standard deviation is another way we measure the spread of a distribution of numbers. It is a better, and more useful, method than either range or interquartile range. The formula actually measures how likely every number in a distribution is to be close to the arithmetic mean. The larger the standard deviation is the more scattered the distribution is.

Two useful formulae for calculating the standard deviation of a group of numbers are given below. Then some worked examples show you how to do these calculations. A practice exercise is included if you wish to 'practise' before using the method in your coursework.

Standard deviation, s, for a set of numbers $x_1, x_2,..., x_n$, having a mean of $\bar{x}$ is given by

$$s = \sqrt{\frac{\Sigma\,(x - \bar{x})^2}{n}} \quad \text{or} \quad s = \sqrt{\frac{\Sigma x^2}{n} - \left\{\frac{\Sigma x}{n}\right\}^2}$$

Worked Examples

1 Find the standard deviation of 4, 7, 8, 10, 11 using the formula

$$s = \sqrt{\frac{\Sigma(x - \bar{x})^2}{n}}.$$

The arithmetic mean $(\bar{x}) = \dfrac{4 + 7 + 8 + 10 + 11}{5} = 8$

The differences of the distribution from the mean, $(x - \bar{x})$ are:

4–8, 7–8, 8–8, 10–8 and 11–8

i.e. $-4, -1, 0, 2, 3$

The squares of these differences, $(x - \bar{x})^2$ are:

16, 1, 0, 4, 9

The mean of these squares of the differences

$$\frac{\Sigma(x - \bar{x})^2}{n} = \frac{16 + 1 + 0 + 4 + 9}{5} = 6$$

The standard deviation is the square root of this value

$$\sqrt{\frac{\Sigma(x - \bar{x})^2}{n}} = \sqrt{6} = 2.45 \text{ (3sf)}.$$

> **NOTE**
> Remember $-4^2 = +16$ etc.

2   Find the standard deviation of 4, 7, 8, 10, 11 using the formula

$$s = \sqrt{\frac{\Sigma x^2}{n} - \left\{\frac{\Sigma x}{n}\right\}^2}$$

The arithmetic mean, $\dfrac{\Sigma x}{n} = \dfrac{4 + 7 + 8 + 10 + 11}{5} = 8$

The squares of the distribution are:

$4^2, 7^2, 8^2, 10^2$ and 11^2

i.e.   16, 49, 64, 100, 121

The mean of these squares, $\dfrac{\Sigma x^2}{n} = \dfrac{16 + 49 + 64 + 100 + 121}{5} = 70$

The standard deviation is

$$\sqrt{\frac{\Sigma x^2}{n} - \left\{\frac{\Sigma x}{n}\right\}^2} = \sqrt{(70 - \{8\}^2)} = \sqrt{(70 - 64)} = \sqrt{6} = 2.45 \text{ (3 sf)}$$

3   The weekly pay for eight shopworkers is as follows:

£180   £180   £200   £220 £240   £260   £290   £310

Find the mean and the standard deviation of the weekly pay.

Using the given formula for the standard deviation of a set of numbers $x_1, x_2, \ldots, x_n$, having a mean of $\bar{x}$, $s = \sqrt{\dfrac{\Sigma(x - \bar{x})^2}{n}}$

The arithmetic mean $(\bar{x})$

$$= \frac{£180 + £180 + £200 + £220 + £240 + £260 + £290 + £310}{8}$$

$$= \frac{£1880}{8} = £235$$

The differences of the distribution from the mean, $(x - \bar{x})$ are:

$-55, \ -55, \ -35, \ -15, \ 5, \ 25, \ 55, \ 75$

The squares of these differences, $(x - \bar{x})^2$ are:

3025, 3025, 1225, 225, 25, 625, 3025, 5625

The mean of these squares of the differences, $\dfrac{\Sigma(x - \bar{x})^2}{n}$

$$= \frac{3025 + 3025 + 1225 + 225 + 25 + 625 + 3025 + 5625}{8}$$

$$= \frac{16\,800}{8} = 2100$$

The standard deviation is $\sqrt{\dfrac{\Sigma(x-\bar{x})^2}{n}} = \sqrt{2100} = 45.825\,756\,949\,5$
$$= 45.8 \text{ (3sf)}$$

Another way to find the mean and standard deviation is to write down the data in tabular form as follows:

x	$(x-\bar{x})$	$(x-\bar{x})^2$
180	-55	3025
180	-55	3025
200	-35	1225
220	-15	225
240	5	25
260	25	625
290	55	3025
310	75	5625
$\Sigma x = 1880$		$\Sigma(x-\bar{x})^2 = 16\,800$

The mean, $\bar{x} = \dfrac{\Sigma x}{n} = \dfrac{1880}{8} = 235$

Standard deviation, $s = \sqrt{\dfrac{\Sigma(x-\bar{x})^2}{n}} = \sqrt{\dfrac{16\,800}{8}} = \sqrt{2100}$

$$= 45.825\,756\,949\,5 = 45.8 \text{ (3 sf)}.$$

4   In the previous worked example all eight shopworkers are given a £40 bonus for Christmas. How does the bonus affect the mean and standard deviation?

After the £40 bonus the pay for the shopworkers is as follows:

£220   £220   £240   £260   £280   £300   £330   £350

Writing the information in tabular form as follows:

x	$(x-\bar{x})$	$(x-\bar{x})^2$
220	-55	3025
220	-55	3025
240	-35	1225
260	-15	225
280	5	25
300	25	625
330	55	3025
350	75	5625
$\Sigma x = 2200$		$\Sigma(x-\bar{x})^2 = 16\,800$

$$\text{The mean, } \bar{x} = \frac{\Sigma x}{n} = \frac{2200}{8} = 275$$

$$\text{Standard deviation, } s = \sqrt{\frac{\Sigma(x - \bar{x})^2}{n}} = \sqrt{\frac{16\,800}{8}} = \sqrt{2100}$$

$$= 45.825\,756\,949\,5 = 45.8 \text{ (3 sf)}.$$

We notice that the mean increases by £40 but that the standard deviation does not alter.

NOTE
The standard deviation has not changed. The same increase on all of the values of a distribution does not affect the spread of the distribution.

5   In the previous worked example each shopworker receives a 5% pay rise the following spring. How does the pay rise affect the mean and standard deviation.

After a 5% pay rise the pay for the shopworkers is as follows:

£189   £189   £210   £231   £252   £273   £304.50   £325.50

Writing the information in tabular form as follows:

x	$(x - \bar{x})$	$(x - \bar{x})^2$
189	−57.75	3335.0625
189	−57.75	3335.0625
210	−36.75	1350.5625
231	−15.75	248.0625
252	5.25	27.5625
273	26.25	689.0625
304.50	57.75	3335.0625
325.50	78.75	6201.5625
$\Sigma x = 1974$		$\Sigma(x - \bar{x})^2 = 18\,522$

$$\text{The mean, } \bar{x} = \frac{\Sigma x}{n} = \frac{1974}{8} = 246.75$$

$$\text{Standard deviation, } s = \sqrt{\frac{\Sigma(x - \bar{x})^2}{n}} = \sqrt{\frac{18\,522}{8}} = \sqrt{2315.25}$$

$$= 48.117\,044\,797 = 48.1 \text{ (3 sf)}.$$

We notice here that the original mean (235) and standard deviation (45.8 to 3 sf) have both increased by 5%.

In general we can show that:

- if we increase (or decrease) all of the values of a distribution by an equal amount then the mean will increase (or decrease) by that amount and the standard deviation (spread) will not be affected,

- if we multiply (or divide) all of the values of a distribution by an equal amount then the mean and the standard deviation will also be multiplied (or divided) by that same amount.

In the last worked example we might find it helpful to use the second formula to find the standard deviation This formula is particularly helpful when we know the value of the mean and avoids having to repeatedly work out the values of $(x - \bar{x})^2$.

$$s = \sqrt{\dfrac{\Sigma x^2}{n} - \left\{\dfrac{\Sigma x}{n}\right\}^2}$$

After a 5% pay rise, we can find the mean and standard deviation as follows:

x	x^2
189	35 721
189	35 721
210	44 100
231	53 361
252	63 504
273	74 529
304.50	92 720.25
325.50	105 950.25
$\Sigma x = 1974$	$\Sigma x^2 = 505\ 606.5$

The mean, $\bar{x} = \dfrac{\Sigma x}{n} = \dfrac{1974}{8} = 246.75$

$$\dfrac{\Sigma x^2}{n} = \dfrac{505\ 606.5}{8} = 63\ 200.8125$$

Standard deviation, $s = \sqrt{\dfrac{\Sigma x^2}{n} - \left\{\dfrac{\Sigma x}{n}\right\}^2} = \sqrt{63\ 200.8125 - 246.75^2}$

$$= \sqrt{63\ 200.8125 - 60\ 885.5625}$$

$$= \sqrt{2315.25}$$

$$= 48.117\ 044\ 797$$

$$= 48.1\ (3\text{sf}) \quad \text{as before}$$

Interpretation of the standard deviation

The standard deviation shows the spread of values about the arithmetic mean. The greater the standard deviation then the greater the spread. For a normal distribution, 68% of the distribution lies within one standard deviation of the mean, 95% of the distribution lies within two standard deviations of the mean and 99% of the distribution lies within three standard deviations of the mean.

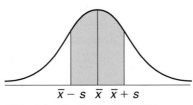

68% of the distribution lies within
one standard deviation of the mean

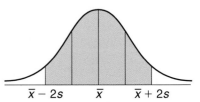

95% of the distribution lies within
two standard deviations of the mean

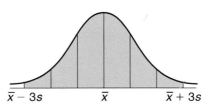

99% of the distribution lies within
three standard deviations of the mean

For example, the height of 500 adults was found to have a mean of 170 cm with a standard deviation of 15 cm. Assuming that these adults are a normal distribution then

68% will lie within one standard deviation of the mean
i.e. 68% of the adults will lie between 155 cm and 185 cm

95% will lie within two standard deviations of the mean
i.e. 95% of the adults will lie between 140 cm and 200 cm

99% will lie within three standard deviations of the mean
i.e. 99% of the adults will lie between 125 cm and 215 cm.

PRACTICE 2.6.1a   Try these questions with a calculator

1 Find the mean and standard deviation of the following data.
  a 1, 2, 3, 4, 5, 6, 7
  b 2, 2, 4, 8
  c −4, −1, 2, 3, 5
  d 2.5, 3.5, 4.5, 5.5, 6.5, 7.5

2 Find the mean and standard deviation of the following information which gives the times needed to complete a task on five successive days:

  23 mins,   42 mins,   36 mins,   29 mins,   45 mins

3 The prices of houses in an estate agent's window are:

  £84 000   £96 000   £118 000   £92 000   £94 000
  £94 000   £90 000   £98 000   £102 000   £92 000

Calculate the means and use the formula

$$s = \sqrt{\frac{\Sigma\,(x - \bar{x})^2}{n}}$$

to find the standard deviation.

4 Use the formula

$$s = \sqrt{\frac{\Sigma x^2}{n} - \left\{\frac{\Sigma x}{n}\right\}^2}$$

to find the standard deviation of the distribution in question **3**.

PRACTICE 2.6.1b   Try these questions without a calculator

1 The mean of the numbers −5, −2, 2, 4, 6 is 1. The standard deviation of the same numbers is 4. Use this information to find the mean and standard deviation of each of the following sets of data.

  a −4, −1, 3, 5, 7
  b 0, 3, 7, 9, 11
  c −6, −3, 1, 3, 5
  d −10, −4, 4, 8, 12
  e −2.5, −1, 1, 2, 3
  f 0, 1.5, 3.5, 4.5, 5.5
  g −0.05, −0.02, 0.02, 0.04, 0.06

Measures of central tendency

The most common statistical measure is the measurement of central tendency or average. Different averages considered include the mode, median and arithmetic mean.

Mode

The mode is the value that occurs the most frequently. If there are two modes the distribution is bimodal. If there are more than two modes the distribution is multimodal.

Median

The median is the middle value when all of the values are arranged in numerical order. When there are an even number of values, we take the two middle numbers and find their mean. A cumulative frequency diagram can also be used to find the median by reading off the middle value, i.e. the $\frac{1}{2}(n + 1)$th value, on the cumulative frequency axis.

Arithmetic mean

The arithmetic mean or mean is found by adding up the values and dividing by the number of values. When we have data arranged in groups we use the mid-point of the interval to represent the group.

Time series

Time series are diagrams that plot information over periods of time. Variations in time series can be 'smoothed out' using moving averages to identify trend.

Cumulative frequency diagram

A cumulative frequency diagram or ogive is constructed by plotting the *cumulative frequencies* (at the end of each boundary) and joining them with a smooth curve.

Range

The range of a distribution is found by working out the difference between the highest value and the lowest value. The range should always be presented as a single value.

Quartiles

Quartiles divide the distribution into four equal parts. The lower quartile is the $\frac{1}{4}(n + 1)$th value and the upper quartile is the $\frac{3}{4}(n + 1)$th value.

Interquartile range

The interquartile range only considers the middle 50% of the distribution and is unaffected by extreme values.

$$\text{Interquartile range} = \text{upper quartile} - \text{lower quartile}$$

Box plots

Box plots (or box and whisker diagrams) are useful means of showing the median and quartiles diagramatically. They can be used to compare different distributions and identify skewed distributions.

Scatter diagrams

The distribution of points on a scatter diagram can be used to give an indication of the relationship or correlation between two sets of data:

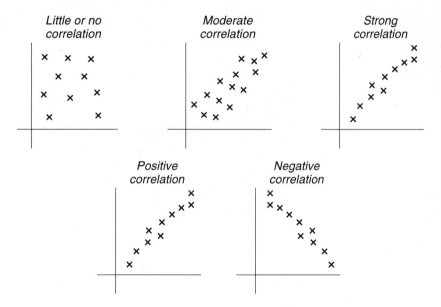

Line of best fit

Where the points on a scatter diagram show moderate or strong correlation, a line of best fit (or regression line) can be drawn and used to predict possible values for the data.

Standard deviation (useful for coursework)

The standard deviation for a set of data can be calculated using the formulae:

$$s = \sqrt{\frac{\Sigma\,(x - \bar{x})^2}{n}} \quad \text{or} \quad s = \sqrt{\frac{\Sigma x^2}{n} - \left\{\frac{\Sigma x}{n}\right\}^2}$$

Using the mean and the standard deviation

If we increase (or decrease) all of the values of a distribution by an equal amount then the mean will increase (or decrease) by that amount and the standard deviation (spread) will not be affected.

If we multiply (or divide) all of the values of a distribution by an equal amount then the mean and the standard deviation will also be multiplied (or divided) by that same amount.

CHAPTER 3
Probability

In this chapter you will need to:

▸ revise how to use fractions, decimals and percentages (see Topics 6.4, 6.5 and 6.6)

▸ understand the terms used in probability

▸ understand the probability scale

Probability

Probability measures how likely an event is to happen, or not to happen.

Worked Example

State whether the following events are **certain, likely, unlikely** or **impossible** to occur.

a You will run a mile in under two minutes.
b You had a birthday last year.
c It will be sunny in June.
d A coin has a head on each side.
e The local supermarket will shut down next Friday.
f You will win the lottery next week.
g You get an odd number when throwing a dice.

Most people would agree with the following answers:

a	You will run a mile in under two minutes.	impossible
b	You had a birthday last year.	certain
c	It will be sunny in June.	likely
d	A coin has a head on each side.	impossible
e	The local supermarket will shut down next Friday.	unlikely
f	You will win the lottery next week.	unlikely
g	You get an odd number when throwing a dice.	

The last question cannot be answered properly since the probability of getting an odd number is the same as the probability of not getting an odd number. When these probabilities are the same we call it **evens**.

Probability scale

The idea of using certain, likely, unlikely and impossible to measure probability is not very accurate. Therefore probability is usually shown on a **probability scale**, shown below:

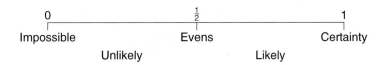

The 0 and 1 values are explained later.

PRACTICE 3.1.1

1 Mark the probabilities of the following events on a probability scale like this one:

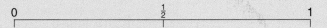

  a The probability of scoring more than 4 on a roll of a fair six-sided dice.

  b The probability that you will have a drink tomorrow.

  c The probability that a number chosen from the list 2, 3, 4, 5, 6 is odd.

  d The probability that a card picked from a standard pack is a diamond.

To calculate the probability of an event occurring we use the following formula:

$$\text{probability} = \frac{\text{number of successful outcomes}}{\text{total number of possible outcomes}}$$

Worked Examples

1 Find the probability of obtaining a three when throwing a dice.

NOTE
Probability can be written as a fraction, as a decimal, or as a percentage.

$$\text{Probability} = \frac{\text{number of successful outcomes}}{\text{total number of possible outcomes}}$$

probability $= \dfrac{1}{6}$ (there is 1 successful outcome i.e. a 3)
(there are 6 possible outcomes)

2 A bag contains 20 coloured cubes. 12 cubes are green and 8 are red. A cube is selected from the bag at random. What is the probability of selecting a green cube?

$$\text{Probability} = \frac{\text{number of successful outcomes}}{\text{total number of possible outcomes}}$$

probability $= \dfrac{12}{20}$ (there are 12 successful outcomes)
(there are 20 possible outcomes)

probability $= \dfrac{3}{5}$ (cancelling down)

NOTE
In probability we sometimes use the shorthand p(green) to mean the probability of getting a green cube and in this example p(green) = $\frac{3}{5}$.

PRACTICE 3.2.1

1 Write down the probability of
  a getting a head if a coin is tossed,
  b getting an odd number if a dice is rolled,
  c selecting a heart from a pack of cards,
  d selecting the ace of clubs from a pack of cards.

2 A letter is selected from the word MISSISSIPPI. What is the probability that it is the letter:
  a M   **b** S   **c** P   **d** R?

3 An eight-sided dice is rolled. Find the probability of getting:
   a a 5,   **b** a prime number,   **c** a multiple of 3.

4 A letter is picked at random from the 26 letters of the alphabet.
   a What is the probability that the letter is in the first half of the alphabet?
   b What is the probability that the letter is in the word RANDOM?
   c What is the probability that the letter is in the word PROBABILITY?

5 Twenty discs marked with the numbers 1 to 20 are placed in a bag. One disc is drawn at random. What is the probability that the number on the disc will be:
   a an odd number,   **d** a factor of 24,
   b a multiple of 3,   **e** greater than 12,
   c a prime number,   **f** less than, or equal to, 6?

6 Viv puts a coin into her money box. It now holds three £2 coins, two £1 coins, five 50p pieces, four 20p pieces and six 10p pieces. Find the probability that the coin she put into the box was:
   a a 50 pence piece,   **d** worth less than 50 pence,
   b a 10 pence piece,   **e** worth at least £1.
   c a 5 pence piece,

7 A machine produces 500 bolts and 35 are found to be faulty.
   What is the probability that a bolt chosen at random will not be faulty?
   Give your answer as a fraction in its lowest terms.

8 A bag contains seven red cubes, eight green cubes and ten blue cubes.
   What is the probability of drawing:
   a a blue cube,   **d** a yellow cube,
   b a green cube,   **e** a red, green or blue cube?
   c a cube that is not red,

9 A box contains 40 counters of different colours. A counter is chosen at random from the box. The probability that the counter chosen is white is $\frac{1}{10}$, the probability that the counter chosen is black is 0.4 and the probability that the counter chosen is red is 30%. The rest of the counters are blue.
   a How many counters are white?
   b How many counters are black?
   c How many counters are red?
   d How many counters are blue?

10 A bag contains 20 counters and the probability of getting a red counter is 0.85.
   a How many red counters are there in the bag?
   b How many counters are not red?

Total probability

From the last two parts of question 8 in Practice 3.2.1, you should have noted that:

$$\text{the probability of a yellow cube} = \frac{0}{25} = 0$$

$$\text{the probability of a red or green or blue cube} = \frac{25}{25} = 1$$

Therefore

if an event is impossible then its probability $\quad\quad = 0$
if an event is certain to happen then its probability $\quad = 1$

The probability that an event occurs plus the probability that the event does not occur should always equal one.

Worked Example

The probability that Sonia passes her driving test is $\frac{7}{9}$. What is the probability that Sonia does not pass her driving test?

The probability that an event occurs plus the probability that the event does not occur should always equal one.

So the probability that Sonia passes her driving test plus the probability that Sonia does not pass her driving test should equal one.

$\frac{7}{9}$ + the probability that Sonia does not pass her driving test = 1

$\frac{7}{9} + \frac{2}{9} = 1$

so the probability that Sonia does not pass her driving test $= \frac{2}{9}$.

> **NOTE**
> The probability of an event occurring is equal to 1 minus the probability of the event not occurring so that the probability that Sonia does not pass her driving test is equal to 1 minus the probability that Sonia does pass her driving test.

PRACTICE 3.2.2   Try these questions without a calculator

1   The probability that it will rain tomorrow is $\frac{1}{3}$. What is the probability that it will not rain tomorrow?

2   The probability that a particular team will win the league title is 0.004. What is the probability that the team will not win the league title?

3   The probability that Jem will be late for work on Monday is 0.002. What is the probability that Jem will not be late for work on Monday?

4   A box of chocolates is such that 35% of the chocolates are plain chocolates. Calculate the probability that a chocolate chosen at random is not a plain chocolate.

5   The probability that a bus arrives early is 0.1 and the probability that the bus arrives on time is 0.5. What is the probability that the bus arrives late?

Theoretical and experimental probability

Toss a coin 10 times.
Did you get 5 heads and 5 tails?

Toss a coin another 10 times.
What happened?

When we toss a coin 10 times, we expect to get 5 heads and 5 tails. We use probability based on **equally likely outcomes** ($\frac{1}{2}$) to tell us how many heads and how many tails we should get (in theory).

i.e. $10 \times \frac{1}{2} = 5$

In reality, we often get slightly different results and these give us the **experimental probability** (from our experiment). If we tossed our coin 10 times and got 7 heads then we would say that the experimental probability or relative frequency of getting a head is $\frac{7}{10}$.

The more times we toss the coin, then the closer the experimental probability or relative frequency should be to the theoretical probability. Sometimes estimates of probability can only be made by using experimental probability or relative frequency, for example:

the probability of a coach arriving on time,
the probability of passing a driving test,
the probability that a car will develop a fault.

Thus we get relative frequency by dividing (each) frequency by the total frequency.

Worked Examples

1   A coin is tossed 500 times.
    What is the expected number of heads?

The probability of getting a head when tossing a coin is $\frac{1}{2}$.

When tossing a coin 500 times,

expected number of heads = $500 \times \frac{1}{2} = 250$

If a coin is tossed 500 times, we would expect to get 250 heads (and 250 tails).

2 A dice is thrown 100 times. How many times would you expect to throw a six?

The probability of throwing a six is $\frac{1}{6}$.

When throwing a dice 100 times,

expected number of sixes $= 100 \times \frac{1}{6} = 16.6$ (recurring).

If a dice is thrown 100 times, we would expect to get 17 sixes (to the nearest whole number).

3 A dice is thrown 150 times and the following frequency distribution is obtained.

Score	1	2	3	4	5	6
Frequency	21	31	26	19	33	20

a What is the relative frequency of getting a score of 6?
b What is the relative frequency of getting an odd number?

a The relative frequency of a score of 6 is $\frac{20}{150} = \frac{2}{15}$ (in its lowest terms).

b The frequency of getting an odd number is $21 + 26 + 33 = 80$.

The relative frequency of getting an odd number is $\frac{80}{150} = \frac{8}{15}$ (in its lowest terms).

4 In the 2001 National Census, 50 families in a street gave the following information about the number of children in their families:

Number of children in the family	0	1	2	3	4	5	>5
Number of families (f)	7	12	15	7	5	2	2

Find the relative frequencies of:

a one child in a family,
b less than 3 children per family,
c more than 4 children per family.

a Relative Frequency $= \dfrac{\text{Actual Frequency}}{\text{Total Frequency}} = \dfrac{12}{50} = 0.24$

b Relative Frequency $= \dfrac{\text{Actual Frequency}}{\text{Total Frequency}} = \dfrac{34}{50} = 0.68$

c Relative Frequency $= \dfrac{\text{Actual Frequency}}{\text{Total Frequency}} = \dfrac{4}{50} = 0.08$

PRACTICE 3.2.3a   Try these questions without a calculator

1 A dice is thrown 60 times. What is the expected frequency of an odd number?

2 The probability that a person living in Brackwell will win a prize on the lottery next week is 0.000 2. If the population is 22 500, how many people living in Brackwell can be expected to win the lottery next week?

3 About one child in five in a particular area is asthmatic. How many Asthmatic children would you expect to find:

   a in a village housing 152 children,

   b in a street where 44 children live,

   c in Mr. Brennan's class of 26 children?

4 The probability that a new scooter will develop a fault in the first month is $\frac{1}{200}$. A garage sells 820 new scooters one year. How many of the new scooters will be expected to develop a fault in the first month?

5 A dice is thrown 200 times and the following frequency distribution is obtained.

Score	1	2	3	4	5	6
Frequency	30	35	38	29	32	36

   a What is the relative frequency of a score of 1?

   b What is the relative frequency of a score of 6?

   c What is the relative frequency of getting an even number?

   d For which score are the relative frequency and theoretical probability the closest?

6 Which of the following probabilities can be determined by considering equally likely outcomes and which can be determined through experimental probability?

   a The probability of a train arriving late.

   b The probability that an unbiased coin will land tails up.

   c The probability of a particular machine breaking down.

2 A counter is selected from a box containing 4 red and 3 green counters at the same time as a six-sided dice, numbered 1 to 6, is thrown. Draw a possibility space for this information and use this information to calculate
  a the probability of a red and a six,
  b the probability of a green and a three,
  c the probability of a red and an odd number.

3 A six-sided dice, numbered 1 to 6, and a four-sided dice, numbered 1 to 4, are thrown at the same time. Draw a possibility space for the two dice and use this information to calculate
  a the probability of a total of 3,
  b the probability of a total of 7,
  c the probability of a total of 10.

4 Two pentagonal spinners with the numbers 1 to 5 are spun and their outcomes added together. Draw a possibility space for the two spinners and use this information to calculate
  a the probability of a total of 2,
  b the probability of a total of 6,
  c the probability of a total of 9.

5 Two coins are tossed and a six-sided dice is rolled. For two heads the score is double the number shown on the dice. For one head the score is the number shown on the dice. For no heads the score equals zero. Draw a possibility space for the scores and use this information to calculate
  a the probability of a score of 4,
  b the probability that the score is more than 4.

6 The following table shows the probabilities of selecting counters from a box. The counters are coloured red, blue and green and numbered 1, 2, 3 and 4.

		Number			
		1	2	3	4
	Red	$\frac{1}{20}$	$\frac{1}{10}$	$\frac{1}{5}$	0
Colour	Blue	$\frac{1}{10}$	0	$\frac{1}{20}$	$\frac{1}{10}$
	Green	$\frac{1}{5}$	$\frac{1}{20}$	$\frac{1}{10}$	$\frac{1}{20}$

  a A counter is taken from the box at random. Calculate the probability that:
     i it is blue and numbered 1,   **iii** it is numbered 3,
     ii it is green,   **iv** it is blue or numbered 4.
  b There are 14 red counters in the box.
     i How many counters are there altogether?
     ii How many blue counters are there altogether?

5 The table shows the sale of raincoats in a department store.

Week	1	2	3	4	5	6	7	8	9	10
Sales	14	20	30	16	12	12	6	8	2	9

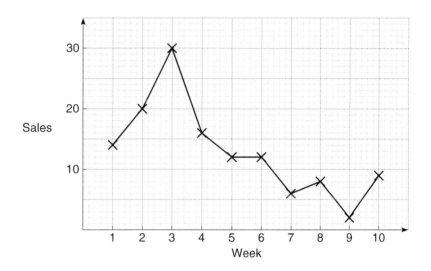

a Calculate the first value of the four-point moving average for the
   data.   *(1 mark)*

The remaining values of the four-point moving average for the data are

                19.5   17.5   11.5   9.5   7.0   6.25

b Plot all the values of the moving average on the graph.   *(1 mark)*

c Use your graph to estimate the sales in the following week.   *(3 marks)*

d Explain why your answer to part **c** is not an accurate reflection
   of the sales.   *(1 mark)*

4.2

WITHOUT A
CALCULATOR

Module 1 – Data handling

1　The ages of people in a class are recorded as:

　　　　23　　18　　23　　27　　19　　22　　36　　31

　　Construct a stem and leaf diagram to show these ages.　　*(2 marks)*

2

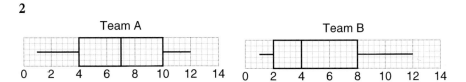

Team A　　　　　　　　　　　　　　　Team B

0　2　4　6　8　10　12　14　　　0　2　4　6　8　10　12　14

　　The box plots summarise the number of points scored by two teams in a
　　competition.

　　a　Find the interquartile range for the points scored by Team A.　　*(1 mark)*

　　b　Describe **two differences** between the two distributions.　　*(2 marks)*

3　Mr Appleton records the favourite colours of the pupils in his class.

Colour	Frequency
Red	15
Blue	12
Green	7
Yellow	2

Draw and label a pie chart to
represent this information.　　*(4 marks)*

4　A seaside resort recorded the rainfall in millimetres and the number of
　　deck chair tickets sold.
　　The scatter diagram illustrates some of these recordings.

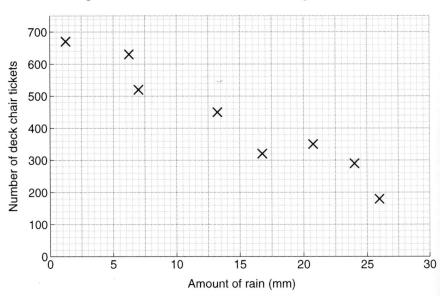

a What does the scatter graph tell you about the connection between the rainfall and the number of deck chair tickets sold? *(1 mark)*

b Draw a line of best fit on the scatter graph. *(1 mark)*

c Use your line of best fit to work out the likely number of deck chair tickets sold when the rainfall is recorded as 10 mm. *(2 marks)*

5 A dice is biased so that the probability of getting a six is $\frac{1}{4}$.
The dice is rolled 100 times.

a How many sixes would you expect to get? *(2 marks)*

b The number three appears 13 times.
Give an estimate of the probability of getting a three when this dice is rolled. *(1 mark)*

6 The weight of tea in a sample of 100 tea-bags is shown in the table.

Weight of tea in tea-bag, w (grams)	Frequency	Cumulative frequency
$2.9 \leqslant w < 3.0$	2	
$3.0 \leqslant w < 3.1$	6	
$3.1 \leqslant w < 3.2$	32	
$3.2 \leqslant w < 3.3$	41	
$3.3 \leqslant w < 3.4$	14	
$3.4 \leqslant w < 3.5$	4	
$3.5 \leqslant w < 3.6$	1	

a Complete the cumulative frequency column of the table. *(1 mark)*

b Draw a cumulative frequency curve for these data on graph paper. *(2 marks)*

c Use your graph to estimate the number of tea-bags with a weight greater than 3.35 grams. *(1 mark)*

CHAPTER 5
Module 2 – The handling data task

Module 2 is the handling data task and is worth 10% of your total marks on the examination.

The handling data task will usually involve you undertaking a statistical investigation on some area of interest using your own data or sampling data from a given data set. This work is all about your statistical thinking … so don't forget to:

- include some statistics,
- show your thinking.

Planning is important so before you start your coursework decide what you are going to investigate and do not be too ambitious!

Most handling data tasks can be split into three areas …

Starting up
- *Decide what your investigation is about and provide a hypothesis (a theory) to test.*
- *Think about how you are going to collect the information.*

Collecting
- *Show your results as tables, charts or graphs.*
- *Write down anything you notice from your tables, charts or graphs.*

Getting results
- *Make comments on your findings and suggest reasons for these.*
- *Relate these findings back to the original hypothesis.*

Comprehensive guidance about how to plan and carry out your handling data task can be found in Chapter 1, see pages 7 and 8.

NOTE
If you want to do really well on your coursework then you must extend the given task. You can do this by writing some further hypotheses and investigating these.

CHOICE OF TASK

The choice of task is important so you can get the best possible marks for your work. Your teacher or lecturer will provide you with some ideas or you may find the following useful:

Reaction times

Grandad told Simon that some people have slower reactions than other people. Simon decided to test the reaction times of some of his friends.
- Write down a hypothesis for him to test.
- Design and carry out an investigation to find out different ways in which reaction times can be affected.

Investigate further.

116

Pulse rate

Not everyone has the same pulse rate – and pulse rate can be affected by a number of different things.

- Write a hypothesis about how someone's pulse rate can be affected.
- Design and carry out an investigation to show different ways in which pulse rate can be affected.

Investigate further.

Your coursework will be marked by your teacher or sent to the examination board for marking. The handling data task is marked under three strands. Each strand is marked out of a total of 8. To get a grade C you should aim to get a total of 14 marks over the three strands. They are:

1 Specifying the problem and planning
2 Collecting, processing and representing the data
3 Interpreting and discussing the results

Each strand assesses a different area of your coursework, as follows:

1 Specifying the problem and planning

This strand is about choosing a problem and deciding how to go about solving it. You should provide clear aims, consider the collection of data, identify practical problems and explain how you might overcome them.

Marks	To be awarded these marks you must…
3–4	set out reasonably clear aims and include a plan. The sample size is of an appropriate size (usually 30 data items).
5–6	set out clear aims and include a plan which is designed to meet those aims. The sample size is an appropriate size and reasons are given for its choice.

2 Collecting, processing and representing the data

You should collect data and use appropriate statistical representations and calculations to process and represent the data.

Marks	To be awarded these marks you must…
3–4	collect data and make use of statistical representations and calculations, such as pie charts, bar charts, stem and leaf diagrams, mean, median and mode.
5–6	collect appropriate data and make use of statistical representations and calculations such as pie charts, bar charts, stem and leaf diagrams, scatter graphs, mean, median and mode (of grouped data).

3 Interpreting and discussing the results

This strand is about commenting, summarising and interpreting your data. You should link your findings back to the original problem and provide an evaluation of your work.

Marks	To be awarded these marks you must…
3–4	summarise and correctly interpret some of your representations and calculations and use them to respond to your original hypothesis.
5–6	summarise and correctly interpret your representations and calculations and use these to respond to your original question. Consideration is given to the strategies included in the work and how successful these are.

And finally …

- Remember to state your aims at the beginning and say how well those aims were met at the end.
- Use appropriate statistical representations to illustrate information with accompanying commentary.
- Projects based on probability only will not score well on the criteria so should be avoided.
- Make sure that the work submitted is your own because if you copy from someone else you might be disqualified.
- Always keep your rough working as it is evidence of your thinking – you might include some comment on why it didn't seem to work.
- You can use a computer for your coursework but remember to interpret any information provided.
- Remember that presentation is important so present your work neatly and clearly.

References to other parts of the book

SECTION TWO

Number (Module 3)

CONTENTS

CHAPTER 6
Number and number problems

In this chapter you will need to:
▸ understand how numbers are grouped
▸ understand squares, square roots and powers
▸ understand the order of doing arithmetic

Grouping numbers

Numbers can be grouped in many different ways. You need to know about the following groups:

counting numbers	1, 2, 3, 4, 5, 6, ...
natural numbers	1, 2, 3, 4, 5, 6, ... the same as counting numbers
odd numbers	1, 3, 5, 7, 9, 11, ...
even numbers	2, 4, 6, 8, 10, 12, ...

integers (whole numbers) ..., $-5, -4, -3, -2, -1, 0, 1, 2, 3, 4, 5, ...$

positive integers	$+1, +2, +3, +4, +5, ...$
negative integers	$-1, -2, -3, -4, -5, ...$

Square numbers

Square numbers are formed when you multiply any whole number by itself. 16 is a square number because 4 multiplied by itself is 16.

Worked Example

The specifications state that you should know the first 15 square numbers.

The first 15 square numbers are:

$1 = 1 \times 1$	$81 = 9 \times 9$
$4 = 2 \times 2$	$100 = 10 \times 10$
$9 = 3 \times 3$	$121 = 11 \times 11$
$16 = 4 \times 4$	$144 = 12 \times 12$
$25 = 5 \times 5$	$169 = 13 \times 13$
$36 = 6 \times 6$	$196 = 14 \times 14$
$49 = 7 \times 7$	$225 = 15 \times 15$
$64 = 8 \times 8$	

NOTE
The square roots of square
numbers are always whole
numbers. Any positive
number has a square root
but most of these are not
whole numbers.

NOTE
Try to remember the
common square roots:

$\sqrt{1} = 1$ $\sqrt{16} = 4$

$\sqrt{4} = 2$ $\sqrt{25} = 5$

$\sqrt{9} = 3$ $\sqrt{36} = 6$ etc.

Alternatively, use the $\boxed{\sqrt{}}$
button on your calculator.

NOTE
Sometimes the answer will
not be exact and we will
need to approximate the
answer.

Square roots

Square roots are numbers which, when multiplied by themselves, give the
required number.
6 is the square root of 36 because $6 \times 6 = 36$
In maths the $\sqrt{}$ sign is used for 'the square root of', so $\sqrt{36} = 6$

Worked Examples

1   6.5 is the square root of 42.25 because $6.5 \times 6.5 = 42.25$

   We write $\sqrt{42.25} = 6.5$

2   8.15 is the square root of 66.4225 because $8.15 \times 8.15 = 66.4225$

   We write $\sqrt{66.4225} = 8.15$

3   Use the $\boxed{\sqrt{}}$ button on a calculator to find the following:

   $\sqrt{25}$ $\sqrt{56.25}$ $\sqrt{80}$ $\sqrt{289}$ $\sqrt{2890}$

   Using your calculator:
   $\sqrt{25} = 5$ exactly
   $\sqrt{56.25} = 7.5$ exactly
   $\sqrt{80} = 8.944\,271\,9\ldots$ approximately
   $\sqrt{289} = 17$ exactly
   $\sqrt{2890} = 53.758\,72\ldots$ approximately

However, **each positive number has TWO square roots!**

If we calculate 5×5 we get 25, so we can say that 5 is the square root of 25.
BUT if we calculate -5×-5 we also get 25 because a negative (minus)
number times another negative number is a positive (plus) number. So we
can say that -5 is also the square root of 25.

Therefore 25 has two square roots, $+5$ and -5.
We already know the sign $\sqrt{}$ means 'the square root of'. Also, $\pm$ means 'plus
and minus'. Thus the above expression could be written:
$$\sqrt{25} = \pm 5.$$

Therefore, strictly speaking, the answers to the worked examples above
should be:
1. ± 6.5 **2.** ± 8.15 **3.** ± 5, ± 7.5, $\pm 8.944\,271\,9$, ± 17 and $\pm 53.758\,72$

Sometimes, depending on the question, only one answer is correct. For
instance, if you were asked to find the length of the side of a square of area
$100\,\text{m}^2$, we would have to calculate $\sqrt{100}$ (= ± 10). However, we cannot
draw a length of -10 m. So only $+10$ is correct in this question.

Cube Numbers

Cube numbers are formed when you multiply any whole number by itself twice.

27 is a cube number because $3 \times 3 \times 3 = 27$

Worked Example

In the syllabus you are expected to know the first 5 cube numbers and the cube of 10.

These are:
$$1 = 1 \times 1 \times 1$$
$$8 = 2 \times 2 \times 2$$
$$27 = 3 \times 3 \times 3$$
$$64 = 4 \times 4 \times 4$$
$$125 = 5 \times 5 \times 5$$
$$1000 = 10 \times 10 \times 10$$

Cube roots

Cube roots are numbers which, multiplied by themselves twice, give the required number, e.g. 2 is the cube root of 8 because $2 \times 2 \times 2 = 8$.

We write **cube root** as $\sqrt[3]{}$. Therefore, from the worked examples above:
$$\sqrt[3]{8} = 2$$
$$\sqrt[3]{27} = 3 \text{ etc.}$$

PRACTICE 6.1.1a   Try these questions without a calculator

1 Find the squares of:
   a 16   **b** 20   **c** 25   **d** 30   **e** 32

2 Find the cubes of:
   a 3   **b** 7   **c** 0   **d** 12   **e** 30

PRACTICE 6.1.1b   Try these questions with a calculator

1 Which of the following are square numbers?
   A 125   **C** 1690   **E** 10 000
   B 169   **D** 1000   **F** 100 000

2 **a** Use the $\boxed{\sqrt{}}$ button on your calculator to find, giving both answers:
   i $\sqrt{49}$ **iii** $\sqrt{90}$ **v** $\sqrt{1233.4144}$
   ii $\sqrt{77.44}$ **iv** $\sqrt{900}$
   b Which of the above answers are exact?

3 Find the exact values of:
   a 45^2 **b** 4.5^2 **c** 13.2^2 **d** 27.8^2 **e** 3.25^2

4 Do this question only if you have a cube root button ($\sqrt[3]{}$) on your calculator. Find the cube roots of:
   a 512   **c** 32 768   **e** 15.625
   b 8000   **d** 1.728   **f** 34 645.976

Simple powers

We know already when we multiply a number by itself we are squaring the number.

The square of 4 is 4×4 ($= 16$) and the square of 7 is 7×7 ($= 49$).

We also know that when we multiply a number by itself and then by itself again we are cubing the number.

The cube of 4 is $4 \times 4 \times 4$ ($= 64$) and the cube of 7 is $7 \times 7 \times 7$ ($= 343$).

Writing out numbers like this can be rather time consuming. Instead we can use a shorthand where

$$4 \times 4 = 4^2 \qquad\qquad 7 \times 7 = 7^2$$
$$4 \times 4 \times 4 = 4^3 \qquad 7 \times 7 \times 7 = 7^3$$

This method of writing can be extended to other numbers of the form:

$$3^5 \quad \longleftarrow \text{ power (or index)}$$
$$ \quad \longleftarrow \text{ base}$$

The **power** or **index** simply tells you how many times the base number is to be multiplied by itself so that 3^5 means that 3 (the base number) is to be multiplied by itself 5 times (the power or index).

$$3^5 = \underbrace{3 \times 3 \times 3 \times 3 \times 3}_{5 \text{ times}}$$

Similarly 5^8 means that 5 (the base number) is to be multiplied by itself 8 times (the power or index).

$$5^8 = \underbrace{5 \times 5 \times 5 \times 5 \times 5 \times 5 \times 5 \times 5}_{8 \text{ times}}$$

The plural of index is **indices**.

PRACTICE 6.1.2   Try these questions without a calculator

1 Write down different ways to say the following:
   a 5^2 c 15^2 e 11^3 g 3^7
   b 9^2 d 4^3 f 6^4 h 2^{10}

2 Work out each of the powers in question **1**.

3 Write down the following as a power.
   a $5 \times 5 \times 5 \times 5$
   b $4 \times 4 \times 4 \times 4 \times 4 \times 4 \times 4$
   c $8 \times 8 \times 8$
   d $16 \times 16 \times 16 \times 16 \times 16 \times 16 \times 16 \times 16 \times 16 \times 16$
   e $3 \times 3 \times 3 \times 3 \times 3 \times 3$

4   Find the value of A when A = 5^4.

5   Find the value of C when C = 7^3.

6   Find the values of:
   a $3^2 + 5^3$
   b $5^2 + 4^3$

7   Which is the greater
   a 3^2 or 2^3
   b 5^2 or 2^5
   c 3^4 or 4^3
   d 2^4 or 4^2?
   Show your workings in each case.

Use your calculator for this question.

8   A man starts with a large piece of paper $\frac{1}{100}$ of an inch thick. He cuts it in half and places the cut piece on top of the first. He does this 50 times (i.e. he cuts the stack). How high is the resulting column of paper?

Order of operations

The word BODMAS is used to help us remember the order in which operations are undertaken:

Brackets
Of
Division
Multiplication
Addition
Subtraction

This tells us the order in which mathematical expressions should be worked out. **Brackets** are always worked out first. **Divisions** and **multiplications** are worked out before **additions** and **subtractions**.

If an expression has only multiplication/division or addition/subtraction then the answer should be worked out from left to right.

NOTE

The word *evaluate* means find the value of or work out.

This word is often used on examination papers so it is important that you are familiar with what it means.

Worked Examples

Evaluate the following:

a $25 - 5 + 1$　　**c** $12 - 3 \times 2$　　**e** $6 \times (3 + 1)$　　**g** $12 - 6 \div 3$
b $6 \times 2 \div 3$　　**d** $(12 - 3) \times 2$　　**f** $6 \times 3 + 1$　　**h** $8 - 6 \div 2 + 5$

   a $25 - 5 + 1$　　　　　working from left to right
      $= 21$
   b $6 \times 2 \div 3$　　　　　working from left to right
      $= 4$

c $12 - 3 \times 2$ multiplication before subtraction
$= 12 - 6$
$= 6$

d $(12 - 3) \times 2$ brackets $(12 - 3)$ first, then multiplication
$= 9 \times 2$
$= 18$

e $6 \times (3 + 1)$ brackets $(3 + 1)$ first, then multiplication
$= 6 \times 4$
$= 24$

f $6 \times 3 + 1$ multiplication before addition
$= 18 + 1$
$= 19$

g $12 - 6 \div 3$ division before subtraction
$= 12 - 2$
$= 10$

h $8 - 6 \div 2 + 5$ division first
$= 8 - 3 + 5$
$= 10$

PRACTICE 6.1.3   Try these questions without a calculator

1 Evaluate the following:
  a $23 - 2 + 5$ and $23 - (2 + 5)$
  b $17 - 2 \times 3$ and $(17 - 2) \times 3$
  c $8 \times 5 - 1$ and $8 \times (5 - 1)$
  d $12 - 6 \div 3$ and $(12 - 6) \div 3$

2 Evaluate the following:
  a $4 \times 3 \div 2$ **c** $6 + 3 \times 1$ **e** $21 - 9 \div 3$
  b $20 - 8 \times 3$ **d** $6 + 6 \div 2$ **f** $15 - 9 \div 3 + 1$

3 Place brackets in the following equations to make them correct.
  a $4 \times 3 - 1 = 8$ **c** $9 + 6 \div 3 = 5$
  b $4 + 5 \times 2 = 18$ **d** $10 \div 5 \times 2 = 1$

4 Work out the answer and find the 'odd one out' in each case.
  a $4 \times 6 + 4$ $5 \times 5 + 3$ $3 \times 7 + 5$
  b $6 \times 5 - 3$ $7 \times 4 - 3$ $4 \times 8 - 5$
  c $5 + 8 \times 3$ $3 + 9 \times 4$ $4 + 7 \times 5$
  d $3 \times (5 + 4)$ $9 \times (2 + 1)$ $6 \times (3 + 2)$
  e $(5 + 6) \times 4$ $(8 + 7) \times 3$ $(14 + 8) \times 2$
  f $(12 - 6) \times 4$ $(9 - 4) \times 5$ $(15 - 7) \times 3$
  g $4 + 6 \times 5$ $5 \times 7 - 5$ $(9 - 4) \times 6$
  h $24 \div 6 + 3$ $20 \div 5 + 6$ $27 \div 3 + 1$
  i $(20 + 16) \div 9$ $(18 + 14) \div 8$ $(18 + 17) \div 7$
  j $40 \div (3 + 5)$ $54 \div (5 + 4)$ $30 \div (5 + 1)$
  k $36 \div 6 \times 3$ $48 \div 12 \times 4$ $54 \div 6 \times 2$
  l $8 \times 12 \div 6$ $9 \times 10 \div 5$ $6 \times 9 \div 3$

Therefore, any fraction with a denominator having factors of 2 and/or 5 will be exact. The others are recurring.

Thus $\frac{1}{2}, \frac{3}{8}, \frac{7}{16}$ etc should be exact – try them!

$\frac{5}{6}, \frac{4}{7}, \frac{11}{12}$ etc should be recurring – try them!

Notice, however, that **the fraction must be in its simplest form.** For example, the prime factors of 6 are 2×3 – so any fraction with a denominator 6 should recur. $\frac{1}{6}, \frac{2}{6}, \frac{4}{6}$ and $\frac{5}{6}$ DO recur, but $\frac{3}{6}$ is exact. This is because $\frac{1}{6}$ and $\frac{5}{6}$ are in their simplest forms; $\frac{2}{6}$ is really $\frac{1}{3}$ and $\frac{4}{6}$ is really $\frac{2}{3}$ – both of which recur because of the 3; $\frac{3}{6}$ is really $\frac{1}{2}$ which has a denominator now of only 2 and is exact.

The same is true for fractions with denominator 12:

$\frac{1}{12}, \frac{2}{12} (= \frac{1}{6}), \frac{4}{12} (= \frac{1}{3}), \frac{5}{12}, \frac{7}{12}, \frac{8}{12} (= \frac{2}{3}), \frac{10}{12} (= \frac{5}{6})$, and $\frac{11}{12}$ are all recurring.

$\frac{3}{12} (= \frac{1}{4}), \frac{6}{12} (= \frac{1}{2})$, and $\frac{9}{12} (= \frac{3}{4})$ are all exact.

Adding and subtracting decimals

To add or subtract decimals the numbers must be lined up properly.

To do the addition $3.62 + 25.1$ we must be careful to line up the decimal points as follows:

$$
\begin{array}{r}
3.62 \\
+\ 25.1 \\
\hline
28.72
\end{array}
$$

Similarly to do the subtraction $9.65 - 2.4$:

$$
\begin{array}{r}
9.65 \\
-\ 2.4 \\
\hline
7.25
\end{array}
$$

Worked Examples

1 Work out $9.6 + 4.78$.

To work out this addition we must be careful to line up the decimal points:

$$
\begin{array}{r}
9.6 \\
+\ 4.78 \\
\hline
14.38
\end{array}
$$

i.e.
$$
\begin{array}{r}
9.60 \\
+\ 4.78 \\
\hline
14.38
\end{array}
$$
(9.60 is identical to 9.6)

2   Work out $8.2 - 3.65$.

> To work out this subtraction we must be careful to line up the decimal
> points. Again, it is helpful to pad out the numbers with zeros:

$$
\begin{array}{r}
8.20 \\
-\ 3.65 \\
\hline
4.55
\end{array}
$$

PRACTICE 6.5.4

1 Work out the following without using a calculator:
   a $0.25 + 0.25$ e $1.3 + 0.65$ i $105 + 0.01$
   b $0.33 + 0.68$ f $0.6 + 0.003$ j $0.35 + 0.04 + 0.1$
   c $0.65 + 0.99$ g $3.2 + 0.5$ k $3.7 + 0.5 + 26$
   d $0.421 + 0.567$ h $7.3 + 2$

2 Work out the following without using a calculator:
   a $0.75 - 0.25$ d $0.84 - 0.003$ g $12.6 - 5$
   b $0.93 - 0.68$ e $4.6 - 0.61$ h $6.8 - 2$
   c $0.55 - 0.19$ f $0.1 - 0.01$ i $15 - 0.001$

3 Deborah paid four cheques into her bank account. The amounts were
   £15.50, £25.75, £3.92 and £38.07. How much did she bank altogether?

4 Jack and Jill fell down the hill. Jack fell 8.25 m. Jill fell 3.075 m further
   than Jack. How far did Jill fall altogether?

5 A quadrilateral has sides of length 2.07 cm, 4.33 cm, 3.48 cm and
   5.07 cm. What is its perimeter?

6 Abbie's puppy, Jake, takes her for walks from Monday to Friday. On
   Monday they walked 2.4 km; on Tuesday they walked 3.7 km; on
   Wednesday they walked 2.96 km and on Thursday they walked
   3.82 km. If Abbie and Jake walked a total of 16 km in the week, how far
   did they walk on Friday?

7 Captain Birdseye took his yacht on a 15 km race. The first leg was
   4.805 km and the second was 4.756 km. How long was the final leg of
   the race?

Multiplying decimals

It is easy to multiply two decimals using a calculator. If this is not allowed then
the following method should be used:

    i Multiply the two numbers together ignoring the decimal points.
    ii Add together the number of digits after the decimal point in each of the
   numbers.
    iii Replace the decimal point so that the number of digits after the decimal
   point is the same as the number in ii above.

Worked Examples

1 Work out 0.3×0.4.

We first multiply the two numbers together ignoring the decimal points:

$3 \times 4 = 12$

The number of digits after the decimal point in each of the numbers is $1 + 1 = 2$.

We now replace the decimal point so that there are 2 digits after the decimal point:

$0.3 \times 0.4 = 0.12$

2 Multiply 2.55×1.2.

We first multiply the two numbers together ignoring the decimal points:

$255 \times 12 = 3060$

The number of digits after the decimal point in each of the numbers is $2 + 1 = 3$.

We now replace the decimal point so that there are 3 digits after the decimal point:

$2.55 \times 1.2 = 3.060$

3 What is the product of 0.000 15 and 0.33?

We first multiply the two numbers together ignoring the decimal points:

$15 \times 33 = 495$

The number of digits after the decimal point in each of the numbers is $5 + 2 = 7$.

We now replace the decimal point so that there are 7 digits after the decimal point:

$0.000\ 15 \times 0.33 = 0.000\ 049\ 5$

> **NOTE**
> Always check that the answer is approximately correct when multiplying decimals.

> **NOTE**
> A quick way to multiply by 33 is to multiply by 11 then multiply by 3.

PRACTICE 6.5.5

1 Work out the following without using a calculator:

a 0.6×0.3	**d** 0.7×0.8	**g** 0.04×120
b 1.2×12	**e** 0.001×0.225	**h** $0.3 \times 0.05 \times 0.001$
c 20×0.6	**f** 30.0×1.2	

2 One kilo of nectarines cost £1.75. How much does 4 kilos cost?

3 Mr. Burton, the tailor, is cutting out material for suits. Each suit takes 4.45 metres of cloth. How much cloth is needed for 12 suits?

4 A car averages 37.6 miles per gallon on a journey. How far is the journey if it uses 6.3 gallons?

5   A rectangle has a length of 12.4 cm and a width of 8.2 cm. Find its area.

6   A triangle has a base of 4.6 feet and a height of 3.2 feet. Find its area.

7   Amelia Jane was 6 pounds and 8 ounces when she was born. On her first birthday she was 5.2 times as heavy. How heavy was she on her first birthday?

8   A concrete block weighs 19.4 kilos. A conservatory is built with walls 5 blocks high and with 46 blocks in each row. How heavy is the wall?

Dividing decimals

Dividing by a whole number is quite straightforward. It isn't so easy to divide a decimal by another decimal. In these cases we treat the division like a fraction and rewrite it as an equivalent fraction.

Worked Examples

1   Divide 6.3 by 0.7.

$$6.3 \div 0.7 \text{ can be written as } \frac{6.3}{0.7}$$

We can make an equivalent fraction by multiplying the numerator and the denominator by 10 as this will make the denominator a whole number.

$$\overset{\times 10}{\frac{6.3}{0.7}} = \frac{63}{7} \underset{\times 10}{}$$

We now need to work out $63 \div 7$:

$$\frac{9}{7)63}$$

So $0.000\,63 \div 0.7 = 9$

2   Divide 43.648 by 1.24.

$$43.648 \div 1.24 \text{ can be written as } \frac{43.648}{1.24}$$

We can make an equivalent fraction by multiplying the numerator and the denominator by 100 as this will make the denominator a whole number.

$$\overset{\times 100}{\frac{43.648}{1.24}} = \frac{4364.8}{124} \underset{\times 100}{}$$

We now need to work out $4364.8 \div 124$:

$$
\begin{array}{r}
35.2 \\
124\overline{)4364.8} \\
372 \\
\overline{644} \\
620 \\
\overline{248} \\
248
\end{array}
$$

or $124\overline{)436^{64}4.^{24}8}\ \ ^{3\ \ 5.\ \ 2}$

So $43.648 \div 1.24 = 35.2$

3   Divide 0.0035 by 0.005.

$0.0035 \div 0.005$ can be written as $\dfrac{0.0035}{0.005}$

We can make an equivalent fraction by multiplying the numerator and the denominator by 1000 as this will make the denominator a whole number.

$$
\dfrac{0.0035}{0.005} = \dfrac{3.5}{5}
$$

We now need to work out $3.5 \div 5$: $5\overline{)3.5}\ \ ^{0.7}$

So $0.0035 \div 0.005 = 0.7$

PRACTICE 6.5.6

1   Work out the following without using a calculator:
    a $2.65 \div 5$ d $12 \div 0.0001$ g $6.25 \div 0.125$
    b $1.44 \div 12$ e $169 \div 1.3$ h $0.888 \div 0.000\,222$
    c $220 \div 0.05$ f $0.001 \div 0.05$

2   Road runner travels 18.2 metres in 3.5 seconds. How fast is this in metres per second?

3   Gary sees 54 suspect cells under his microscope in an area $0.06\ \text{cm}^2$. How many cells would he find in $1\ \text{cm}^2$?

4   A bag of sweets weighing 95 grams includes wrappings of 0.5 grams. If each sweet weighs 4.5 grams, how many sweets are in the bag?

5   'Aller United' have a stadium holding $125\,500\ \text{m}^2$ of seating for its fans. If each fan is allowed $4.8\ \text{m}^2$ of space, how many fans does the stadium hold when full?

6 How many pieces of cotton, each 2.4 metres long, can a dressmaker cut from a reel of length 100 metres? How much is left over?

7 One kilo is approximately 2.2 pounds. Approximately how many pounds are there in   **a** $6\frac{1}{2}$ **b** $18\frac{1}{2}$ **c** $32\frac{3}{4}$ kilos?

6.6 PERCENTAGES

Percentages are fractions with a denominator of 100.

11% means 11 parts per 100 or $\frac{11}{100}$

79% means 79 parts per 100 or $\frac{79}{100}$

Sometimes we can simplify the fractions so that:

50% means 50 parts per 100 or $\frac{50}{100}$ or $\frac{1}{2}$

25% means 25 parts per 100 or $\frac{25}{100}$ or $\frac{1}{4}$

Changing fractions to percentages

To change a fraction to a percentage we just multiply the fraction by 100.

Worked Examples

1 Convert $\frac{1}{2}$ to a percentage.

To change a fraction to a percentage we multiply the fraction by 100.

$\frac{1}{2} \times 100 = 50$ so $\frac{1}{2} = 50\%$

2 Convert $\frac{4}{5}$ to a percentage.

To change a fraction to a percentage we multiply the fraction by 100.

$\frac{4}{5} \times 100 = 80$ so $\frac{4}{5} = 80\%$

Changing percentages to fractions

To change a percentage to a fraction we just divide the percentage by 100.

Worked Examples

1 Convert 34% to a fraction.

To change a percentage to a fraction we divide the percentage by 100.

$34\% = \frac{34}{100} = \frac{17}{50}$ so $34\% = \frac{17}{50}$

2 Convert $27\frac{1}{2}\%$ to a fraction.

To change a percentage to a fraction we divide the percentage by 100.

$27\frac{1}{2}\% = \frac{27\frac{1}{2}}{100} = \frac{55}{200} = \frac{11}{40}$ so $27\frac{1}{2}\% = \frac{11}{40}$

NOTE

The fraction $\frac{27\frac{1}{2}}{100}$ needs to be written as an equivalent fraction (avoiding fractions in the numerator) i.e. $\frac{55}{200}$

Changing decimals to percentages

To change a decimal to a percentage we just multiply the decimal by 100.

Worked Examples

1   Convert 0.5 to a percentage.

  To change a decimal to a percentage we multiply the decimal by 100.

   $0.5 \times 100 = 50$ so $0.5 = 50\%$

2   Convert 0.01 to a percentage.

  To change a decimal to a percentage we multiply the decimal by 100.

   $0.01 \times 100 = 1$ so $0.01 = 1\%$

Changing percentages to decimals

To change a percentage to a decimal we just divide the percentage by 100.

Worked Example

Convert 34% to a decimal.

  To change a percentage to a decimal we divide the percentage by 100.

   $\dfrac{34\%}{100} = 0.34$ so $34\% = 0.34$

Comparing fractions, decimals and percentages

In order to compare fractions, decimals and percentages it is helpful to change all numbers into percentages.

Worked Example

Place these numbers in order with the smallest first:

$$\frac{23}{100}, \quad \frac{1}{5}, \quad 0.22, \quad 25\%, \quad 25.6\%, \quad 0.255, \quad \frac{6}{25}, \quad 0.300$$

Changing each of these numbers to percentages we get:

$\frac{23}{100} \quad = \frac{23}{100} \times 100\% \quad = 23\% \quad ③$

$\frac{1}{5} \quad = \frac{1}{5} \times 100\% \quad = 20\% \quad ①$

$0.22 \quad = 0.22 \times 100\% \quad = 22\% \quad ②$

$25\% \quad\quad\quad\quad\quad\quad\quad\quad = 25\% \quad ⑤$

$25.6\% \quad\quad\quad\quad\quad\quad\quad = 25.6\% \quad ⑦$

$0.255 \quad = 0.255 \times 100\% \quad = 25.5\% \quad ⑥$

$\frac{6}{25} \quad = \frac{6}{25} \times 100\% \quad = 24\% \quad ④$

$0.300 \quad = 0.300 \times 100\% \quad = 30\% \quad ⑧$

So the order is:

$$\frac{1}{5}, \quad 0.22, \quad \frac{23}{100}, \quad \frac{6}{25}, \quad 25\%, \quad 0.255, \quad 25.6\%, \quad 0.300.$$

PRACTICE 6.6.3   Try these questions without a calculator

1   Copy the table below and fill in the blank spaces:

Decimal	Fraction	Percentage
0.3		
0.55		
0.875		
	$\frac{1}{3}$	
	$\frac{3}{4}$	
	$\frac{4}{5}$	
		1
		$2\frac{1}{2}$
		48
1.25		
	$2\frac{2}{3}$	
		320

2 Place these numbers in order with the smallest first:
   $\frac{1}{2}$, $\frac{26}{50}$, 47.9%, $\frac{48}{100}$, $\frac{505}{1000}$, 0.46, 0.488, 51.0%

3 Which of these numbers are the same?
   a $\frac{3}{4}$, 0.76, 75.5%, $\frac{19}{25}$ **c** $\frac{4}{7}$, 57%, $\frac{11}{20}$, 0.57
   b $\frac{3}{8}$, 38%, 0.375, $\frac{37}{100}$

4 A shop had two identically priced pairs of jeans in a sale. One pair was labelled '$\frac{1}{4}$ off'. the other said '20% discount'. Which pair of jeans was the lower price?

5 Two boys dropped balls on to a surface from the same height. The first rebounded by $\frac{3}{8}$ of the height, the second by 35%. Which ball rebounded most?

6 A house has two flights of stairs. The first flight has 14 steps out of a total of 25. What percentage is taken up by the second flight?

NOTE

See the work of Topic 6.4 on 'One number as a fraction of another' to remind you.

One number as a percentage of another

To calculate one number as a percentage of another, we write the first number as a fraction of the second number and then change to a percentage by multiplying by 100.

Worked Examples

1 Write down 20 p as a percentage of 50 p.

   To calculate one number as a percentage of another, we write the first number as a fraction of the second number and then change to a percentage by multiplying by 100.

   20 p as a fraction of 50 p is $\frac{20}{50} = \frac{2}{5}$ cancelling down to the lowest terms

   We now change the fraction to a percentage by multiplying by 100.

   20 p as a percentage of 50 p is $\frac{2}{5} \times 100 = 40\%$

   We would say that 20 p is 40% of 50 p.

2 Write down 5 grams as a percentage of 200 grams.

   To calculate one number as a percentage of another, we write the first number as a fraction of the second number and then change to a percentage by multiplying by 100.

   5 g as a fraction of 200 g is $\frac{5}{200} = \frac{1}{40}$ cancelling down

   We now change the fraction to a percentage by multiplying by 100.

   5 g as a percentage of 200 g is $\frac{1}{40} \times 100 = \frac{100}{40}\% = \frac{5}{2}\% = 2\frac{1}{2}\%$

   We would say that 5 g is $2\frac{1}{2}\%$ of 200 g.

3 Express 8 yards as a percentage of 64 feet.

First of all we must make sure that both values are given in the same units. 8 yards is the same as 24 feet so the question can be written as:

Express 24 feet as a percentage of 64 feet.

Next, to calculate one number as a percentage of another, we write the first number as a fraction of the second number and then change to a percentage by multiplying by 100.

24 feet as a fraction of 64 feet is $\frac{24}{64} = \frac{3}{8}$ cancelling down

We now change the fraction to a percentage by multiplying by 100.

24 feet as a percentage of 64 feet is $\frac{3}{8} \times 100 = 37.5\%$

We would say that 24 feet is 37.5% of 64 feet.

PRACTICE 6.6.4   Try these questions without a calculator

1 Write down 60 p as a percentage of 120 p.

2 Write down 80 p as a percentage of 400 p.

3 Write down 6 litres as a percentage of 60 litres.

4 Write down 3 miles as a percentage of 21 miles.

5 What is 25 p as a percentage of £6.25?

6 What is 150 cm as a percentage of 3 km?

7 Express 6 feet as a percentage of 10 yards.

8 What is 5 pints as a percentage of 3 gallons?

9 David has bought Victoria an 18 carat gold bracelet. Pure gold is 24 carat. What percentage of Victoria's bracelet is gold?

10 Of the 150 people attending a conference 66 are men. What percentage are women?

Percentage of an amount or quantity

These are the three main methods for finding percentages of an amount or quantity:

Method 1

The first method uses the idea that any percentage can be written as a fraction with a denominator of 100. This fact is then used to convert the expression into a mathematical form which can be worked out.

Worked Examples

1 Find 45% of £16.

45% means 45 hundredths of something, so the expression can be written as $\frac{45}{100} \times £16$

$= £7.20$

2 A supermarket sells 550 apples a day and it is expected that 2% of these apples will be rotten. How many rotten apples does the supermarket sell in a day?

The question requires us to find 2% of 550, or two hundredths $\left(\frac{2}{100}\right)$ of £550.

$2\% = \frac{2}{100}$, so the expression can be written as $\frac{2}{100} \times 550$

$= 11$ apples

Method 2

The second method uses the idea that any percentage can be written as a decimal. This fact is then used to convert the expression into a mathematical form which can be worked out.

Worked Examples

1 Find 45% of £16.

45% = 0.45, so the expression can be written as $0.45 \times £16$
$= £7.20$

2 A supermarket sells 550 apples a day and it is expected that 2% of these apples will be rotten. How many rotten apples does the supermarket sell in a day?

2% = 0.02, so the expression can be written as 0.02×550
$= 11$ apples

Method 3

The third method involves us finding 1% of the given amount or quantity (by dividing by 100) and then multiplying to find the required percentage.

Worked Examples

1 Find 45% of £16.

1% of £16 $= \dfrac{£16}{100}$ $= £0.16$

45% of £16 $= 45 \times £0.16 = £7.20$

2   A supermarket sells 550 apples a day and it is expected that 2% of these apples will be rotten. How many rotten apples does the supermarket sell in a day?

$$1\% \text{ of } 550 \quad = \frac{550}{100} \quad = 5.5 \text{ apples}$$

$$2\% \text{ of } 550 \quad = 2 \times 5.5 \quad = 11 \text{ apples}$$

PRACTICE 6.6.5a   Try these questions without a calculator

1   Work out: **a** 25% of £16   **c** 12% of 150 apples
                     b 30% of 900 m   **d** 35% of 2000 g

2   A building society pays 7% interest on each account. How much is paid out on an account containing £3000?

3   A factory makes 620 cars a month and it is expected that 3% of these cars will be returned to the garage. How many cars will be returned to the garage?

4   My journey to work takes me 40 minutes, 30% of which finds me in traffic jams. How long am I in traffic jams?

5   A DJ has 200 CDs, 65% of which are dance music. How many dance music CDs does she have?

6   Guy Fawkes bought a box of 75 matches with which to light his bonfire. The wood was damp and it took him 16% of his matches to light the fire. How many matches did he use?

7   The cricket team's leading batsman scored $37\frac{1}{2}$% of the total of 256 runs. How many runs did he score?

PRACTICE 6.6.5b   Try these questions with a calculator

1   Work out: **a** 36% of £260   **c** 84% of 260 litres
                     b 58% of 300 m   **d** 92% of 4 ft 2 inches

2   A shopkeeper is paid 8% of all furniture sales as a bonus at the end of the month. What bonus will the shopkeeper receive on sales of £4600?

3   A bank charges $2\frac{1}{2}$% interest on overdraft amounts. How much will be charged on an overdraft of £450?

4   At Grange Hall school 92% of the students were present today. The school roll contains 1300 students. How many were absent?

5   A door to door salesman knocks at all of the 240 houses in a street. There is no one home in $7\frac{1}{2}$% of the houses. How many houses had occupants at home? If he made a successful sale at 11.3% of them, how many sales did he make?

6 In her garden, Lizzie planted flowers in 23% of the total area. The total area was 420 m^2. What area did she use for flowers? 31% of the <u>remainder</u> of her garden was taken up by a patio. What is the area of Lizzie's patio? Give your answer to the nearest m^2.

Percentage change

To work out the **percentage change** you:

i   work out the increase or decrease,

ii add or subtract it from the original amount.
    This is shown in the following examples.

Worked Examples

1 A person earning £600 per month is awarded a pay increase of 4%. What are his new monthly earnings?

   The increase in earnings is equivalent to 4% of £600

$$1\% \text{ of } £600 = \frac{£600}{100} = £6$$

$$4\% \text{ of } £600 = 4 \times £6 = £24$$

   So his new monthly earnings are £600 + £24 = £624

2 A shopper buys a wardrobe for £240 and receives a cash discount of 12%. How much does the shopper pay for the wardrobe?

   The discount is equivalent to 12% of £240.

$$1\% \text{ of } £240 = \frac{£240}{100} = £2.40$$

$$12\% \text{ of } £240 = 12 \times £2.40 = £28.80$$

   So the amount paid is £240 − £28.80 = £211.20.

The two worked examples on percentage change can be worked out more quickly by using the following information:

If an amount is increased by 4% then the new amount
   = 100% of the original amount + 4% of the original amount
   = 104% of the original amount

Similarly, if an amount is decreased by 12% then the new amount
   = 100% of the original amount − 12% of the original amount
   = 88% of the original amount

Worked Examples

1 A person earning £600 per month is awarded a pay increase of 4%. What are his new monthly earnings?

   His new monthly earnings = 104% (100% + 4%) of £600.

$$1\% \text{ of } £600 = \frac{£600}{100} = £6$$

$$104\% \text{ of } £600 = 104 \times £6 = £624 \text{ (as before)}$$

2 A shopper buys a wardrobe for £240 and receives a cash discount of 12%.
   How much does the shopper pay for the wardrobe?
   The cost of the wardrobe = 88% (100% − 12%) of £240.

$$1\% \text{ of } £240 = \frac{£240}{100} = £2.40$$

   88% of £240 = 88 × £2.40 = £211.20 (as before)

3 The population of a village is 6375 and this number decreases by 16%
   over a period of 10 years. What is the new population of the village?
   The percentage decrease = 84% (100% − 16%) of the original population
                           = 84% of 6375

$$1\% \text{ of } 6375 = \frac{6375}{100} = 63.75$$

   84% of 6375 = 84 × 63.75 = 5355

4 Jane invests £2500 in her building society account and receives 4%
   interest per year.
   a What amount is there in her account after one year?
   b What amount is there in her account after two years assuming the
      interest is reinvested?

   a   The percentage increase   = 104% (100% + 4%) of the original
                                     amount
                                   = 104% of £2500

$$1\% \text{ of } £2500 = \frac{£2500}{100} = £25$$

      104% of £2500 = 104 × £25 = £2600

   b   The percentage increase = 104% (100% + 4%) of the amount after
                                  the first year
                                = 104% of £2600

$$1\% \text{ of } £2600 = \frac{£2600}{100} = £26$$

      104% of £2600 = 104 × £26 = £2704

5 A baker reduces the price of bread by 10% and her sales increase by 20%.
   What is the percentage increase in the takings from bread?

   One way to solve this problem is to take an imaginary amount for the
   takings such as £100.

   After a reduction of 10%, the takings
       = 90% (100% − 10%) of the original takings (£100)
       = 90% of £100   (1% = £1 so 90% = £90)
       = £90

   After an increase of 20%, the takings
       = 120% (100% + 20%) of £90
       = 120% of £90   (1% = £0.90 so 120% = £108)
       = £108

   £108 represents an increase of 8% on £100 so the percentage increase
   is 8%.

PRACTICE 6.6.6a   Try these questions without a calculator

1   An amount of £500 is increased by 25%. What is the new amount?

2   An amount of £300 is increased by 30%. What is the new amount?

3   An amount of £68 is decreased by 25%. What is the new amount?

4   £5000 is invested in an offshore account which pays 10% interest at the end of the year. What is the new amount after:
    a   one year,   **b**   two years?

5   A bag of sand is said to contain 50 kilograms. It actually contains 2.5% more. How much sand does it contain?

6   A piece of elastic, originally 80 cm long is stretched by 5%. What is the new length?

7   Ms Berry is making jam. She needs $1\frac{1}{2}$ kilos of blackberries, but, after picking them she finds she has only 80% of that weight. What weight did she pick?

8   A discount warehouse reduces the price of computers by 15% and the sales increase by 20%. What is the percentage increase in the takings from computers?

PRACTICE 6.6.6b   Try these questions with a calculator

1   An amount of £220 is increased by 18%. What is the new amount?

2   An amount of £30 is increased by 2.5%. What is the new amount?

3   An amount of £320 is decreased by 90%. What is the new amount?

4   £3600 is invested in a building society which pays 7% interest at the end of the year. What is the new amount after:
    a   one year,
    b   two years?

5   The value of a car depreciates by 14% each year. How much is a car valued at £6500 worth after:
    a   one year,
    b   two years?

6   A vat of whisky originally held 55 litres. However, it reduced in volume due to evaporation, by 16%. What was the final amount in the vat?

7   Sam bought a bike for £40 and, after repairing and cleaning it, sold it at a profit of 18%. What was the selling price?

8   A car depreciates by 15% per year. How long will it take before its value is half its original value?

Percentage change

Percentage change is found as an increase or a decrease in the original amount or quantity.

$$\text{Percentage change} = \frac{\text{actual change}}{\text{original amount}} \times 100\%$$

These changes can be in any sort of amount or quantity, including money. In money, percentage increase is called profit and percentage decrease is called loss. The important thing to remember is that the figure on the bottom of the formula is the **original value** and **not** necessarily the largest.

The following worked examples show the formula used in several situations.

Worked Examples

1 A woman's wages increase from £25 000 to £27 000 per annum. What is the percentage increase?

$$\text{Percentage increase} = \frac{\text{increase}}{\text{original amount}} \times 100\%$$

$$\text{Percentage increase} = \frac{£27\,000 - £25\,000}{£25\,000} \times 100\%$$

$$= \frac{£2000}{£25\,000} \times 100\%$$

$$= 8\%$$

2 A firm produces 55 000 toys in one year and 53 500 toys the following year. Calculate the percentage decrease.

$$\text{Percentage decrease} = \frac{\text{decrease}}{\text{original amount}} \times 100\%$$

$$\text{Percentage decrease} = \frac{55\,000 - 53\,500}{55\,000} \times 100\%$$

$$= \frac{1500}{55\,000} \times 100\%$$

$$= 2.727\,27\% = 2.73\% \ (3\text{ sf})$$

3 Oranges are bought in boxes of 48 costing £10 and sold at 25p each. What is the percentage profit?

Selling price = $48 \times 25\,\text{p} = £12$

Profit = selling price − buying price

$\qquad = £12 - £10$

$\qquad = £2$

$$\text{Percentage profit} = \frac{\text{profit}}{\text{buying price}} \times 100\%$$

$$= \tfrac{2}{10} \times 100\%$$

$$= 20\%$$

4 A car was bought for £650 and sold one year later for £600. What is the percentage loss over the year?

Loss = buying price − selling price
= £650 − £600
= £50

Percentage loss = $\dfrac{\text{loss}}{\text{buying price}} \times 100\%$

= $\frac{50}{650} \times 100\%$

= 7.6923%

= 7.69% (3sf)

5 A caravan is bought for £450 and sold at a profit of 20%. What was the selling price?

Buying price = £450

Profit = 20% of selling price
= 20% of £450
= $\frac{20}{100} \times £450$
= £90

Selling price = buying price + profit
= £450 + £90
= £540

PRACTICE 6.6.7a　Try these questions without a calculator

1 A person's wage increases from £300 to £330 per week. What is the percentage increase?

2 A secretary's hours are decreased from 40 to $37\frac{1}{2}$ hours per week. What percentage decrease is this?

3 A house increases in value from £1 250 000 to £1 500 000. What is the percentage increase?

4 Toad of Toad Hall bought his latest car for £18 000. A week later he crashed it and, after repair, sold it for £11 700. What was his percentage loss?

5 A book is designed to have 650 pages. When the author finishes the manuscript he finds he has written 754 pages. What percentage increase is this?

6 A box of 144 pens is bought for £10 and individual pens are sold at 10 p each. What is the percentage profit?

7 A picture is bought at £400 and sold at a profit of 15%. What is the selling price?

8 A diamond bought for £2800 is sold at a profit of 22%. What is the selling price?

PRACTICE 6.6.7b   Try these questions with a calculator

1   The turnover at a restaurant increases from £45 000 to £48 000 per year. What was the percentage increase in turnover?

2   The number of students in a college decreases from 845 to 825. Calculate the percentage decrease.

3   The number of buses operating on a route is reduced from 22 per day to 18. What percentage decrease is this?

4   The time taken to complete a journey increases by 12 minutes to 3 hours. What is the percentage increase in the time taken?

5   A motorist's speedometer was reading 70 mph when the police stopped him and told him he was actually travelling at 73.5 mph. What percentage increase is this?

6   A rectangle is supposed to measure 7 cm by 5 cm. However it is wrongly drawn as 7.12 cm by 5.08 cm. What is the percentage error in the area?

7   Annwyn makes a calculator error. She wants to find the value of $\sqrt{112}$ but instead finds $\sqrt{121}$. What is the percentage error in her calculation?

8   A car is bought for £380 and sold for £350. What is the percentage loss?

9   100 apples are bought for £17 but 5% are found to be damaged and not saleable. The rest are sold for 20 p each. What is the percentage profit?

10   A suite originally costing £850 is valued at £475. What is the percentage loss?

Reverse percentages

Questions are sometimes set where the amount is given after a percentage change has been applied. The following worked examples show how this type of question is solved.

Worked Examples

1   After an increase of 8%, a worker's take home pay is equal to £237.60. What was the original wage?

We know that 108% (100% + 8%) of the original wage is equal to £237.60.

108% of the original wage = £237.60

$$1\% \text{ of the original wage} = \frac{£237.60}{108} = £2.20$$

100% of the original wage = 100 × £2.20 = £220

4 Evaluate $(5.74 \times 10^{-12}) \div (8.2 \times 10^{-8})$.

$$(5.74 \times 10^{-12}) \div (8.2 \times 10^{-8}) = \frac{(5.74 \times 10^{-12})}{(8.2 \times 10^{-8})}$$

$$= (5.74 \div 8.2) \times (10^{-12} \div 10^{-8})$$
$$= 0.7 \times 10^{-12 - -8}$$
$$= 0.7 \times 10^{-12+8}$$
$$= 0.7 \times 10^{-4}$$
$$= 7 \times 10^{-5} \text{ (rewriting in standard form}$$
$$\text{where } 0.7 = 7 \times 10^{-1})$$

PRACTICE 7.3.4a   Try these questions without a calculator

1 $(3 \times 10^2) \times (2 \times 10^7)$ **6** $(4.8 \times 10^{-3}) \times (3 \times 10^{-6})$

2 $(2 \times 10^8) \times (2 \times 10^3)$ **7** $(6 \times 10^4) \div (3 \times 10^3)$

3 $(3 \times 10^8)^2$ **8** $(7 \times 10^9) \div (2 \times 10^7)$

4 $(4 \times 10^3) \times (6 \times 10^4)$ **9** $(3.6 \times 10^{10}) \div (4.8 \times 10^6)$

5 $(3.5 \times 10^4) \times (2 \times 10^{-5})$ **10** $\dfrac{(3 \times 10^7) \div (4 \times 10^{13})}{6 \times 10^1}$

NOTE

Another way to answer
questions involving
standard form is to use
your calculator with the
$\boxed{\text{EXP}}$ or $\boxed{\text{EE}}$ button – see
Topic 7.4 'Using a
calculator'.

PRACTICE 7.3.4b   Try these questions with a calculator

Work out the following as shown in the previous worked examples (you
must show all of your working).

1 $(3.15 \times 10^2) \times (2.26 \times 10^5)$ **6** $(3.52 \times 10^4) \times (2.2 \times 10^{-3})$

2 $(4.185 \times 10^5) \times (2.01 \times 10^4)$ **7** $(7.65 \times 10^4) \times (3.6 \times 10^{-3}) \times (2.8 \times 10^3)$

3 $(4.7 \times 10^3) \times (4.25 \times 10^4)$ **8** $(5.423 \times 10^3) \div (6.38 \times 10^1)$

4 $(3.62 \times 10^8) \times (4.89 \times 10^{11})$ **9** $(3.458 \times 10^7) \div (4.55 \times 10^{-3})$

5 $(5.888 \times 10^{15}) \times (3 \times 10^{16})$ **10** $(1.4365 \times 10^{-5}) \div (6.5 \times 10^{-4})$

11 The Western Electricity Company employs 4.7×10^3 people and
produced 6.298×10^5 kilowatt hours of electricity. What was the
electricity production per employee?

12 The mass of a hydrogen atom is 1.7×10^{-24} g. One litre of air contains
2.5×10^{22} atoms of hydrogen. What is the mass of the hydrogen atoms in
one litre of air?

7.4 USING A CALCULATOR

You will be expected to use a calculator for the examination (except for the aural paper) and a scientific calculator is the best one for the course. When you are asked to use your calculator in the examination, it is important that you show your working otherwise marks may be lost for incorrect solutions.

Try this sum on your calculator: $2 + 3 \times 4 =$

If the answer is 14 then you are using a scientific calculator.

If the answer is 20 then you are *not* using a scientific calculator.

If you have any other answer then you have made a mistake!

Recent advances in calculator technology have seen the introduction of programmable calculators and, more recently, calculators which have direct algebraic logic which do not require users to transpose figures and functions such as $\boxed{\sqrt{}}\ \boxed{2}\ \boxed{5}$ to $\boxed{2}\ \boxed{5}\ \boxed{\sqrt{}}$.

The following functions represent those found on a variety of different types of calculators but you should carefully read the user manual accompanying your calculator for further information.

Function	Explanation
$\boxed{\text{C}}$	Clear – used to clear an error before an operation.
$\boxed{\text{AC}}$	All clear – used to clear all data.
$\boxed{\text{MODE}}$	Sets the mode for normal calculations, statistical calculations, etc.
$\boxed{\text{DRG}}$	Sets the units for angular measurement between degrees, radians and grads – normally set to degrees.
$\boxed{\text{M in}}$ or $\boxed{\text{STO}}$	Stores displayed values in the memory (memory location may need to be specified).
$\boxed{\text{MR}}$ or $\boxed{\text{RCL}}$	Recalls values stored in the memory (memory location may need to be specified).
$\boxed{\text{M+}}$	Adds the displayed value to the value stored in the memory and stores the result.
$\boxed{\text{M−}}$	Subtracts the displayed value from the value stored in the memory and stores the result.
$\boxed{\text{+/−}}$	Used to change sign – changes positive numbers to negative numbers (and negative to positive).
$\boxed{1/x}$ or $\boxed{x^{-1}}$	Calculates the reciprocal of the value in the calculator display.
$\boxed{x^2}$	Calculates the square of the value in the calculator display.
$\boxed{\sqrt{}}$	Calculates the square root of the value in the calculator display.
$\boxed{x^3}$	Calculates the cube of the value in the calculator display.
$\boxed{\sqrt[3]{}}$	Calculates the cube root of the value in the calculator display.

Make sure you know how to use these buttons correctly and efficiently **before** you sit your examination. Information on some important function buttons is provided here in a little more detail along with further worked examples.

The fraction function

The $a^{b/c}$ button is used to work with fractions as follows:

Worked Examples

1 Calculate $\frac{3}{4} - \frac{1}{8}$.

The following keys should be pressed:

$\boxed{3}\ \boxed{a^{b/c}}\ \boxed{4}\ \boxed{-}\ \boxed{1}\ \boxed{a^{b/c}}\ \boxed{8}\ \boxed{=}$

The calculator display will show $5\lrcorner8$

The display is then interpreted as $\frac{5}{8}$

2 Calculate $12\frac{1}{4} \times \frac{1}{7}$.

The following keys should be pressed:

$\boxed{1}\ \boxed{2}\ \boxed{a^{b/c}}\ \boxed{1}\ \boxed{a^{b/c}}\ \boxed{4}\ \boxed{\times}\ \boxed{1}\ \boxed{a^{b/c}}\ \boxed{7}\ \boxed{=}$

The calculator display will show $1\lrcorner3\lrcorner4$

The display is then interpreted as $1\frac{3}{4}$

3 Calculate $14\frac{2}{5} \times 1.2$

The following keys should be pressed:

$\boxed{1}\ \boxed{4}\ \boxed{a^{b/c}}\ \boxed{2}\ \boxed{a^{b/c}}\ \boxed{5}\ \boxed{\times}\ \boxed{1}\ \boxed{.}\ \boxed{2}\ \boxed{=}$

The calculator display will show 17.28

Some calculators can also be used to convert improper fractions to mixed numbers using this function.

PRACTICE 7.4.1

Use your calculator to work out the addition and subtraction questions given in Practice 6.4.3, 6.4.4 and 6.4.5 and the multiplication and division questions given in Practice 6.4.6. 6.4.7 and 6.4.8.

The power function

The $\boxed{x^y}$ or $\boxed{y^x}$ button is used to work with powers as follows:

Worked Examples

1 Calculate 3^4

The following keys should be pressed: $\boxed{3}$ $\boxed{x^y}$ $\boxed{4}$ $\boxed{=}$

The calculator display will show $81.$

2 Calculate 2^{-4}

The following keys should be pressed: $\boxed{2}$ $\boxed{x^y}$ $\boxed{-4}$ $\boxed{=}$

The calculator display will show 0.0625

3 Calculate $81^{1/4}$

The following keys should be pressed:

$\boxed{8}$ $\boxed{1}$ $\boxed{x^y}$ $\boxed{(}$ $\boxed{1}$ $\boxed{\div}$ $\boxed{4}$ $\boxed{)}$ $\boxed{=}$

The calculator display will show $3.$

PRACTICE 7.4.2

Use your calculator to work out the following:

1 3^4	**4** 8^0	**7** 10^{-2}	**10** $(\frac{2}{5})^4$	**13** $27^{\frac{1}{3}}$
2 4^3	**5** 127^0	**8** 20^{-2}	**11** $(0.0009)^{\frac{1}{2}}$	**14** $(\frac{1}{4})^{-\frac{1}{2}}$
3 5^1	**6** 4^{-1}	**9** 0.5^2	**12** $49^{\frac{1}{2}}$	**15** $32^{-\frac{4}{5}}$

The standard form function

The $\boxed{EXP}$ or $\boxed{EE}$ button is used to work with standard form as follows:

Worked Examples

1 Calculate $3 \times 10^2 + 2 \times 10^{-1}$

The following keys should be pressed:

$\boxed{3}$ $\boxed{EXP}$ $\boxed{2}$ $\boxed{+}$ $\boxed{2}$ $\boxed{EXP}$ $\boxed{-1}$ $\boxed{=}$

The calculator display will show 300.2

2 Work out $4.3 \times 10^6 \times 2.8 \times 10^2$

The following keys should be pressed:

$\boxed{4}$ $\boxed{\cdot}$ $\boxed{3}$ $\boxed{EXP}$ $\boxed{6}$ $\boxed{\times}$ $\boxed{2}$ $\boxed{\cdot}$ $\boxed{8}$ $\boxed{EXP}$ $\boxed{2}$ $\boxed{=}$

The calculator display will show $1.204 \quad 09$

The display is then interpreted as 1.204×10^9

12-hour and 24-hour clock

Worked Examples

1 A commuter leaves home at 08 25 and arrives at her meeting at 11 18.
How long did the journey take?

To work out the time taken divide the time up as follows:

	hours	minutes
08 25 to 09 00		35
09 00 to 11 00	2	
11 00 to 11 18		18
	2	53

The journey takes 2 hours and 53 minutes.

2 A train leaves Edinburgh at 12.26 pm and arrives in London at 6.45 pm.
How long did the journey take?

Dividing the time up as follows:

	hours	minutes
12.26 pm to 1.00 pm		34
1.00 pm to 6.00 pm	5	
6.00 pm to 6.45 pm		45
	5	79

The answer 5 hours and 79 minutes must be wrong since there are 60
minutes in an hour. 79 minutes is 1 hour and 19 minutes so the answer
is 5 hours + (1 hour and 19 minutes) = 6 hours and 19 minutes.

3 A coach arrived in London at 16 32 and the journey took 4 hours and
20 minutes. What time did the journey start?

A useful method here is to subtract 4 hours and then subtract 20
minutes as follows:

$$16\ 32 - 4\ \text{hours} \qquad = 12\ 32$$
$$12\ 32 - 20\ \text{minutes} \qquad = 12\ 12$$

The coach left at 12 12 (or 12.12 pm).

4 A lorry must reach its destination by a quarter past four in the afternoon and the journey takes 2 hours and 34 minutes. What is the latest time that the lorry driver should set out?

> Here we must subtract 2 hours and 34 minutes from 4.15 pm (or 16 15). We shall first subtract 2 hours and then subtract 34 minutes as follows:
>
> 4.15 pm − 2 hours   = 2.15 pm
> 2.15 pm − 34 minutes   = 1.41 pm

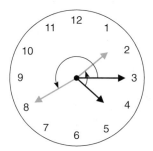

(it may be helpful to imagine or draw a clock to solve this part)

The lorry driver should set out at 1.41 pm.

NOTE
You do not need a calculator for questions like these.

PRACTICE 8.2.1

1 Convert the following to the 24-hour clock.
   a 3.00 am   **c** 8.05 pm   **e** 5.30 am   **g** 10.15 am
   b 3.20 pm   **d** 12.45 pm   **f** 7.55 pm   **h** 11.59 pm

2 Convert the following to the 12-hour clock.
   a 10 00 hrs   **c** 12 50 hrs   **e** 11 59 hrs   **g** 22 01hrs
   b 11 30 hrs   **d** 15 05 hrs   **f** 23 50 hrs   **h** 00 01hrs

3 A television programme starts at a quarter past 3 and finishes at twenty to 5. How many minutes does the programme last?

4 A train leaves London at 11 25 hrs and arrives at its destination at 13 20 hrs. How long was the train journey?

5 A film starts at 11.20 pm and finishes at 1.10 am. How long is the film?

6 A plane leaves London Heathrow at 19 30 hrs and arrives at Amsterdam 55 minutes later. What time does the plane arrive in Amsterdam?

7 At twenty past ten in the evening a student sets her alarm for five to 8 the next day. How much sleep does the student get?

8 A coach leaves London Victoria at 15 40 and arrives at its destination at 17 25.
   a What was the arrival time in 12-hour clock time?
   b How many minutes did the journey take?

9 A ferry journey takes $3\frac{1}{4}$ hours and leaves at 21 40 hrs. If the ferry is delayed $1\frac{1}{2}$ hours, when will the ferry arrive at its destination?

8.3 IMPERIAL AND METRIC UNITS

Imperial measure

Imperial measure was the originally accepted series of weights and measures.

Length	12 inches (in)	= 1 foot (ft)
	3 feet	= 1 yard (yd)
	1760 yards	= 1 mile
	5280 feet	= 1 mile
Capacity	20 fluid ounces (fl oz)	= 1 pint (pt)
	2 pints	= 1 quart (qt)
	8 pints	= 1 gallon (gal)
Weight	16 ounces (oz)	= 1 pound (lb)
	14 pounds	= 1 stone (st)
	8 stone	= 1 hundredweight (cwt)
	20 hundredweights	= 1 ton

> **NOTE**
>
> **In common usage, mass and weight are used to mean the same thing although in science they are not.**

Metric (SI) measure

The metric system is a system of measurement based on the metre, litre and gram as a standard of measurement.

Length	10 millimetres (mm)	= 1 centimetre (cm)
	100 centimetres	= 1 metre (m)
	1000 millimetres	= 1 metre
	1000 metres	= 1 kilometre (km)
Capacity	10 millilitres (ml)	= 1 centilitre (cl)
	100 centilitres	= 1 litre (l)
	1000 millilitres	= 1 litre
	1000 litres	*= 1 kilolitre (kl)*
Weight	*10 milligrams (mg)*	*= 1 centigram (cg)*
	100 centigrams	*= 1 gram (g)*
	1000 milligrams	= 1 gram
	1000 grams	= 1 kilogram (kg)
	1000 kilograms	= 1 tonne (t)

> **NOTE**
>
> **Units such as kilolitres and centigrams are not often used in the metric system but are included so that the patterns existing between metric units of length, capacity and weight can be seen clearly.**

You will need to know the following conversions for the examination:

1 kilogram is approximately 2.2 pounds
1 inch is approximately 2.5 centimetres
1 foot is approximately 30 centimetres
5 miles is approximately 8 kilometres
1 gallon is approximately 4.5 litres
1 litre is approximately 1.75 pints
1 pound is approximately 450 grams
1 mile is approximately 1600 metres
1 pint is approximately 550 millilitres
1 metre is approximately 39 inches or 1.1 yards
1 ounce is approximately 30 grams

Worked Examples

1 How many inches in $2\frac{1}{2}$ yards?

Using the fact that | 12 inches | = 1 foot
                    | 3 feet | = 1 yard

then | $2\frac{1}{2}$ yards | $= 2\frac{1}{2} \times 3$ feet $= 7\frac{1}{2}$ feet
     | $7\frac{1}{2}$ feet | $= 7\frac{1}{2} \times 12$ inches $= 90$ inches

There are 90 inches in $2\frac{1}{2}$ yards.

2 Convert 55 millilitres to litres.

Since | 1000 millilitres | = 1 litre
then | 1 millilitre | $= \frac{1}{1000}$ litre
and | 55 millilitres | $= 55 \times \frac{1}{1000}$ litres
      | | $= \frac{55}{1000} = \frac{11}{200}$ litre (cancelling down)

55 millilitres $= \frac{11}{200}$ litre or 0.055 litre (giving the answer in decimal form).

3 A gallon of fuel costs £2.65. What is the price per litre?

A gallon is approximately 4.5 litres so 4.5 litres of fuel costs £2.65 and
1 litre of fuel costs $\dfrac{£2.65}{4.5} = £0.588\,888\,88\ldots$
A litre of fuel costs £0.59 (to the nearest penny).

PRACTICE 8.3.1a   Try these questions without a calculator

1 How many feet in $2\frac{1}{4}$ miles?

2 How many fluid ounces in 5 pints?

3 How many millimetres in $4\frac{3}{4}$ metres?

4 Convert 3200 centimetres to metres.

5 Convert 4570 milligrams to grams.

6 Convert 765 millimetres to kilometres.

7 How many feet in 75 cm?

8 Two feet of material cost £1.80. What is the cost per metre?

PRACTICE 8.3.1b   Try these questions with a calculator

Write your answers to 2 sf.

1 How many pounds in $2\frac{1}{4}$ hundredweights?

2 Convert 4650 grams to tonnes.

3 Convert 0.5 centimetre to metres.

4 How many inches in 45 cm?

5 How many ounces in 200 g?

6 How many fluid ounces in 2.25 litres?

7 How many metres in 10 yards?

8 A gallon of oil costs £8.65. What is the price per litre?

9 500 g of butter cost £1.82. What is the cost per pound?

10 A car travels at 50 mph. What is the speed in km/h?

8.4 CHARTS AND TABLES

Examination questions will be set to test your ability to 'interpret and use mathematical information presented in written or visual form when solving problems'.

The following exercises gives examples of typical questions under this heading.

PRACTICE 8.4.1   Try these questions without a calculator

1 The following information provides details of the TV programmes one evening.

6.00	News and Weather	9.00	News and Weather
7.00	Consumer Watch	9.30	Feature Film
7.30	Soap Street	11.55	Weatherwatch
8.00	First Monday	12.05	Nightime
8.50	Your Views	1.20	Close

   a How long is the Feature Film?
   b How long is the Nightime programme?
   c I have 3 hours on my videotape. If I record Consumer Watch and First Monday, how long will I have left on my video?
   d I have 1 hour and 25 minutes left on my videotape. If I record Soap Street and Your Views, how long will I have left on my video?

2 The following information provides details of the night service buses to Trafalgar Square.

Sunbury				00 55		01 55		02 55
Feltham Station				01 04		02 04		03 04
Heathrow Airport	23 25		00 25		01 25		02 25	
Hounslow	23 42	00 12	00 42	01 12	01 42	02 12	02 42	03 12
Hammersmith	23 59	00 29	00 59	01 29	01 59	02 29	02 59	03 29
Earls Court Station	00 08	00 38	01 08	01 38	02 08	02 38	03 08	03 38
Hyde Park	00 18	00 48	01 18	01 48	02 18	02 48	03 18	03 48
Trafalgar Square	00 25	00 55	01 25	01 55	02 25	02 55	03 25	03 55

a I arrive at Sunbury at 00 45. How long will I have to wait for the bus to Hounslow?

b I arrive at Hounslow at 23 45. How long will I have to wait for the bus to Hyde Park?

c How long does the journey take from Earls Court Station to Trafalgar Square?

d How long does the journey take from Sunbury to Hammersmith?

e I arrive at Heathrow Airport at 11.30 pm. What is the earliest time that I can get to Hammersmith by bus?

f I arrive at Feltham Station at 1.45 am. What is the earliest time that I can get to Trafalgar Square by bus?

3 The following information details the rail service between Southampton and London.

					Also at these minutes after each hour		Until	
Southampton	07 45	08 01	08 40	09 07	15	35	18 15	18 42
Parkway	07 54	08 09	08 47	09 16	22	43	18 22	18 49
Eastleigh	07 58		08 51	09 20		47		18 53
Winchester	08 09	08 19	09 01		32	57	18 32	19 03
Basingstoke	08 29	08 36	09 18			14		19 20
Woking	09 02	08 55	09 38			33		19 41
Clapham Jn		09 15	09 58			55		20 02
London	09 35	09 26	10 08		28	05	19 29	20 12

a I arrive at Southampton at 07 55. What is the time of the next train to Eastleigh?

b I arrive at Winchester at 12 30. How long will I have to wait for a train to Basingstoke?

c How long does the 14 15 from Southampton take to reach London?

d How long does the 14 57 from Winchester take to reach London?

e What is the shortest journey time from Parkway to Woking?

f I arrive at Winchester station at 08 05. What is the earliest time that I can arrive in London?

g I arrive at Parkway at 16 15. What is the earliest time that I can arrive at Clapham Junction?

4 The following information provides details of day trips from Newhaven to Dieppe.

24-HOUR RETURN TRIPS BY CAR				
	Jan – Mar		Apr – Dec	
	Sun – Fri	Sat	Sun – Fri	Sat
BY FERRY				
Car and 1 person	£42	£42	£64	£76
Car and 2 people	£50	£50	£70	£82
Car and up to 6 people	£59	£59	£76	£88
BY HOVERCRAFT				
Car and 1 person	£50	£52	£72	£86
Car and 2 people	£58	£60	£78	£92
Car and up to 6 people	£67	£69	£84	£98

a What is the cost for a car and 2 people on a Thursday in May on the ferry?

b How much more would it cost to travel by hovercraft?

c What is the cost for a family of 2 adults and 4 children travelling by hovercraft on a Friday in September?

d What would be the extra cost if they travelled on the ferry the following day?

5 The following information provides details of prices for a holiday in Europe.

Departure dates	1 Jan – 26 Mar			27 Mar – 27 Aug			28 Aug – 31 Dec		
Number of nights	3	4	extra nights	3	4	extra nights	3	4	extra nights
HOTEL									
Ambassador	305	335	26	355	393	35	299	329	24
Castello	329	365	31	395	445	46	335	369	33
Excelsior	335	372	34	399	455	48	335	375	34
Grande	349	389	36	409	462	49	349	385	35
Reduction of £30 for infants under 2 years old **Reduction of £25 for children aged 2–11 years old**									

a   What is the total cost for 2 adults staying 3 nights at the Excelsior Hotel if they take the holiday in April?

b   How much would they save in total if they took their holiday at the beginning of March?

c   What is the total cost for 4 adults staying 5 nights at the Ambassador Hotel if they take their holiday in September?

d   What is the total cost for 2 adults and their 2 children aged 8 and 14 years old if they stay 4 nights at the Grande Hotel and take their holiday in July?

e   How much would they save in total if they stayed at the Ambassador Hotel?

f   What is the total cost for 2 adults and their 2 children aged 2 and 6 years old if they stay 3 nights at the Hotel Castello and take their holiday in October?

g   What is the cost of a holiday at the Excelsior Hotel if I fly out on the 29th August and fly back on the 2nd September?

6   The following information provides details of single (Sgl) and return (Ret) coach fares.

Boarding points	Heathrow Airport		Gatwick Airport		Manchester Airport		Birmingham Airport	
	Sgl	Ret	Sgl	Ret	Sgl	Ret	Sgl	Ret
Manchester Airport	£28	£36	£30	£38			£15	£18
Wolverhampton	£22	£29	£24	£32	£13	£17	£7	£11
Birmingham Airport	£21	£27	£23	£30	£15	£18		
Coventry	£20	£26	£22	£28	£16	£18	£5	£6
Heathrow Airport			£13	£23	£28	£36	£21	£27
London Victoria	£7	£10	£13	£23	£28	£36	£21	£27
Gatwick Airport	£13	£23			£30	£38	£23	£30
Children under 16 travel at half the adult fare								

a   What is the cost of a single fare from Wolverhampton to Heathrow Airport?

b   What is the cost of a single fare from Coventry to Gatwick Airport?

c   What is the cost of a return fare from London Victoria to Manchester Airport?

d   How much do I save by buying a return ticket instead of two single tickets on the journey from Heathrow Airport to Gatwick Airport?

e   What is the total cost for 2 adults and their 2 children under 16 years of age from Coventry to Manchester Airport if they buy a single ticket?

f   What is the total return cost for 2 adults and their 2 children aged 14 and 16 years of age from Wolverhampton to Gatwick Airport?

3 Emily receives a monthly income of £785.20 from her investments. Her allowances total £4910. How much tax does she pay each month?

Annual income	$= £785.20 \times 12 = £9422.40$
Taxable income	$=$ Annual income $-$ personal allowances
	$= £9422.40 - £4910$
	$= £4512.40$

Emily pays 10% tax (lower rate) on the first £1520 of taxable income and 22% tax (basic rate) on income between £1520 and £28 400.

On £4512.40, Emily pays 10% tax on the first £1520 and 22% tax on the remaining £2992.40 (£4512.40 − £1520 = £2992.40).

Tax at lower rate	$= 10\%$ of £1520
	$= \dfrac{10}{100} \times £1520$
	$= £152$
Tax at basic rate	$= 22\%$ of £2992.40
	$= \dfrac{22}{100} \times £2992.40$
	$= £658.328$
	$= £658.33$ (to the nearest penny)
Total tax	$= £152 + £658.328$ (using original amount before rounding)
	$= £810.328$
	$= £810.33$ (to the nearest penny)

The question asks how much tax does she pay each month?

Tax each month	$= \dfrac{£810.328}{12}$
	$= £67.527\,33\ldots$

Emily pays £67.53 tax each month (to the nearest penny).

PRACTICE 8.5.2   Try these questions with a calculator

1 Jenny earns £125 per week. She has a personal allowance of £4385. What is her taxable income?

2 Steven earns £580.56 per month. He has a personal allowance of £4385 plus a further allowance of £105. What is his taxable income?

3 A pensioner earns £512.50 per month from her investments. She has a tax allowance of £5790. What is her taxable income?

4   Phil has a part-time job and earns £58.50 per week. His personal allowance is £4385. What is his taxable income?

5   A librarian is paid £54.20 per week for part-time work. His personal allowance is £4385. How much extra can he earn each week before he is liable to pay any tax?

6   Jackie earns £7300 one year. She has a tax allowance of £4195 and pays 20 p in the £ on her taxable income. Calculate how much tax Jackie pays per year.

7   A businesswoman earns £26 500 one year. She has a tax allowance of £4195 and pays 20% on the first £4300 of her taxable income and 23% on the rest of her taxable income. How much tax does she pay in the year?

8   Ruth earns £480.68 per week. She has a tax allowance of £4385 and pays 10% on the first £1520 of her taxable income and 22% on the rest of her taxable income. How much tax does she pay in the year?

9   Parminder earns £22 600 per annum and has a personal allowance of £4385 plus a further allowance of £1250. He pays 10% tax on the first £1520 of his taxable income and 22% on the remainder. How much tax does he pay?

10 Mr Donovan earns £855.25 per month from his investments. He has a tax allowance of £6050 altogether. He pays 10% tax on the first £1520 of his taxable income and 22% on the remainder. How much tax does he pay?

8.6 HOUSEHOLD FINANCE

Value Added Tax

Value Added Tax (VAT) is a tax on goods or services which is paid to the government. Some goods such as basic food, children's clothes, books and newspapers do not have VAT and are called zero rated.

NOTE

Before undertaking this work, you may wish to revise Topic 6.6 to remind you about percentage change and reverse percentages.

Worked Examples

1   A washing machine is priced at £840 plus VAT at $17\frac{1}{2}$%. How much is the VAT and what is the total cost of the washing machine?

We need to find $17\frac{1}{2}$% of £840 as follows:

$$1\% \text{ of } £840 \qquad = \frac{£840}{100} \qquad = £8.40$$

$$17\frac{1}{2}\% \text{ of } £840 \quad = 17\frac{1}{2} \times £8.40 \quad = £147$$

So the VAT is £147 and the total cost is £840 + £147 = £987.

NOTE

An alternative way to find $17\frac{1}{2}\%$ is to find 10%, 5% and $2\frac{1}{2}\%$ and add these together. Remember 5% is half of 10% and $2\frac{1}{2}\%$ is half of 5%.

Alternatively:

10% of £840	$=$	$\dfrac{£840}{10}$	$= £84$
5% of £840	$=$	$\dfrac{£84}{2}$	$= £42$
$2\frac{1}{2}\%$ of £840	$=$	$\dfrac{£42}{2}$	$= £21$

VAT $= £84 + £42 = £21 = £147$

So the VAT is £147 and the total cost is $£840 + £147 = £987$.

2   A television set is priced at £799 which includes VAT at $17\frac{1}{2}\%$. What is the cost of the television set without the VAT?

The price of £799 includes the actual cost of the television set plus VAT at $17\frac{1}{2}\%$, so £799 represents $117\frac{1}{2}\%$ ($100\% + 17\frac{1}{2}\%$) of the actual cost of the television set.

117.5% of the actual cost of the television set $= £799$

1% of the actual cost of the television set $= \dfrac{£799}{117.5} = £6.80$

100% of the actual cost of the television set $= 100 \times £6.80 = £680$

NOTE

For the purposes of using a calculator it is better to write $117\frac{1}{2}$ as 117.5.

NOTE

It is helpful when dealing with reverse percentages to check the answer by adding on the VAT at $17\frac{1}{2}\%$ to your answer.

PRACTICE 8.6.1a   Try these questions without a calculator

For the following questions assume that the rate of VAT is $17\frac{1}{2}\%$ or else complete the exercise using any other appropriate value.

1   Find the total purchase price for the following items:
   a   An audio system priced £590 + VAT.
   b   A refrigerator priced £460 + VAT.
   c   A camera priced £235 + VAT.
   d   A fitted kitchen priced £1865 + VAT.
   e   A new car priced £9885 + VAT.

2   A bill is received for £92.00 excluding VAT at 17.5%. What is the total cost of the bill with VAT?

PRACTICE 8.6.1b   Try these questions with a calculator

1   Check your answers to question **1** in Practice 8.6.1a using a calculator.

2   Check your answers to question **2** in Practice 8.6.1a using a calculator.

3   A microwave oven is priced at £376 which includes VAT at $17\frac{1}{2}\%$. What is the cost of the microwave oven without VAT?

4   A fitted bedroom is priced at £3290 which includes VAT at $17\frac{1}{2}\%$. What is the cost of the fitted bedroom without VAT?

5   A dishwasher is priced at £575.75 which includes VAT at $17\frac{1}{2}\%$. What is the VAT?

NOTE

Questions might also be set on electricity or gas bills.

Telephone bills

Telephone bills are calculated according to the number, duration, time and distance of telephone calls made. In addition to the call charges the bill also includes a rental charge (for the line and other facilities) and VAT at $17\frac{1}{2}\%$.

Worked Example

During one quarter a householder is charged £14.15 for telephone calls along with a rental charge of £21.09. VAT at $17\frac{1}{2}\%$ is added to the final amount. Calculate the cost of the telephone bill.

$$
\begin{aligned}
\text{Cost of bill} \quad &= \text{cost of calls} + \text{quarterly rental} \\
&= £14.15 + £21.09 \\
&= £35.24
\end{aligned}
$$

$$
\begin{aligned}
\text{VAT} \quad &= 17\tfrac{1}{2}\% \text{ of } £35.24 \\
&= £6.17 \text{ (to the nearest penny)}
\end{aligned}
$$

$$
\begin{aligned}
\text{Total cost} \quad &= \text{cost of bill} + \text{VAT} \\
&= £35.24 + £6.17 \\
&= £41.41
\end{aligned}
$$

NOTE

The total cost can be found more quickly by calculating $117\frac{1}{2}\%$

$(100\% + 17\frac{1}{2}\%)$ of £35.24

PRACTICE 8.6.2   Try these questions with a calculator

1 During one quarter a householder is charged £35.84 for telephone calls along with a rental charge of £21.09. VAT at $17\frac{1}{2}\%$ is added to the final amount. Calculate the cost of the telephone bill.

2 Using the following information, calculate the cost of the following telephone bills for one quarter.

   Quarterly charge is £21.09.
   VAT at $17\frac{1}{2}\%$ is added to the final amount.

   a £26.72 for telephone calls
   b £96.25 for telephone calls
   c £78.43 for telephone calls
   d £25.92 for telephone calls

3 Mr Stephens' quarterly telephone bill includes the following charges:

   £24.98 for telephone calls under £0.42
   £27.41 for itemised telephone calls
   £21.09 for line rental
   £6.00   for Premier Line membership

   VAT at $17\frac{1}{2}\%$ is added to the final amount. Calculate the cost of Mr Stephens' telephone bill.

CHAPTER 9

Sample exam papers

Module 3 – Number

1 A hotel in Italy charges 79 euros for bed and breakfast. Mr Thomas is billed for 4 nights bed and breakfast The exchange rate was 1.58 euros to the pound sterling (£). How much was Mr Thomas' bill in pounds sterling. *(3 marks)*

2 Steven receives his gas bill. The charge for the gas is £60 plus VAT at 5%.
   a Calculate the VAT charged. *(3 marks)*
   b Hence find the total amount Steven has to pay. *(1 mark)*

3 **a** Work out $\sqrt{7}$.
      Give your answer correct to 2 decimal places. *(2 marks)*
   b Bob states that $a^2 + b^2$ is always an even number when a and b are prime numbers.
      By means of an example show that Bob is not correct. *(1 mark)*

4 Paint is sold in two sizes, large and regular. The large size costs £11.50 and contains $2\frac{1}{2}$ litres. The regular size costs £4.99 and contains 1 litre. Which size is better value for money? You **must** show all your working. *(3 marks)*

5 Use your calculator to find the value of

$$\frac{2.61 + 4.83}{1.19 + 2.76}$$

Give your answer to 2 significant figures. *(2 marks)*

6 Calculate $\dfrac{420}{3.2 \times 10^6}$

Give your answer in standard form. *(2 marks)*

7 Meena put £4000 in a building society account that offered 6% interest per year. Interest was added to the account at the end of each year. How much did she have in her account three years later, after the final interest had been added? *(3 marks)*

9.2 WITHOUT A CALCULATOR

Module 3 – Number

1 Sue wishes to travel by train from Exeter (Central) to Salisbury.

Exeter St. Davids . . . . dp	1330	–	*1450*	1545	1620	1700	1741	1822	2029
Exeter Central . . . . dp	1334	–	1459	1549	1624	1704	1745	1826	2033
Pinhoe.	1339	–	–	–	1629	1709	1750	–	2038
Whimple	1346	–	1508	–	1636	1716	1757	1835	2045
Feniton	1351	–	1514	–	1641	1721	1802	1841	2050
Honiton . . . . ar	1358	–	1521	1605	1648	1729	1809	1847	2057
dp	1358	–	1521	1605	1648	1729	1809	1851	2057
Axminster	1409	–	1532	1616	1659	1740	1820	1902	2108
Crewkeme.	1422	–	1545	1629	1713	1753	1842	1923	2133
Yeovil Junction . . . . ar	1431	–	1554	1638	1722	1802	1851	1932	2142
dp	1432	–	1556	1639	1723	1803	1903	1938	2143
Sherborne.	1439	–	1603	1646	1730	1810	1910	1944	2150
Templecombe	1446	–	1610	1653	1737	1817	1917	1952	2157
Gillingham. . . . . ar	1454	1553	1617	1701	1745	1824	1924	1959	2205
dp	1454	1553	1624	1701	1745	1829	1931	1959	2205
Tisbury	1504	1603	1634	–	1755	1839	1941	2010	2215
Salisbury . . . . ar	1519	1625	1649	1723	1809	1853	1955	2036	2235
Southampton Central. . . . . ar	*1559*	*1659*	*1736*	*1759*	*1907*	*2004*	*2104*	*2202*	*2322v*
Portsmouth & S'sea . . . . ar	*1643*	*1743*	–	*1843*	*1948*	*2048*	*2147*	*2243*	*0004v*
Salisbury . . . . dp	1523	1636	–	1725	1815	1915	–	2045	2240
Grateley.	–	1648	–	–	1827	1927	–	2057	2252
Andover	1541	1655	–	1743	1834	1934	–	2104	2259
Whitechurch (Hants).	–	1703	–	–	1842	1942	–	2112	2307
Overton.	–	1709	–	–	1848	1948	–	2118	2313
Basingstoke. . . . . ar	1557	1717	–	1801	1856	1956	–	2126	2321
Reading. . . . . ar	*1628*	*1747*	–	*1846*	*1928*	*2028*	–	*2203*	*0003*
Woking . . . . ✈ ar	1617	1741	–	1820	1916	2017	–	2146	*0007*
Clapham Junction . . . . ar	1642	1802	–	1844	1936	2037	–	2211	*0046*
London Waterloo. . . . . ⊖ ar	1650	1810	–	1852	1944	2051	–	2219	*0055*

She arrives at Exeter (Central) station at 1530 and catches the first train going to Salisbury.
How long does the train journey take in hours and minutes? *(3 marks)*

2 Mr and Mrs Collins and their three children are planning a week's holiday. The cost of staying at the hotel for one week is £150 for each adult and £100 for each child. The return rail fare is £35 for each adult and half price for children.

    a Calculate the total hotel costs. *(1 mark)*

    b Calculate the total rail fare. *(2 marks)*

3 **a** Find the value of 4×2^3 *(1 mark)*

    b Find an approximate value of $\dfrac{4.96}{26.2 + 23.9}$ *(2 marks)*

    c Evaluate 7^{-2}. Give your answer as a fraction. *(1 mark)*

CHAPTER 11
Formulae and equations

We all know that the area of this rectangle is found by multiplying the length (L) by the width (W).

Length (L)

Width (W)

Area A = LW

If the area is given the letter A, we can write this as A = L × W, or A = LW.

This is an example of a **formula**.

We can put numbers in place of any two of the letters to work out what the value of the third letter is. For example if the length L was 8 cm and the width W was 5 cm, then we could write A = 8 × 5 = 40.
i.e. The area of this rectangle is 40 cm^2.
If L and W were different values we could use the same formula to work out A.
We can write all sorts of formulae like this for different situations.
We look at formulae in more detail in Topic 11.3.

Indices

For further information on indices and powers see Topics 7.1 and 7.2.

Two basic laws of arithmetic

NOTE
This rule does not work for subtraction or division. For example, 5 − 3 is not the same as 3 − 5 and 10 ÷ 5 is not the same as 5 ÷ 10.

1 When we add or multiply two numbers, it doesn't matter which comes first

i.e. $a \times b = b \times a$

For example	$4 + 7 = 7 + 4 = 11$	and	$4 \times 7 = 7 \times 4 = 28$
	$6 + {}^-8 = {}^-8 + 6 = {}^-2$	and	$6 \times {}^-8 = {}^-8 \times 6 = {}^-48$
In algebra	$a + b = b + a$	and	$a \times b = b \times a$

2 When we add or multiply three (or more) numbers then

$a \times (b \times c) = (a \times b) \times c$ or $a + (b + c) = (a + b) + c$

For example $2 + 3 + 4 \ = \ (2 + 3) + 4 \ = \ 2 + (3 + 4)$
i.e. $\qquad\qquad\quad 9 \ = \ 5 \ + 4 \ = \ 2 + \ 7$
and $\qquad 3 \times 5 \times 2 \ = \ (3 \times 5) \times 2 \ = \ 3 \times (5 \times 2)$
i.e. $\qquad\qquad\quad 30 \ = \ 15 \ \times 2 \ = \ 3 \times \ 10$

In algebra $\quad a + b + c \ = \ (a + b) + c \ = \ a + (b + c)$
and $\qquad\quad a \times b \times c \ = \ (a \times b) \times c \ = \ a \times (b \times c)$

Order of operations

For further information on the order in which we can do these operations see Topic 6.1.

245

Notation means **the way we write things down**.

In algebra:

x means $1 \times x$		or	$1x$ (we don't usually write the 1)
$-x$ means $-1 \times x$		or	$-1x$ (we don't usually write the 1)
$4x$ means 4 times x		or	$4 \times x$ or $x + x + x + x$
$\dfrac{x}{4}$ means x divided by 4		or	$x \div 4$ or $\frac{1}{4}$ of x
xy means x times y		or	$x \times y$
$3xy$ means 3 times x times y		or	$3 \times x \times y$
$\dfrac{x}{y}$ means x divided by y		or	$x \div y$

11.2 INDICES

Using indices in algebra

We saw, for example, in Topic 7.1 that 6^4 means $6 \times 6 \times 6 \times 6 = 1296$.

In algebra	x^2 means	$x \times x$	(we say x *squared*)
	x^3 means	$x \times x \times x$	(we say x *cubed*)
	x^4 means	$x \times x \times x \times x$	(we say x *to the power 4*), etc.
i.e.	x^n means	$x \times x \times x \times$ ...etc	(multiplied n times)
			(we say x to the power n).

Also
$3x^2$ means $3 \times x^2$ or $3 \times x \times x$ or $(x^2 + x^2 + x^2)$
$(3x)^2$ means $3x \times 3x$ or $3 \times x \times 3 \times x = 9x^2$
$2a^2b^3$ means $2 \times a^2 \times b^3$ or $2 \times a \times a \times b \times b \times b$ or $(a^2b^3 + a^2b^3)$
$x + y$ means *the sum of the unknown numbers x and y*

The laws of indices

We have already seen in Topic 7.2 that, for example,

$5^3 \times 5^4 = 5^{3+4} = 5^7$ and that $4^8 \div 4^5 = 4^{8-5} = 4^3$.

In algebra these basic laws can be written as:

a $x^a \times x^b = x^{a+b}$ for example, $a^3 \times a^4 = a^7$
b $x^a \div x^b = x^{a-b}$ for example, $b^7 \div b^4 = b^3$
c $(x^a)^b = x^{ab}$ for example, $(c^2)^3 = c^{2\times3} = c^2 \times c^2 \times c^2 = c^6$

Worked Examples

a $a^2 \times a^3 = a^{2+3} = a^5$ **d** $2d \times 5e = 10de$

b $b^5 \div b^3 = b^{5-3} = b^2$ **e** $3f \times (-4g) = -12fg$

c $(2c)^3 = 2c \times 2c \times 2c = 8c^3$ **f** $(-7h) \times (-3i) = 21hi$

g $m^3 \div m^4 = m^{3-4} = m^{-1}$ (see Topic 7.2)

h $14n^5 \div 7n^8 = (14 \div 2)(n^{5-8}) = 2n^{-3} = \dfrac{2}{n^3}$ (see Topic 7.2)

i $2j \times 3k \times 4l = 24jkl$

j $3m^4n^2 \times 5m^3n^9 = 3 \times 5 \times m^{4+3} \times n^{2+9} = 15m^7n^{11}$

k $15pq^3 \div 3p^3q = (15 \div 3) \times (p \div p^3) \times (q^3 \div q) = \dfrac{5q^2}{p^2}$

l $8r^5s^3 \div 20s^2t^3 = \dfrac{2r^5s}{5t^3}$ 　　　　　 **n** $\sqrt[3]{w^6} = w^{6\div3} = w^2$

m $\sqrt{v^6} = v^{6 \div 2} = v^3$ 　　　　　　 **o** $\sqrt{9x^8} = 3x^4$

PRACTICE 11.2.1 Try these questions without a calculator

1 Simplify the following:

a $2x \times 3y$	**f** $e^8 \times e^4$	**k** $18w^8 \div 6w^4$	**p** $(-3p)^3$
b $5x \times 4y$	**g** $f^8 \div f^2$	**l** $4v^2 \div 12v^6$	**q** $(-4p)^3$
c $5c \times (-3d)$	**h** $f^{15} \div f^5$	**m** $(2m)^3$	**r** $(-2p)^5$
d $-6c \times 4d$	**i** $j^3 \div j^4$	**n** $(3m)^4$	**s** $(-2q) \times (-5r)$
e $e^5 \times e^3$	**j** $k^6 \div k^9$	**o** $(-3p)^2$	**t** $(-5q) \times (-6r)$

2 Simplify the following:

a $\frac{1}{2}s \times 8t$	**i** $(-2x) \times (-4y) \times 5z$
b $\frac{3}{4}s \times 20t$	**j** $(-3x) \times 5y \times (-6z)$
c $\frac{1}{2}u \times \frac{4}{9}v$	**k** $5x \times (-7y) \times (-4z)$
d $\frac{2}{3}u \times 15v$	**l** $(-9a) \times (-2b) \times (-5c)$
e $2w \times 3x \times 4y$	**m** $2d \times 3d \times 4d$
f $5w \times 4x \times 6y$	**n** $3e \times 5e \times 6e^2$
g $2w \times 3x \times (-4y)$	**o** $2d \times 3e \times 4f$
h $5w \times (-4x) \times 6y$	**p** $2d \times 3e \times 4f^2$

3 Simplify the following:

a $gh \times 2g \times 3h$	**k** $21q^3 \div 3q^6$
b $g^2h^3 \times g^4h^5 \times gh^2$	**l** $14r^4s^2 \div 2r^3s^4$
c $3mn \times 2m^2n^3 \times 5m^4n^2$	**m** $36u^2 \div (-9u)$
d $7j^4k^6 \times 8j^8k$	**n** $(-45u) \div (-9u^2)$
e $24p \div 8p$	**o** $(-54c^3d^4) \div 6c^2d$
f $24p^6 \div 8p^2$	**p** $(-36w^9v^5) \div (-3w^3v^7)$
g $20fg \div 5f$	**q** $(x^2)^3$
h $20f^4g^3 \div 4fg^2$	**r** $(m^7)^4$
i $4q \div 12q$	**s** $(3h^3)^3$
j $4q \div 12q^2$	**t** $(2k^5)^4$

4
  a If $2^n = 8$, find n
  b If $3^m = 81$, find m
  c If $4^n = 1024$, find n
  d If $3 \times 2^n = 48$, find n
  e If $4 \times 5^m = 500$, find m
  f If $m \times 6^2 = 108$, find m
  g If $n \times 7^3 = 343$, find n
  h If $2^{3s} = 64$, find s
  i If $x^3 = 125$, find x
  j If $m^5 = 243$, find m
  k If $2 \times p^3 = 432$, find p
  l If $3^{2z} = 9$, find z
  m If $d^2 = \frac{1}{4}$, find d
  n If $c^3 = \frac{1}{8}$, find c
  o If $6^{2t+1} = 216$, find t
  p If $(2^{2b})(2^{6b}) = 256$, find b

11.3 WORKING WITH EXPRESSIONS & FORMULAE

Basic algebra

Algebra is simply arithmetic using letters and numbers. In algebra letters are used to represent numbers. The mathematical rules that work for arithmetic also work for algebra.

When we write down that Jane is 26 years old we are making an *exact* statement, but when we say that John is P years old we are making a *general* statement.

Worked Examples

1 Write in algebraic notation:
  a the sum of the number p plus three times the number q, $p + 3q$
  b four times the number m subtracted from three times the number n, $3n - 4m$
  c the number x divided by the number y, $\dfrac{x}{y}$
  d twice the number p plus three times the number q, $2p + 3q$
  e the number z squared, z^2
  f the number y cubed (i.e. multiplied by itself three times), y^3
  g four times the number m squared, $4m^2$
  h the square root of z. $\sqrt{z}$

2 Jane is 26 years old and John is P years old. How old will they be
  a in five years,   **b** last year?

  a In five years: Jane will be $26 + 5 = 31$ John will be $P + 5$
  b Last year: Jane was $26 - 1 = 25$ John was $P - 1$

PRACTICE 11.3.1

1 Write the following in algebraic notation.
  a The sum of five times the number x plus four times the number y.
  b Three times the number c minus 2.
  c Double the number p and divide it by the number q squared.
  d The cost of 4 pounds of apples plus 2 pounds of bananas, where a is the cost of 1 pound of apples and b is the cost of 1 pound of bananas.
  e The value of a number divided by four and added to the cube of the number, where x is the number.
  f The value of the number, x, when it is divided by 4 and added to the square of the same number.

2 a is the cost of 1 kg of apples, b is the cost of 1 kg of bananas. What is the cost of 4 kg of apples and 2 kg of bananas?

3 What is the cost of 2 CDs at £c each together with 3 DVDs at £d each?

4 Ally is y years old now. Write down:
   a her dad's age if he is four times as old as Ally is now,
   b Ally's age in six year's time,
   c her dad's age seven years ago,
   d her dad's age when Ally was half as old as she is now,
   e Ally's age when her dad will be five times as old as Ally is now.

Words and terms

- Any letter used to represent a number is called a *variable* or *unknown*. They are called variables because their values can change.
- Anything whose value does not change is called a *constant*.
- 2 or 0.5 or π are constants because their values do not change.
- Any number in front of a variable is called a *coefficient*.
  When we write the term $7x^2$ we say that 7 *is the coefficient of* x^2.
- An algebraic collection of terms is called an *expression*.
- An expression is a collection of constants and variables. For example, $4x^3 + 7x^2 - 5x + 9$ is a statement of three variable terms and one constant. The terms in any expression must be connected by plus ($+$) or minus ($-$) signs.
- Any term may have more than one variable in it. For example, the area of a rectangle of length l and width w could be written as lw.
- Usually we put letters in alphabetical order in a term and the number always comes first. For example, we would write $5a^3bc^2$ rather than a^3c^25b.
- If any expression has more than one term of the same *type* in it then these can be combined. These are called *like* terms. In the expression $5x^2 + 8x - 4 + 6x^2 - 3x$, the $5x^2$ and $6x^2$ are *like* terms. The $8x$ and $-3x$ are also like terms. The expression could be simplified into $11x^2 + 5x - 4$.
- When we are deciding whether terms are *like*, don't forget that the order of letters inside a term is *not* important. Thus $5cd$ and $4dc$ are like terms.

> **NOTE**
> The $11x^2$ and $5x$ terms are *not* like terms. They are in fact *unlike* terms.

Worked Examples

Simplify:
a $2f + 7f - 3f$
b $2a + 3b + 6a + 9b$
c $x - y - 2z + 5x - 4y + z$

d $4b^2 - 7b + 4 - 2b^2 - 9b - 5$
e $3pqr + 7qrp - 4rqp$
f $2cd^2 + 4c^2d + 8cd^2 - c^2d$

   a $2f + 7f - 3f = 6f$

   b $2a + 3b + 6a + 9b$
      $= 2a + 6a + 3b + 9b$
      $= 8a + 12b$

   c $x - y - 2z + 5x - 4y + z$
      $= x + 5x - y - 4y - 2z + z$
      $= 6x - 5y - z$

   d $4b^2 - 7b + 4 - 2b^2 - 9b - 5$
      $= 4b^2 - 2b^2 - 7b - 9b + 4 - 5$
      $= 2b^2 - 16b - 1$

   e $3pqr + 7qrp - 4rqp = 6pqr$

   f $2cd^2 + 4c^2d + 8cd^2 - c^2d$
      $= 2cd^2 + 8cd^2 + 4c^2d - c^2d$
      $= 10cd^2 + 3c^2d$

PRACTICE 11.3.2   Try these questions without a calculator

1 Simplify:

a $4a + 7a + 9a$

b $5b - 9b + 6b$

c $4c + c - 7c$

d $4d + 7e + 8d + 8e$

e $5f - 3g - 2f + 6g$

f $2h - 7k - 9l - 5h - 5k + 4l$

g $x + 3y + 6x - 1 - 7m$

h $8p - 7q + 3 - 6q - 7p$

i $2r + \frac{3}{2}s - \frac{1}{2}r + \frac{5}{4}s$

j $7t + 9u - 6u - t^2$

k $11v^2 - 4v + 9$

l $4w + 3w^2 - w^2 - 5w - 8$

m $2x^2 + (2x)^2$

n $\dfrac{4}{y} + \dfrac{7}{y} - \dfrac{3}{y}$

o $\dfrac{2}{z} - \dfrac{5}{z^2} + \dfrac{9}{z^2} - \dfrac{3}{z}$

p $2 - 3x + 4x^2 + 9x^3 - 5 + 4x - 4x^2 + 2x^3$

q $\dfrac{b}{c} + \dfrac{4b}{c} - \dfrac{2b}{c}$

r $3de + 5ef - 7fg + 4gd$

s $4x^3y + 5x^2y^2 - 3xy^3 + 2x^2y^2 - 2xy^3 + 8x^3y$

t $(2z)^3 + 4z^2 + 5z^3$

Using brackets in algebra

We saw in Topic 6.1 that there is a definite order for doing operations. We use the word **BODMAS**. The **B** for **B**rackets is used in algebra as well. Brackets are used when we wish to group terms together. **Anything written inside brackets should be done before any other operations.**

For example, Mrs Lavers has three pints of milk, m, and two cartons of cream, c, delivered each day for a week.

So, for 1 day, we say	$3m + 2c$
Thus, for 7 days, we say	$7(3m + 2c)$
If we removed the brackets we would get	$21m + 14c$

> **NOTE**
> $7(3m + 2c)$ means
> 7 times $(3m + 2c)$.

The two expressions $7(3m + 2c)$ and $21m + 14c$ are said to be **mathematically equivalent**.

When removing brackets, each term *inside* the bracket is multiplied by the term *outside*.

Remember to use the rules for multiplying signs when removing the brackets. A term without a sign in front of it is always taken as positive $(+)$. The rules are simple:

when multiplying or dividing:

  if the signs are the same, i.e. both $(+)$ or both $(-)$, the result is $(+)$,
  if the signs are different, i.e. one $(+)$ and one $(-)$, the result is $(-)$.

Simplify:

a $3(x + 2y)$

b $4(2a - 3b)$

c $2(-4c - 5d)$

d $-5(3e + 7f)$

e $-4(6g - 2h)$

f $-8(-2x - 5y)$

g $3x(2x + 4y - 5z)$

h $5p + 4(p - 2q + 5)$

i $6r - 3(5r + 4s - 3t)$

j $2(a + 3b) + 4(2a - 2b)$

a $3(x + 2y) = 3 \times x + 3 \times 2y$
$$= 3x + 6y$$

b $4(2a - 3b) = 4 \times 2a + 4 \times -3b$
$$= 8a - 12b$$

c $2(-4c - 5d) = 2 \times -4c + 2 \times -5d$
$$= -8c - 10d$$

d $-5(3e + 7f) = -5 \times 3e + -5 \times 7f$
$$= -15e - 35f$$

e $-4(6g - 2h) = -4 \times 6g + -4 \times -2h$
$$= -24g + 8h$$

f $-8(-2x - 5y) = -8 \times -2x + -8 \times -5y$
$$= 16x + 40y$$

g $3x(2x + 4y - 5z) = 3x \times 2x + 3x \times 4y + 3x \times -5z$
$$= 6x^2 + 12xy - 15xz$$

h $5p + 4(p - 2q + 5) = 5p + 4 \times p + 4 \times -2q + 4 \times 5$
$$= 5p + 4p - 8q + 20$$
$$= 9p - 8q + 20$$

i $6r - 3(5r + 4s - 3t) = 6r - 3 \times 5r - 3 \times 4s - 3 \times -3t$
$$= 6r - 15r - 12s + 9t$$
$$= -9r - 12s + 9t$$

j $2(a + 3b) + 4(2a - 2b) = 2 \times a + 2 \times 3b + 4 \times 2a + 4 \times -2b$
$$= 2a + 6b + 8a - 8b$$
$$= 10a - 2b$$

PRACTICE 11.3.3　Try these questions without a calculator

1 Remove the brackets:

a $2(a + 3)$	**f** $-4(3x + 2y)$	**k** $3w(x + 2y - 3z)$
b $2(3a - 1)$	**g** $-3(4y - 3z)$	**l** $-3w(4w - 5x + 3)$
c $3(2b - 7)$	**h** $-7(-3a + 2b)$	**m** $5(3x^2 + 2x + 7)$
d $4(2b + 3c)$	**i** $-6(-4c - 3d)$	**n** $4y(7y^2 - y + 3)$
e $5(6f - 3g)$	**j** $\frac{2}{3}(9e - 15f)$	

2 Remove the brackets, collect like terms and simplify:

a $2z + 3(z + 5)$

b $2z - 3(z + 5)$

c $2z - 3(z - 5)$

d $4(a - 3) + 2(a + 7)$

e $5(2b - 3) - 3(2b + 1)$

f $-2(-2c - 3) - (4c - 7)$

g $-(5d + 3e - 2f) + 3(2d - e + 3f)$

h $-(5d + 3e - 2f) - 3(2d - e + 3f)$

i $2(x^2 + 2x - 1) + 3(x^2 - x - 7)$

j $5(2y^2 - 3y + 4) - 2(y^2 - 3y - 5)$

k $2x(x^2 + 3x - 1) + 3(4x^2 - 6x + 2)$

l $4xy - 3x(y + 2)$

m $5m(n - 3) - 2n(m + 4)$

n $4p(2p + 3q) + 3p(5p - q)$

o $4p(2p + 3q) - 3p(5p - q)$

p $7y(5z + \dfrac{3}{y})$

q $-2t(4 - \dfrac{8}{t})$

r $7(2z + 3y) - 3(y - 2x) + 4(2x + 3z)$

Multiplying brackets together

Sometimes we want to multiply two brackets together. For example, $(x + 2)(x + 3)$ means 'multiply the bracket $(x + 2)$ by the bracket $(x + 3)$'. Now, x^2 can be shown as the area of a square of side x units.

Therefore, $(x + 2)(x + 3)$ can be shown as the area of a rectangle $(x + 2)$ units by $(x + 3)$ units. We can see this in the next diagram.

$x \times x$
$= x^2$

Looking at this diagram we can see that there are four areas to add together. These are: x^2, $2x$, $3x$ and 6 square units respectively.
Thus $(x + 2)(x + 3)$ must equal $x^2 + 2x + 3x + 6 = x^2 + 5x + 6$ when we collect like terms,

i.e. $(x + 2)(x + 3) = x^2 + 5x + 6$.

It takes too long to draw diagrams like these every time we want to multiply two brackets together. Luckily there is an algebraic way of doing the same thing.

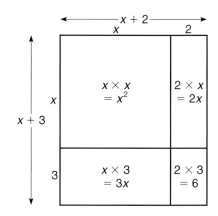

The rule is:

Multiply *each term* in the second bracket by *each term* in the first.

There are *two* easy algebraic ways to do this.

Method one

Draw up a multiplication table.

×	x	$^+2$
x	x^2	^+2x
$^+3$	^+3x	$^+6$

Both the like terms can be found in the diagonal marked on the diagram. Collecting these up we have $(x + 2)(x + 3) = x^2 + 3x + 2x + 6 = x^2 + 5x + 6$.

Method two

Multiply the second bracket by each term in the first bracket.
We can see how this is done by following the example:

$$(x + 2)(x + 3) = x(x + 3) + 2(x + 3) = x^2 + 3x + 2x + 6 = x^2 + 5x + 6.$$

Another way of doing the multiplication is shown below:

F   L   **F   O   I   L**
$$(x + 2)(x + 3) = x^2 + 3x + 2x + 6 = x^2 + 5x + 6$$
I
$2x$
$3x$
O
(collecting like terms)

In the above diagram we can see that there are four multiplications: the **First** two terms, the **Outer** two terms, the **Inner** two terms, and the **Last** two terms.

> **NOTE**
> FOIL is a very good way of remembering all the multiplication we have to do. But don't forget the two like terms in the middle.

These can easily be remembered by the word **FOIL.**

Remembering this word is a very useful way of dealing with the multiplication. It doesn't matter which method we choose to remember as long as we can do the multiplication.

The examples below show some more solutions involving the use of differing signs.

Worked Examples

1 Calculate $(b + 3)(b - 5)$.

$\times$	b	$^{+}3$
b	b^2	$^{+}3b$
$^{-}5$	$^{-}5b$	$^{-}15$

Hence $(b + 3)(b - 5) = b^2 - 5b + 3b - 15 = b^2 - 2b - 15$.

2 Calculate $(x - 4)(x - 9)$.

F O I L

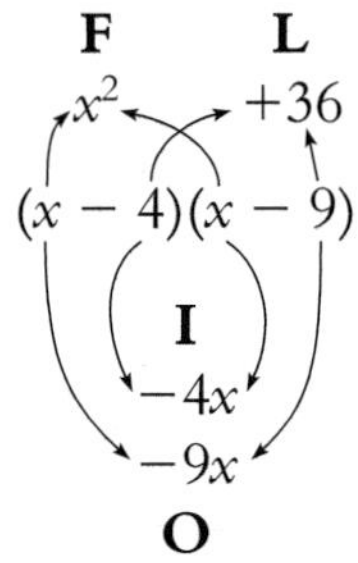

$(x - 4)(x - 9) = x^2 - 9x - 4x + 36 = x^2 - 13x + 36$
(collecting like terms)

3 Calculate $(3h + 8)(5h - 7)$.

$\times$	$5h$	$^{-}7$
$3h$	$15h^2$	$^{-}21h$
$^{+}8$	$^{+}40h$	$^{-}56$

Hence $(3h + 8)(5h - 7) = 15h^2 - 21h + 40h - 56 = 15h^2 + 19h - 56$

4 $$\begin{aligned}(a + 4)(a + 7) &= a(a + 7) + 4(a + 7)\\ &= a^2 + 7a + 4a + 28\\ &= a^2 + 11a + 28\end{aligned}$$

5 $$\begin{aligned}(x + 8)(x - 2) &= x(x - 2) + 8(x - 2)\\ &= x^2 - 2x + 8x - 16\\ &= x^2 + 6x - 16\end{aligned}$$

6 $$\begin{aligned}(d - 3)(d + 7) &= d(d + 7) - 3(d + 7)\\ &= d^2 + 7d - 3d - 21\\ &= d^2 + 4d - 21\end{aligned}$$

3 Solve the equations $2x + 3y = -4$, $4x - 3y = 10$.

The coefficients of y are the same but of different sign. Therefore we add the equations.

$$2x + 3y = -4$$
$$4x - 3y = 10$$

(adding) $\quad 2x + 4x + 3y - 3y = -4 + 10$

i.e. $\qquad\qquad\qquad 6x = 6$

i.e. $\qquad\qquad\qquad x = 1$

Substituting $x = 1$ back in the first original equation gives $2(1) + 3y = -4$

i.e. $\qquad\qquad\qquad 3y = -6$

i.e. $\qquad\qquad\qquad y = -2$

Checking in the second original equation gives: $4(1) - 3(-2) = 10$. This is correct.

Thus $x = 1$, $y = -2$ is the only solution to the simultaneous equations $2x + 3y = -4$, $4x - 3y = 10$.

4 Solve the equations $4x + 7y = 17$, $4x + 5y = 11$.

The coefficients of x are the same and of the same sign. Therefore we subtract the equations.

$$4x + 7y = 17$$
$$4x + 5y = 11$$

(subtracting) $\quad 4x - 4x + 7y - 5y = 17 - 11$

i.e. $\qquad\qquad\qquad 2y = 6$

i.e. $\qquad\qquad\qquad y = 3$

Substituting $y = 3$ back in the first original equation gives $4x + 7(3) = 17$

i.e. $\qquad\qquad\qquad 4x = -4$

i.e. $\qquad\qquad\qquad x = -1$

Checking in the second original equation gives $4(-1) + 5(3) = 11$. This is correct.

Thus $x = -1$, $y = 3$ is the only solution to the simultaneous equations $4x + 7y = 17$, $4x + 5y = 11$.

5 Solve, simultaneously, the equations $4x - 3y = -5$, $2x - 3y = -1$.

The coefficients of y are the same and of the same sign. Therefore we subtract the equations.

$$4x - 3y = -5$$
$$2x - 3y = -1$$

(subtracting) $\quad 4x - 2x - 3y - (-3y) = -5 - (-1)$

i.e. $\qquad\qquad\qquad 2x = -4$

i.e. $\qquad\qquad\qquad x = -2$

Substituting $x = -2$ back in the first original equation gives $4(-2) - 3y = -5$

i.e. $\qquad\qquad\qquad -3y = 3$

i.e. $\qquad\qquad\qquad y = -1$

Checking in the second original equation gives $2(-2) - 3(-1) = -1$. This is correct.

Thus $x = -2$, $y = -1$ is the only solution to the simultaneous equations $4x - 3y = -5$, $2x - 3y = -1$.

PRACTICE 11.4.6   Try these questions without a calculator

1 Use the method of elimination to solve the following simultaneous equations.

a $a + b = 7$ **d** $3g - 4h = -15$ **g** $3p + 4q = 24$
    $2a + b = 11$ $-3g - h = 0$ $4p - 4q = 32$

b $2c - d = 13$ **e** $-3j + 4k = 5$ **h** $-2r + 3s = 1$
    $c - d = 5$ $-3j - 7k = -50$ $2r + 9s = 7$

c $4e + 2f = 2$ **f** $7m + 4n = 12$
    $5e - 2f = 7$ $-5m + 4n = 12$

Further simultaneous linear equations

In the above questions, there was always one variable with the same coefficients. So how can we solve a pair of simultaneous equations where they are different?

We do this by multiplying the equations by constants such that the coefficients of one of the variables is the same in both equations.

It doesn't matter which variable you use so long as it has the same coefficient in both equations.

Then we solve the equations as we did in the last practice exercise.

The following examples show how this is done.

Worked Examples

1 Solve the simultaneous equations $2x + 3y = 19$, $3x - y = 1$.

If we multiply the second equation throughout by 3 we would then have $3y$ in each equation.

Hence: (equation 1) $2x + 3y = 19$
        (3 × equation 2) $9x - 3y = 3$

        (adding) $2x + 9x + 3y - 3y = 19 + 3$
        i.e. $11x = 22$
        i.e. $x = 2$

Substituting $x = 2$ back in the first equation gives $2(2) + 3y = 19$
        i.e. $3y = 15$
        i.e. $y = 5$

Checking in the second original equation gives $3(2) - 5 = 1$.
This is correct.

Thus $x = 2$, $y = 5$ is the only solution to the simultaneous equations $2x + 3y = 19$, $3x - y = 1$.

2 Solve the simultaneous equations $3x + 4y = 9$, $6x + y = -3$.

If we multiply the first equation throughout by 2 we would then have $6x$ in each equation.

Hence: (2 × equation 1) $\qquad\qquad 6x + 8y = 18$

(equation 2) $\qquad\qquad\qquad 6x + y = -3$

(subtracting) $\qquad 6x - 6x + 8y - y = 18 - (-3)$

i.e. $\qquad\qquad\qquad\qquad 7y = 21$

i.e. $\qquad\qquad\qquad\qquad y = 3$

Substituting $y = 3$ back in the first equation gives $3x + 4(3) = 9$

i.e. $\qquad\qquad\qquad\qquad 3x = -3$

i.e. $\qquad\qquad\qquad\qquad x = -1$

Checking in the second original equation gives $6(-1) + 3 = -3$. This is correct.

Thus $x = -1$, $y = 3$ is the only solution to the simultaneous equations $3x + 4y = 9$, $6x + y = -3$.

3 Solve the simultaneous equations $2x - 5y = -6$, $3x + 4y = 37$.

Here we cannot multiply one equation to get two coefficients the same. Therefore we must multiply **both** equations to get two coefficients equal.

We could get $6x$ in each by multiplying the first equation by 3 and the second by 2.
We could get $20y$ in each by multiplying the first equation by 4 and the second by 5.

It does not matter which we select, the answer will be the same in either case.

To prove this, the example is done in both ways. Hence:

a (3 × equation 1) $\qquad\qquad 6x - 15y = -18$

(2 × equation 2) $\qquad\qquad\quad 6x + 8y = 74$

(subtracting) $\qquad 6x - 6x - 15y - 8y = -18 - 74$

i.e. $\qquad\qquad\qquad\qquad -23y = -92$

i.e. $\qquad\qquad\qquad\qquad y = 4$

Substituting $y = 4$ back in the first equation gives $2x - 5(4) = -6$

i.e. $\qquad\qquad\qquad\qquad 2x = 14$

i.e. $\qquad\qquad\qquad\qquad x = 7$

Checking in the second original equation gives $3(7) + 4(4) = 37$. This is correct.

Thus $x = 7$, $y = 4$ is the only solution to the simultaneous equations $2x - 5y = -6$, $3x + 4y = 37$.

b (4 × equation 1) $8x - 20y = -24$
   (5 × equation 2) $15x + 20y = 185$

   (adding) $8x + 15x - 20y + 20y = -24 + 185$
   i.e. $23x = 161$
   i.e. $x = 7$

   Substituting $y = 7$ back in the first equation gives $2(7) - 5y = -6$
   i.e. $-5y = -20$
   i.e. $y = 4$

   Checking in the second original equation gives $3(7) + 4(4) = 37$. This
   is correct.

   Thus $x = 7$, $y = 4$ is the only solution to the simultaneous equations
   $2x - 5y = -6$, $3x + 4y = 37$.

PRACTICE 11.4.7   Try this question without a calculator

1 Use the method of elimination to solve the following simultaneous
   equations.

   a $2a + 3b = 15$ **d** $3g + 4h = -29$ **g** $4p - 3q = 1$
         $a + 2b = 8$ $4g - 3h = 3$ $6p + 2q = 5\frac{5}{6}$

   b $4c - 6d = -24$ **e** $5j + 3k = -15$ **h** $5r + 3s = 0$
         $3c + 3d = -3$ $3j - 2k = -9$ $4r - 2s = 11$

   c $5e + f = 3$ **f** $7m - 3n = 20$ **i** $6u - 8v = 2$
         $e + 2f = -3$ $3m - 5n = 3$ $5u + 4v = -5$

Equations in context

Worked Examples

1 In a local election John Trustme was elected with a majority of 346. The
   total number of votes cast was 1418. How many votes did each of the two
   candidates receive?

   Let the votes for the two candidates be m and n where m is the number
   cast for John Trustme.

   The sum is 1418 i.e. $m + n = 1418$. The difference is 346 i.e. $m - n = 346$.

   Hence: $m + n = 1418$
                                             $m - n = 346$

   (adding) $2m = 1764$
   i.e. $m = 882$

   Substituting in the first equation $882 + n = 1418$
   i.e. $n = 536$

   Checking in the second equation $882 - 536 = 346$. This is correct.

   Hence John Trustme polled 882 votes and his opponent 536.

2 On a package tour, two adults and one child can go for £1190. Similarly the fare for one adult and three children is £1320. How much does it cost for an adult and for a child?

Let the cost of an adult ticket be £a and for a child £c.

Therefore $2a + c = 1190$
and $a + 3c = 1320$

We can make the coefficients of a the same by multiplying the second equation by 2.

Hence (first equation) $\qquad 2a + c = 1190$
(2 × second equation) $\qquad 2a + 6c = 2640$

(subtracting) $\qquad -5c = -1450$
Hence $\qquad c = 290$

Substituting in the first equation $2a + 290 = 1190$
Hence $\qquad 2a = 900$
Hence $\qquad a = 450$

Checking in the second equation $450 + 3(290) = 1320$. This is correct.

Hence an adult ticket costs £450 and a child £290.

PRACTICE 11.4.8   Try these questions without a calculator

1 Batman and Robin are a and b years old respectively. The sum of their ages is 44. Batman is eight years older than Robin. How old is each of them?

2 Romeo and Juliet had dinner. Romeo's meal cost £2 more than Juliet's. Romeo paid the bill which totalled £15. How much did each meal cost?

3 A CD costs £x and a cassette £y. 4 CDs and 3 cassettes cost £70 and 2 CDs and 5 cassettes cost £63. How much does each cost?

4 On a train journey, adult tickets cost £a and child tickets £c. 2 adults and 3 children travel for £37.50. 1 adult and 4 children travel for £35. How much does each ticket cost?

5 Sam needs bait to go fishing. He can either buy 4 maggots and 3 worms for 47 p or 2 maggots and 5 worms for 41 p. How much do maggots and worms cost each?

6 Farmer Barleymow goes to market with £2000. For this money he can buy either 8 sheep and 4 pigs or 4 sheep and 7 pigs. How much do sheep and pigs cost each?

7 Henrietta the goose can lay either golden or brown eggs. 4 golden and 3 brown eggs together weigh 360 g, but 2 golden and 5 brown weigh 320 g. Find the weight of a golden egg.

8 The canteen coffee machine takes 20 p or 50 p coins. When emptied, it was found to contain 36 coins totalling £10.50 in value. How many of each sort of coin did the machine contain?

9 A club secretary bought 40 tickets for Torville and Dean's farewell tour. Some tickets cost £20 and the rest £12.50. The money received for the dearer tickets was £110 less than that received for the cheaper tickets. How many tickets at each price were bought?

10 This triangle is equilateral. Find m and n.

11 This triangle is isosceles. It has a perimeter of 200 cm. Find p and q.

12 The line $y = mx + c$ passes through points (4, 10) and (7, 19). Find the values of m and c.

13 The ages of Florence and Zebedee are in the ratio 2 : 3. In four year's time they will be in the ratio 3 : 4. How old are Florence and Zebedee now?

14 Johnny Herbert drove x miles up the M5 averaging 70 mph. He then left the M5 and drove for y miles averaging 40 mph. He drove a total of 163 miles in 2.5 hours. How far did he drive along the M5?

11.5 QUADRATIC EQUATIONS

We learned how to factorise quadratic expressions in Topic 11.3.

Any quadratic expression written as an equation is called a **quadratic equation**.

Any quadratic equation can be written as $x^2 + ax + b = 0$. a and b are constants. There are three main methods of solving quadratic equations – by factorising, by using a formula and by graphs.

See Topic 12.4, pages 342–343, for solving quadratic equations by graphs. Solutions by using the formula are in the Higher specifications only.

Solving quadratic equations by factorising

Consider the equation $P \times Q = 0$. Clearly $P \times Q = 0$ is only possible if *either* $P = 0$ *or* $Q = 0$. We use this fact to solve quadratic equations.

NOTE
You may like to revise pages 256–260 before you read this page.

Worked Examples

1 Solve the equation $a^2 - 5a + 6 = 0$.

Factorising: $(a - 2)(a - 3) = 0$
Remembering $P \times Q = 0$ above we can say that if $(a - 2)(a - 3) = 0$
then *either* $a - 2 = 0$ *or* $a - 3 = 0$.

If $a - 2 = 0$ then $a = 2$ and
if $a - 3 = 0$ then $a = 3$.

Hence the solutions of $a^2 - 5a + 6 = 0$ are $a = 2$ or $a = 3$.

2 Solve the equation $b^2 + 9b + 20 = 0$.

Factorising: $(b + 4)(b + 5) = 0$
Remembering $P \times Q = 0$ above we can say that if $(b + 4)(b + 5) = 0$
then *either* $b + 4 = 0$ *or* $b + 5 = 0$.

If $b + 4 = 0$ then $b = -4$ and
if $b + 5 = 0$ then $b = -5$.

Hence the solutions of $b^2 + 9b + 20 = 0$ are $b = -4$ or $b = -5$.

3 Solve the equation $c^2 - 5c - 14 = 0$.

Factorising: $(c + 2)(c - 7) = 0$
Remembering $P \times Q = 0$ above we can say that if $(c + 2)(c - 7) = 0$
then *either* $c + 2 = 0$ *or* $c - 7 = 0$.

If $c + 2 = 0$ then $c = -2$ and
if $c - 7 = 0$ then $c = 7$.

Hence the solutions of $c^2 - 5c - 14 = 0$ are $c = -2$ or $c = 7$.

4 Solve the equation $d^2 - 10d + 25 = 0$.

Factorising: $(d - 5)(d - 5) = 0$
Remembering $P \times Q = 0$ above we can say that if $(d - 5)(d - 5) = 0$
then *either* $d - 5 = 0$ *or* $d - 5 = 0$.

If $d - 5 = 0$ then $d = 5$.

Since both brackets are the same we get the same answer $d = 5$ from
each of them.
We say that $d = 5$ *twice*.
Any quadratic equation like this is called a **perfect square.**

Hence the solutions of $d^2 - 10d + 25 = 0$ are $d = 5$ *twice*.

5 Solve the equation $x^2 - 4 = 0$ (special case where $a = 0$).

$x^2 - 4 = 0$

therefore $x^2 = 4$

i.e. $x = 2$ or -2

However, $x^2 - 4 = 0$ could also be factorised as $(x - 2)(x + 2) = 0$

Remembering $P \times Q = 0$ above we can say that if $(x - 2)(x + 2) = 0$ then *either* $x - 2 = 0$ *or* $x + 2 = 0$.

If $x - 2 = 0$ then $x = 2$ and
if $x + 2 = 0$ then $x = -2$.

Hence the solutions of $x^2 - 4 = 0$ are $x = 2$ or $x = -2$.

> **NOTE**
> Since $2 \times 2 = 4$ and also $-2 \times -2 = 4$, then 4 has two square roots, 2 and -2.
> Any positive number has two square roots.
> Any negative number has *no* square roots since two negative numbers or two positive numbers multiplied together can only form a positive result.

6 Solve the equation $y^2 - 3y = 0$ (special case where $b = 0$).

$y^2 - 3y = 0$

Factorising $y(y - 3) = 0$

Remembering $P \times Q = 0$ above we can say that if $y(y - 3) = 0$ then *either* $y = 0$ *or* $y - 3 = 0$.

If $y - 3 = 0$ then $y = 3$.

Hence the solution of $y^2 - 3y = 0$ is $y = 0$ or $y = 3$.

Differences of two squares

The worked example **5** above showed $x^2 - 4$ being factorised as $(x - 2)(x + 2)$.

Any quadratic expression $x^2 - a^2$ can be written as $(x - a)(x + a)$.

For example $x^2 - 25$ is the same as $x^2 - 5^2$ so can be written $(x - 5)(x + 5)$.

i.e. $x^2 - 25 = (x - 5)(x + 5)$.

This is known as 'The difference of two squares' and can be very useful in simplifying expressions and solving equations.

Identities

We said above, that $x^2 - 25$ is the same as $x^2 - 5^2$ so can be written $(x - 5)(x + 5)$.

i.e. $x^2 - 25 = (x - 5)(x + 5)$.

This is known as an **identity**. The left hand side is identical to the right hand side. We show an identity is different from an equation by replacing the $=$ sign with $\equiv$.

i.e. $x^2 - 25 \equiv (x - 5)(x + 5)$.

We can see this by substituting **any** value for x in the identity, for example:

When $x = 6$ $6^2 - 25 = (6 - 5)(6 + 5)$
  i.e. $36 - 25 = 1 \times 11$
  i.e. $11 = 11$

When $x = 10$ $10^2 - 25 = (10 - 5)(10 + 5)$
  i.e. $100 - 25 = 5 \times 15$
  i.e. $75 = 75$

When $x = 3$ $3^2 - 25 = (3 - 5)(3 + 5)$
  i.e. $9 - 25 = -2 \times 8$
  i.e. $-16 = -16$

This works whatever number you substitute for x. Try some for yourself!

An identity is slightly different from an equation. In an equation there are only a set number of solutions, i.e. values of x that 'fit' the equation.

For example, the solution of $3x + 2 = 14$ has only one value of x that fits i.e. $x = 4$ since $3 \times 4 = 14$.

No other value of x fits the equation.

Similarly, worked example **1** on page 000 gives the solution of $a^2 - 5a + 6 = 0$ as $a = 2$ and $a = 3$. Only the values $a = 2$ and $a = 3$ fit.

But, the identity $a^2 - 5a + 6 = (a - 2)(a - 3)$ is true for all values of a, for example :

When a = 2 $2^2 - 5 \times 2 + 6 = (2 - 2)(2 - 3)$
  i.e. $4 - 10 + 6 = 0 \times -1$
  i.e. $0 = 0$

When a = 3 $3^2 - 5 \times 3 + 6 = (3 - 2)(3 - 3)$
  i.e. $9 - 15 + 6 = 1 \times 0$
  i.e. $0 = 0$

When a = 6 $6^2 - 5 \times 6 + 6 = (6 - 2)(6 - 3)$
  i.e. $36 - 30 + 6 = 4 \times 3$
  i.e. $12 = 12$

When a = 10 $10^2 - 5 \times 10 + 6 = (10 - 2)(10 - 3)$
  i.e. $100 - 50 + 6 = 8 \times 7$
  i.e. $56 = 56$

Worked Examples

1 Complete the identities:

    a $a^2 - 49$ **b** $2b^2 - 72$ **c** $m^2 - m - 12$ **d** $9e^2 - 25f^2$

    a $a^2 - 49 \equiv a^2 - 7^2 \equiv (a - 7)(a + 7)$

    b In this question notice that both terms have a common factor of 2. Using that fact we can now write:

      $2b^2 - 72 \equiv 2(b^2 - 36) \equiv 2(b^2 - 6^2) \equiv 2(b - 6)(b + 6)$

c Using methods for factorising quadratic expressions (see Topic 11.5), we get

$$m^2 - m - 12 \equiv (m + 3)(m - 4)$$

d In this question notice that $9e^2$ is, in fact, $(3e)^2$ and that $25f^2$ is $(5f)^2$. Using these facts we can now write:

$$9e^2 - 25f^2 = (3e)^2 - (5f)^2 = (3e - 5f)(3e + 5f)$$

2 Solve the equations: **a** $n^2 - 225 = 0$ **b** $4d^2 - 9 = 0$

a $n^2 - 225 = n^2 - 15^2 = (n - 15)(n + 15)$
Hence $(n - 15)(n + 15) = 0$; Thus $n - 15 = 0$ or $n + 15 = 0$;
i.e. $n = \pm 15$

b In this question notice that $4d^2$ is, in fact, $(2d)^2$. Using this fact we can write:

$$4d^2 - 9 = (2d)^2 - 3^2 = (2d - 3)(2d + 3)$$

Hence $(2d - 3)(2d + 3) = 0$; Thus $2d - 3 = 0$ or $2d + 3 = 0$;
i.e. $n = \pm 1.5$

3 Without using a calculator, find the exact values of:

a $7^2 - 6^2$ **b** $9^2 - 5^2$ **c** $64^2 - 36^2$ **d** $650^2 - 350^2$

a $7^2 - 6^2 = (7 - 6)(7 + 6) = 1 \times 13 = 13$
b $9^2 - 5^2 = (9 - 5)(9 + 5) = 4 \times 14 = 56$
c $6.4^2 - 3.6^2 = (6.4 - 3.6)(6.4 + 3.6) = 2.8 \times 10 = 28$
d $650^2 - 350^2 = (650 - 350)(650 + 350) = 300 \times 1000 = 3\,000\,000$

4 Simplify the following expressions:

a $(w^2 - 9) + (w^2 + w - 12)$ **b** $\dfrac{2(w^2 + 2w + 1)}{w + 1}$ **c** $\dfrac{p^2 - p - 12}{p^2 - 6p + 8}$

a $(w^2 - 9) + (w^2 + w - 12) = (w - 3)(w + 3) + (w - 3)(w + 4)$
$= (w - 3)(w + 3 + w + 4) = (w - 3)(2w + 7)$

b $\dfrac{2(w^2 + 2w + 1)}{w + 1} = \dfrac{2(w + 1)(w + 1)}{(w + 1)} = 2(w + 1)$

c $\dfrac{p^2 - p - 12}{p^2 - 6p + 8} = \dfrac{(p + 3)(p - 4)}{(p - 2)(p - 4)} = \dfrac{(p + 3)}{(p - 2)}$

PRACTICE 11.5.1   Try these questions without a calculator

1 Solve the following quadratic equations.

a $x(x - 5) = 0$ **e** $(x - 2)(x - 6) = 0$ **i** $(x + 3)(x - 11) = 0$
b $x(x + 4) = 0$ **f** $(x - 3)(x - 7) = 0$ **j** $(y - 6)(y + 9) = 0$
c $(x - 3)(x + 3) = 0$ **g** $(x + 1)(x + 2) = 0$ **k** $(z + 4)(z + 4) = 0$
d $(x - 5)(x + 5) = 0$ **h** $(x - 6)(x - 6) = 0$

2 Solve the following quadratic equations.

a $a^2 - 9 = 0$ **c** $c^2 + 5c = 0$ **e** $e^2 - 11e = 0$

b $b^2 - 144 = 0$ **d** $d^2 + 1.8d = 0$ **f** $x^2 - 2\frac{1}{2}x = 0$

3 Solve the following quadratic equations.

a $x^2 - 8x + 12 = 0$ **h** $z^2 + 3z - 70 = 0$ **o** $w^2 + w - 42 = 0$

b $x^2 - 9x + 20 = 0$ **i** $q^2 + 9q + 14 = 0$ **p** $x^2 - 2x - 99 = 0$

c $x^2 + 13x + 30 = 0$ **j** $r^2 + 5r - 14 = 0$ **q** $y^2 + 3y - 40 = 0$

d $x^2 + 20x + 99 = 0$ **k** $s^2 - 5s - 14 = 0$ **r** $z^2 - z - 72 = 0$

e $x^2 - 5x - 36 = 0$ **l** $t^2 - 9t + 14 = 0$ **s** $a^2 - 20a + 100 = 0$

f $x^2 - x - 30 = 0$ **m** $u^2 - 6u - 27 = 0$ **t** $b^2 + 18b + 81 = 0$

g $y^2 + 2y - 99 = 0$ **n** $v^2 + 6v - 16 = 0$

4 a Write down the factors of the quadratic equation which has solutions $x = 2$ and $x = 4$.

b Write the quadratic equation in factor form.

c Hence multiply out the brackets and find the quadratic equation which has $x = 2$ and $x = 4$ as solutions.

5 a Write down the factors of the quadratic equation which has solutions $y = -5$ and $y = -3$.

b Write the quadratic equation in factor form.

c Hence multiply out the brackets and find the quadratic equation which has $y = -5$ and $y = -3$ as solutions.

6 a Write down the factors of the quadratic equation which has solutions $z = 2$ and $z = -1$.

b Write the quadratic equation in factor form.

c Hence multiply out the brackets and find the quadratic equation which has $z = 2$ and $z = -1$ as solutions.

7 Complete the identities:

a $c^2 - 16$ **b** $g^2 - 81$ **c** $2m^2 - 8$ **d** $5r^2 - 125$

8 Complete the identities and solve the equations

a $w^2 - 4 = 0$ **b** $u^2 - 121 = 0$ **c** $2v^2 - 288 = 0$ **d** $25g^2 - 36 = 0$

9 Without using a calculator, find the exact values of

a $4^2 - 2^2$ **b** $14^2 - 6^2$ **c** $2.7^2 - 2.6^2$ **d** $671^2 - 329^2$

10 Simplify the following expressions:

a $(x - 3)^2 + x^2 - 9$ **c** $\dfrac{3x^2 + 3x - 18}{x^2 - 4}$

b $x^2 + 8x + 7 + x^2 - 1$ **d** $\dfrac{(x + 4)^2}{x^2 - 16}$

Equations in context

Worked Examples

1   A rectangle has sides of length $(x + 3)$ and $(x - 2)$ cm. The area is 36 cm^2.
    Find the value of x and the lengths of the sides.

Area $=$ length $\times$ width $= (x + 3)(x - 2)$.

Since the area $= 36$ we can write $(x + 3)(x - 2) = 36$

(multiplying out) $x^2 + 3x - 2x - 6 = 36$

(collecting like terms) $x^2 + x - 42 = 0$

(factorising) $(x - 6)(x + 7) = 0$

Remembering $P \times Q = 0$, we can say that if $(x - 6)(x + 7) = 0$ then
either $x - 6 = 0$ *or* $x + 7 = 0$.

If $x - 6 = 0$ then $x = 6$ and
if $x + 7 = 0$ then $x = -7$.

Hence $x = 6$ is the only practical solution in this case.
Therefore the sides of the rectangle are $6 + 3 = 9$ cm and $6 - 2 = 4$ cm.

NOTE

We must have $= 0$ to be able to solve a quadratic equation.

NOTE

$x = -7$ is not possible in this case since this would make the sides of the rectangle equal to $-7 + 3 = -4$ and $-7 - 2 = -9$. The rectangle would have *negative* length and width.

2   Jane and Gary's wedding portrait is 10 in. by 8 in. It is mounted on a card
    with a border x in. wide all the way round. The area of the card is 168 in^2.
    Find the width of the border and the dimensions of the card.

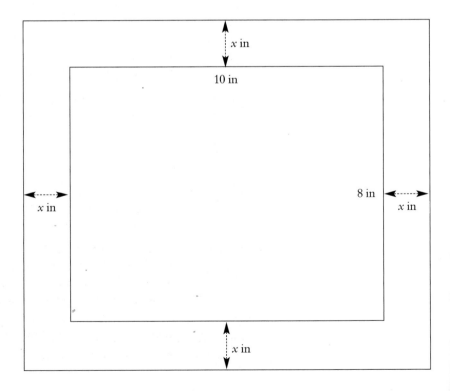

Length of the card = $(10 + 2x)$ in. (i.e. x in. on *each* side)

Similarly, width of the card = $(8 + 2x)$ in.

Therefore the area of the card = $(10 + 2x)(8 + 2x)$

Since the area = 168, we can write $(10 + 2x)(8 + 2x) = 168$

(multiplying out) $80 + 20x + 16x + 4x^2 = 168$

(collecting like terms) $4x^2 + 36x - 88 = 0$

(dividing through by 4) $x^2 + 9x - 22 = 0$

(factorising) $(x - 2)(x + 11) = 0$

Remembering $P \times Q = 0$, we can say that if $(x - 2)(x + 11) = 0$ then *either* $x - 2 = 0$ **or** $x + 11 = 0$.

If $x - 2 = 0$ then $x = 2$ and
if $x + 11 = 0$ then $x = -11$.

Therefore the dimensions of the card are $4 + 10 = 14$ in. by $4 + 8 = 12$ in.

NOTE

$x = -11$ is not possible in this case. It would make the sides of the card equal to $-22 + 10 = -12$ and $-22 + 8 = -14$.
The card would have *negative* length and width. Hence the width of the border, $x = 2$, is the only practical solution in this case.

PRACTICE 11.5.2   Try these questions without a calculator

1 Twice a number subtracted from the square of the number equals 15. Find the two possible values of the number.

2 Two consecutive numbers are multiplied together. The product is 56. Find the numbers.

3 One number is 7 more than another. The sum of the squares of the two numbers is 289. Find the two numbers.

4 The sum of the numbers $1 + 2 + 3 + \dots + n$ is given by the formula $\frac{1}{2}n(n + 1)$. The sum is 55. Find the value of n.

5 A polygon with n sides has d diagonals. n and d are connected by the formula $2d = n(n-3)$. A certain polygon has 20 diagonals. How many sides does it have?

6 A rectangle has a length $(d + 4)$ cm and a breadth $(d - 2)$ cm. It has an area of 40 cm^2. Find the value of d.

7 Joe Cleverclogs scores x marks in 4 tests. In another x tests he scores an additional 36 marks. His mean (average) score remains the same. How many marks did he score in the first 4 tests?

8 Nasser Hussain throws a cricket ball straight up into the air after making a catch. The height of the ball after t seconds is given by the formula $h = 4 + 30t - 5t^2$. The ball rises to a maximum height of 49 metres. How long did the ball take to get to this height?

9 One square has a side of length y cm. Another square has a side 5 cm longer than the first. The total area of the two squares is 97 cm^2. Find the length of side of the smaller square.

We know that $P = a + b + c$ is the formula for the perimeter, P, of a triangle whose sides are of lengths a, b and c.

We call P the **subject** of the formula because it starts with $P = \ldots$ and there are no terms in P on the other side.

We could rearrange the formula into $a = P - b - c$, or $b = P - a - c$, or $c = P - a - b$, making either a, b or c the subject.

This process is called **transposing the formula** or **changing the subject**.

There are two main methods used to rearrange simple formulae or equations and to change the subject:

> **1** by using a number diagram,
>
> or
>
> **2** by using the laws of algebra that we already know for equations, and rearranging.

1 Number diagram method.
   a Reconstruct the original equation, step by step, starting with the required subject, using the *number diagram* technique.
   b Reverse the number diagram formed, ending with a rearranged formula and our required subject.

2 Laws of algebra method.
   In this method we simply use our previous knowledge of the laws of algebra in rearranging the formula.
   It is like solving the equation but using letters as well as numbers to find the value of another variable.
   Whatever we do, we must remember that we do *exactly the same to both sides* and that at all times our equation is *balanced*.
   It is usually, *but not always*, best to do operations in the following order:
   a clear roots by squaring, cubing, etc.,
   b clear fractions by multiplying through the equation,
   c multiply out brackets where necessary,
   d put all terms containing the subject required on one side of the equation and the rest on the other side,
   e do whatever is necessary to obtain the required subject as a single term – this might need multiplying, dividing, factorising, taking roots, etc.,
   f rewrite the equation with only the required subject on one side.

Worked Examples

1 The area of a square of side x is given by the formula $A = x^2$. Make x the subject.

Method 1
Build up the formula from x: $x \rightarrow \boxed{\text{square}} \rightarrow x^2 \; (= A)$

Reverse: $\sqrt{A} \leftarrow \boxed{\text{square root}} \leftarrow A$

Hence $x = \sqrt{A}$

Method 2
$A = x^2$
square root both sides $\sqrt{A} = x$

PRACTICE 11.6.3   Try these questions with a calculator (take $\pi = 3.14$ or use the π button on your calculator)

1 The circumference of a circle is given by the formula $C = 2\pi r$, where r is the radius.
   a Make r the subject of the formula.
   b Find the radius of a circle with a circumference of 50 cm.

2 The area of a circle is given by the formula $A = \pi r^2$, where r is the radius.
   a Make r the subject of the formula.
   b Find the radius of a circle with an area of 50 cm^2.

3 The volume of a cone, of height h and base radius r, is given by the formula $v = \frac{1}{3}\pi r^2 h$.
   a Make h the subject of the formula.
   b Find the height of a cone with a base of radius 4.5 cm containing a volume of 233 cm^3.

4 The kinetic energy of a body of mass m is given by the formula $E = \frac{1}{2}mv^2$, where v is its velocity.
   a Make v the subject of the formula.
   b Find the velocity of an athlete of mass 40 kg running with kinetic energy 1280 joules.

5 The period of swing, in seconds, of a simple pendulum is given by the formula $T = 2\pi\sqrt{\dfrac{L}{10}}$, where L is the length of the pendulum.

   a Make L the subject of the formula.
   b A pendulum has a swing of 3 seconds. Find its length.
      (take $\pi = 3.14$)

6 A floor tile is the shape of the pentagon shown in the diagram. All five sides are of length x cm. The area of the tile is given by the formula

   $$A = \frac{(4 + \sqrt{3})}{10}x^2$$

   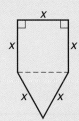

   a Make x the subject of the formula.
   b What is the length of the side of a tile whose area is 91.71 cm^2?

7 The amount, after compound interest has been added, on a sum of money, £P, invested in a building society for 2 years, is given by the formula $A = P\left(1 + \dfrac{r}{100}\right)^2$, where r is the rate of interest.

   a Make r the subject of the formula.
   b £1000 invested for 2 years yields compound interest of £144.90. Find the rate of interest.

We say that 5 *is greater than* 3, or that -1 *is less than* 2.

Such statements are called **inequalities**. We use symbols to make the writing of them easier.

The above two inequalities would be written:

$$5 > 3 \quad \text{and} \quad -1 < 2$$

If an algebraic inequality is written there may be more than one possible solution.

For example, $x > 2$ means that x can take any value above 2.

However, if we write $x \geqslant 2$, (i.e. x is greater or equal to 2), then $x = 2$ is included, in addition to the values given above.

The four basic inequality symbols are:

$>$ which means *greater than*,
$<$ which means *less than*,
$\geqslant$ which means *greater than or equal to*,
$\leqslant$ which means *less than or equal to*.

The number line

Algebraic inequalities can be represented by a *number line*. For instance, $x > 4$ can be shown:

(The **o** indicates that $x = 4$ *is not* included.)
Similarly $x \geqslant 4$ can be shown:

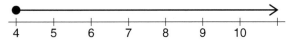

(The **●** indicates that $x = 4$ *is* included.)
Not all algebraic inequalities are represented by arrowed lines.
For instance, x is an integer and $x < 1$ is drawn on a number line as

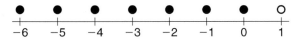

More than one inequality may be written in a single expression. For instance, the number line diagram for $-1 \leqslant x < 4$ is drawn as:

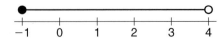

and the statement $-1 \leqslant x < 4$ and x is an integer is drawn as:

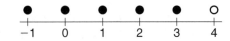

PRACTICE 11.7.1

1 Draw number line diagrams to illustrate the following inequalities:

    a $a>5$ **d** $d\geqslant0$ **g** $2<g<7$ **j** $3\leqslant j<6$

    b $b<3$ **e** $e\geqslant-3$ **h** $-2<h<3$ **k** $-1<k\leqslant5$

    c $c\leqslant2$ **f** $f\leqslant-2$ **i** $-5<i<-1$ **l** $-7\leqslant l\leqslant-3$

2 Repeat question 1, but where the variables are only integers.

NOTE

You may like to read pages 325–330 before reading this.

Regions of inequalities

We can find areas on a graph which represent inequalities. For example, $x>2$ could be drawn as the shaded area opposite.

(The dotted line means that $x=2$ is *not* included in the region.)

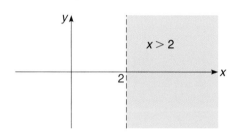

Similarly $y\leqslant5$ could be drawn as the shaded area below.

(The solid line means that $y=5$ *is* included in the region.)

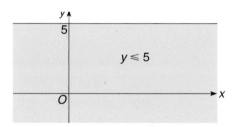

If the two expressions are combined we have the region below.

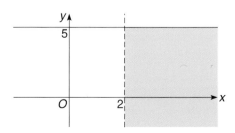

We can also find the region if we have a combined expression for x and y. The method is best shown in the following examples.

Worked Examples

1 Shade the region indicated by the inequality $y - 2x \leqslant 6$.

Step 1 Draw the graph of $y - 2x = 6$.
   (For a revision of how to draw straight line graphs see Chapter 12.)

Step 2 Substitute $x = 0$ and $y = 0$ into the inequality.

  a If the resulting numerical statement is true – shade the side of the line which includes the point (0,0).

  b If the resulting numerical statement is untrue – shade the side of the line which does *not* include the point (0,0).

  In our case $0 - 0 \leqslant 6$ which *is* true. Therefore we shade the side of the line including the point (0,0). The result can be seen below.

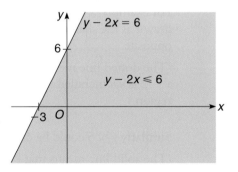

2 Shade the region indicated by the inequality $y + 3x > 8$.

Step 1 Draw the graph of $y + 3x = 8$.

Step 2 Substitute $x = 0$ and $y = 0$ into the inequality.
   In this case $0 - 0 > 8$ which is untrue. Therefore we shade the side of the line opposite to the point (0,0).

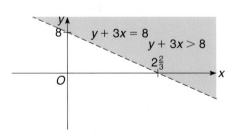

Note the solid line(for the $\leqslant$) and the dotted line (for the $>$) in the two examples.

3 Shade the region indicated by the inequalities $2y < 3x + 11$, $3y + 4x > 12$ and $x \leqslant 4$.

Step 1 Draw the graphs of $2y = 3x + 11$, $3y + 4x = 12$ and $x = 4$.

Step 2 Substitute $x = 0$ and $y = 0$ into the inequalities.
In the first case, $0 < 0 + 11$ which is true. Therefore we shade the side of the line containing point $(0,0)$.
In the second case, $0 + 0 > 12$ which is untrue. Therefore we shade the side of the line opposite the point $(0,0)$.
In the third case we shade the left side of the line $x = 4$.

The resulting area which is true for *all three inequalities* is shown below.

NOTE

If any line passes through $(0,0)$ then substituting $x = 0$ and $y = 0$ will not work. In this case it is possible to use any point we like and to follow the same rules for this point as we did for $(0,0)$.

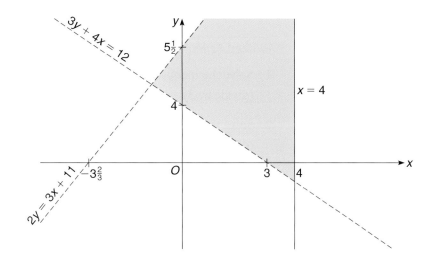

PRACTICE 11.7.2   Try these questions without a calculator

1 Show, on graph paper, the regions covered by the following inequalities:

a $x > -3$	**c** $x \leqslant -1$	**e** $x + y < 5$	**g** $2y - 3x < 6$
b $y > 1$	**d** $y \geqslant 5$	**f** $y - x \geqslant 3$	**h** $3y + 4x \geqslant 12$

2 Shade the regions covered by all the inequalities in each case:

a $y - x < 5$, $x \leqslant -1$, $y \geqslant 1$

b $3y + 5x \leqslant 10$, $x \geqslant -1$, $y > 1$

c $5y + 3x > 10$, $x < 3$, $y \leqslant 5$

d $2y > 3x + 6$, $2y + 3x < 12$, $x \geqslant -3$

Inequations

Algebraic inequalities are also known as **inequations**.

The rules for solving inequations are exactly the same as for equations – *but with one extra rule* which is as follows:

when we multiply or divide by a negative number we reverse the sign.

Looking at some arithmetical examples we can see this is true:

1 $5 > 2$
      (multiply by -1) $-5 < -2$

2 $-3 < 2$
      (multiply by -2) $6 > -4$

3 $8 > -6$
      (divide by -2) $-4 < 3$

Worked Examples

1   Solve the inequation $3a < 12$
      (divide by 3) $a < 4$

2   Solve the inequation $4b \geqslant -20$
      (divide by 4) $b \geqslant -5$

3   Solve the inequation $-2c > 8$
      (divide by -2) $c < -4$

4   Solve the inequation $-3d \geqslant -15$
      (divide by -3) $d \leqslant 5$

5   Solve the inequation $\frac{1}{2}e > -1$
      (multiply by 2) $e > -2$

6   Solve the inequation $-\frac{1}{3}f \leqslant 8$
      (multiply by -3) $f \geqslant -24$

7   Solve the inequation $4g - 2 > -3$
      (add 2) $4g > -1$
      (divide by 4) $a > -\frac{1}{4}$

8   Solve the inequation $-2h + 3 \leqslant 1$
      (subtract 3) $-2h \leqslant -2$
      (divide by -2) $h \geqslant 1$

9   Solve the inequation $3x - 2 > 4x + 1$
      (add 2) $3x > 4x + 3$
      (subtract $4x$) $-x > 3$
      (divide by -1) $x < -3$

11.9
SUMMARY

Two basic laws of arithmetic

1 When we add or multiply two numbers, it doesn't matter which comes first;
$a + b = b + a$ and $a \times b = a \times a$
This law does *not* work for subtraction or division;
$5 - 3$ is *not* the same as $3 - 5$, $10 \div 5$ is *not* the same as $5 \div 10$.

2 When we add or multiply three (or more) numbers then:
$a + b + c = (a + b) + c = a + (b + c)$
$a \times b \times c = (a \times b) \times c = a \times (b \times c)$

Basic algebraic notation

Notation means 'the way we write things down'.

In algebra:

x	means	$1 \times x$ or $1x$ (we don't usually write the 1)
$-x$	means	$-1 \times x$ or $-1x$ (we don't usually write the 1)
$4x$	means	4 times x or $4 \times x$ or $(x + x + x + x)$
$\dfrac{x}{4}$	means	x divided by 4 or $x \div 4$ or $\frac{1}{4}$ of x
xy	means	x times y or $x \times y$
$3xy$	means	3 times x times y or $3 \times x \times y$
$\dfrac{x}{y}$	means	x divided by y or $x \div y$

Index notation

x^n means $x \times x \times x \times \ldots$etc ($n$ times)

The laws of indices

$x^a \times x^b = x^{a + b}$
$x^a \div x^b = x^{a - b}$
$(x^a)^b = x^{ab}$

Basic algebra

Algebra is simply arithmetic using letters and numbers.
In algebra letters are used to represent numbers.

Words and terms

Any letter used to represent numbers is called a *variable* or *unknown*.
Anything whose value does not change is called a *constant*.
Any number in front of a variable is called a *coefficient*.
An algebraic collection of terms is called an *expression*.
An expression is a collection of constants and variables.
Any term may have more than one variable in it.
Usually we put letters in alphabetical order in a term and the number always comes first. If any expression has more than one term of the same *type* in it then these terms can be combined.
These are called *like* terms.

Using brackets

There is a definite order in doing operations.
We use the word **BODMAS**.
Brackets are used when we wish to group terms together.
Anything written inside brackets should be done before any other operations.
When removing brackets, each term *inside* the bracket must be multiplied by the term *outside*.
A term without a sign in front of it is always taken as positive (+).

When multiplying:
if the signs are the same the result is (+),
if the signs are different the result is (−).

Multiplying brackets together

Sometimes we want to multiply two brackets together.
Multiply *each term* in the second bracket by *each term* in the first.

Factorisation

Some series of terms have the same factor in each.
This is called a *common factor*.
Sometimes we find that there is another common factor after we have originally found one. This means that we can find a common factor a second time and factorise again. The second common factor is usually in a bracket.
Example of quadratic factorisation:

$$x^2 + 5x + 6 = (x + 2)(x + 3)$$

Any expression like $ax^2 + bx + c$, where a, b and c are constants, is called a *quadratic expression*.

Simple substitution

If we put a number in place of a letter in an expression we are said to *substitute* the value.

Number diagrams

Number diagrams create sequences of numbers by substituting values into a formula stored in a diagram.

Linear equations and formulae

Formulae are like *equations* – they contain an equals (=) sign and have terms on each side.
The difference between a formula and an equation is that in a formula the variables stand for definite quantities.
In an equation the variables stand for unknown quantities.
The solution may possibly be found – but not always.
We often write equations (and formulae) with one letter on one side of the = sign.
This letter is called the *subject* of the equation (or formula).
The subject is usually on the left hand side of the equation but can be on either.

Balancing equations

Equations are like balances.
They must have the same value on both sides of the = sign.

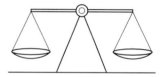

Simple linear equations

Algebraic equations use letters to represent the *unknown* quantity.
In an equation the *left hand side* must be equal to the *right hand side*.

The rules for solving linear equations

Both sides must *balance* at all times.
We must do *exactly* the same to both sides in order to keep it balanced.
To do this we can:

● add the same amount to both sides,
● subtract the same amount from both sides,
● multiply each side by the same amount (this means *each* term on both sides),
● divide both sides by the same amount (this means *each* term on both sides).

Equations are easiest to solve if we collect all the unknown terms on one side and all the constant terms on the other.
It is best to put the unknown terms on the side that gives the positive value.
If an equation has brackets in it, it is usually best to multiply out the brackets, collect like terms and then solve.

Simultaneous linear equations

We always need two equations with the two variables to produce one solution that fits both.

There are five main rules for solving simultaneous equations:

- Find a variable with the same coefficient in both equations.
- If the signs of these two terms are the same *subtract* one equation from the other. If the signs of these two terms are different *add* the equations together.
- Solve the resulting equation in one variable.
- Substitute this value for the first variable back in one of the original equations and solve the resulting equation in the other variable.
- Check the solution by substituting both values back into the other original equation.

Quadratic equations

Any quadratic expression written as an equation is called a *quadratic equation*. Any quadratic equation can be written as $x^2 + ax + b = 0$, where a and b are constants.

Solving quadratic equations by factorising

Consider the equation $P \times Q = 0$.

$P \times Q = 0$ is only possible if *either* $P = 0$ *or* $Q = 0$.

If P and Q are factors from a quadratic expression we can use this fact to solve quadratic equations like $x^2 + ax + b = 0$.

Changing the subject

We know that $P = a + b + c$ is the formula for the perimeter, P, of a triangle whose sides are of lengths, a, b and c.

We call P the *subject* of the formula because it starts with $P = \ldots$ and there are no terms in P on the other side.

We could rearrange the formula into $a = P - b - c$, or $b = P - a - c$, or $c = P - a - b$, making either a or b or c the subject.

This process is called *transposing the formula* or *changing the subject*.

There are two main methods used to rearrange simple formulae or equations and to change the subject:

1 By using a *number diagram* or by reconstructing the original equation, step by step, starting with the required subject, using the *number diagram* technique. Reverse the *number diagram* formed, ending with a rearranged formula and our required subject.

2 Laws of algebra method.
   In this method we simply use our previous knowledge of the laws of algebra in rearranging the formula.

It is like solving the equation but using letters as well as numbers and finding the value of another variable.

Whatever we do, we must remember that we do *exactly the same to both sides* and that at all times our equation is *balanced*.

It is usually, *but not always*, best to do operations in the following order:

a clear roots by squaring, cubing, etc.,

b clear fractions by multiplying through the equation,

c multiply out brackets where necessary,

d put all terms containing the subject required on one side of the equation and the rest on the other side,

e do whatever is necessary to obtain the required subject as a single term – this might need multiplying, dividing, factorising, taking roots, etc.,

f rewrite the equation with only the required subject on one side.

Inequalities

We say that 5 *is greater than* 3, or that -1 *is less than* 2.

Such statements are called *inequalities* and we have symbols to make the writing of them easier.

The above two inequalities would be written: $5 > 3$ and $-1 < 2$.

The symbol always points towards the smaller of the two quantities.

If an algebraic inequality is written there may be more than one possible solution.

For example, $x > 2$ means that x can take any value above 2.

However, if we write $x \geqslant 2$ (i.e. x is greater or equal to 2), then $x = 2$ is included, in addition to the values given above.

The four basic inequality symbols are:

> which means *greater than*,

< which means *less than*,

$\geqslant$ which means *greater than or equal to*,

$\leqslant$ which means *less than or equal to*.

The number line

Algebraic inequalities can be represented by a *number line*.

Regions of inequalities

It is possible to find areas on a graph which represent inequalities.

Inequations

Algebraic inequalities are also known as *inequations*.

The rules for solving inequations are exactly the same as for equations – but with one addition:

when we multiply or divide by a negative number we reverse the sign.

Trial and improvement

Sometimes a quadratic equation has a solution but will not factorise.
Sometimes we want to find a solution to an equation that has a power higher than x^2.

We can solve equations like these using a method called *trial and improvement*.

CHAPTER 12

Sequences and graphs

You may need to revise Topics 6.1 and 6.2 before you continue with this chapter.

Sequences

Sequence are patterns of numbers. Each one follows a rule.
For instance, 2, 4, 6, 8, ____, ____, is the sequence of even numbers.
It is usually possible to find the rule that creates the sequence.
Sometimes the rule is algebraic.

Worked Examples

Find the next two terms in the following sequences and state the rule that creates them.

a Monday, Tuesday, Wednesday, _____, _____

b F, G, H, I, J, _____, _____

c 5, 10, 15, 20, _____, _____

d .   ..   ...
         ..   ...
              ...   _____, _____

e .   .   .
         ..   ..
              ...   _____, _____

f 4, 12, 36, 108, _____, _____

a Monday, Tuesday, Wednesday, Thursday, Friday (days of the week, in order)

b F, G, H, I, J, K, L (letters of the alphabet)

c 5, 10, 15, 20, 25, 30 (each term is 5 more than the previous one)

d
.　　　　..　　　...　　　....　　.....
　　　　..　　　...　　　....　　.....
　　　　　　　...　　　....　　.....
square　　　　　　　　....　　.....
numbers　　　　　　　　　　　.....
(1)　　　(4)　　　(9)　　　(16)　　　(25)

e
.　　　.　　　.　　　.　　　.
　　　..　　　..　　　..　　　..
　　　　　　...　　　...　　　...
triangle　　　　　　　....　　....
numbers　　　　　　　　　　.....
(1)　　　(3)　　　(6)　　　(10)　　　(15)

f 4, 12, 36, 108, 324, 972 (each term is 3 times the previous term)

PRACTICE 12.2.1

1 Write down the next two terms of the following sequences.
State the rule that creates the sequence.

a 1, 3, 5, 7, ..., ...

b 2, 7, 12, 17, ..., ...

c b, e, h, k, ..., ...

d 2, 8, 32, 128, ..., ...

e March, April, May, ..., ...

f 8, 6, 4, 2, ..., ...

g 3, ⁻3, 3, ⁻3, ..., ...

h 2, 6, 5, 8, 8, 10, 11, 12, ..., ...

A number pattern that is formed by some common rule is called a sequence or a **series.**

Each number in the sequence is called a **term**.
Each term in the sequence is linked by a rule.

By studying the patterns that we see between the terms we are often able to work out the rule that creates the way the sequence is made up.
It often helps if we write down the numbers in the sequence in the form of a diagram, chart or table.

Worked Examples

Find the next two terms in each of the following sequences.

1

1st term	2nd term	3rd term	4th term
5	9	13	17

In this example each term is found by adding 4 to the previous term.

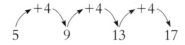

Use the rule to write down the next two terms.

17   21   21   25

The next two terms are 21 and 25.

2

1st term	2nd term	3rd term	4th term
2	6	18	54

In this example each term is found by multiplying the previous term by 3.

2   6   18   54

Use the rule to write down the fifth and sixth terms.

$$54 \times 3 = 162 \qquad 162 \times 3 = 486$$

The fifth and sixth terms are 162 and 486.

3

1st term	2nd term	3rd term	4th term
2	3	5	9

In this example each term is found by multiplying the previous term by 2 and then subtracting 1.

2   3   5   9

Use the rule to write down the next two terms.

$$9 \times 2 - 1 = 17$$
$$17 \times 2 - 1 = 33$$

The next two terms are 17 and 33.

Some sequences are very well known. For example:

     2,   4,   6,   8,   10,   ...   and   1,   3,   5,   7   9,   ...

are the sequences creating the even and odd numbers. You can write down many others!

     1,   4,   9,   16   25,   ...

are known as 'square numbers' because all the terms in the sequence are the squares of consecutive integers (whole numbers) –

i.e. $1^2 = 1$, $2^2 = 4$, $3^2 = 9$, $4^2, = 16$, $5^2 = 25$,   etc.

You have already seen these in the previous worked examples where dotted diagrams of squares are shown.

     1,   8,   27,   64,   125,   ...

are known as 'cube numbers' because all the terms in the sequence are the cubes of consecutive integers (whole numbers) –

i.e. $1^3 = 1$, $2^3 = 8$, $3^3 = 27$, $4^3, = 64$, $5^3 = 125$,   etc.

Other sequences are powers of numbers, for example :

     2,   4,   8,   16,   32,   ...   and   10,   100,   1000,   10 000,   100 000,   ...
i.e. 2^1, 2^2, 2^3, 2^4, 2^5,   ...   and 10^1, 10^2, 10^3, 10^4, 10^5,   ...

     1,   3,   6,   10,   15,   ...

are known as 'triangular numbers'.

You have already seen these in the previous worked examples where dotted diagrams of triangles are shown.

PRACTICE 12.2.2

Write down the rule and the next two terms of the following sequences:

1   3, 5, 7, 9, ..., ...

2   8, 10.5, 13, ..., ...

3   2, 4, 8, 16, ..., ...

4   16, 12, 8, 4, ..., ...

5   27, 9, 3, ..., ...

6   −1, −4, −7, ..., ...

7   5, −10, 20, ..., ...

8   3, 7, 15, 31, ..., ...

9   1, 3.5, 13.5, 53.5, ..., ...

10   2, −2, 2, −2, 2, ..., ...

The Fibonacci sequence

This famous sequence is named after the mathematician, Leonardo of Pisa, also called Fibonacci.

The sequence often occurs in science and natural history.

1, 1, 2, 3, 5, 8, 13, ..., ..., ...

Each term is found by adding together the two previous terms.

What are the next three terms of the Fibonacci sequence?

Invent your own sequences by using your own starting numbers.

Finding the nth term of a sequence

Worked Examples

1 Find the nth term of the sequence 3 5 7 9 ... .
How many terms are needed to reach 41?

Consider the sequence:

1st	2nd	3rd	4th	...	10th	...	50th	...	nth
term	term	term	term		term		term		term
3	5	7	9		...		...		...

The 1st term is 3 and the rule is *add 2*.

The 2nd term is found by adding 2 to the 1st term.

The 3rd term is found by adding 2 to the 2nd term, and so on ...

$$\begin{aligned}
\text{1st term} \quad &= 3 \\
\text{2nd term} \quad &= 3 + 2 = 5 \\
\text{3rd term} \quad &= 5 + 2 = 3 + (2 \times 2) & = 7 \\
\text{4th term} \quad &= 7 + 2 = 3 + (3 \times 2) & = 9 \\
\text{5th term} \quad &= 9 + 2 = 3 + (4 \times 2) & = 11 \\
\text{6th term} \quad &= 11 + 2 = 3 + (5 \times 2) & = 13 \\
\text{10th term} \quad & \quad\quad = 3 + (9 \times 2) & = 21 \\
\end{aligned}$$

Thus, the nth term $= 3 + ((n - 1) \times 2) = 3 + 2n - 2 = 2n + 1$

If the nth term is 41, we can say that $2n + 1 = 41$

i.e. $2n = 40$
$n = 20$

Thus, the 20th term is 41.

NOTE
You may like to revise solving linear equations on pages 269–284.

2 Find the nth term of the sequence 2 6 18 54 ..., ...
How many terms are needed to reach 13 122?

Consider the sequence:

1st	2nd	3rd	4th	...	15th	...	60th	...	nth
term	term	term	term		term		term		term
2	6	18	54		...		...		...

The 1st term is 2 and the rule is 'multiply by 3'.

The 2nd term is found by multiplying the 1st term by 3.

The 3rd term is found by multiplying the 2nd term by 3, and so on ...

$$
\begin{aligned}
\text{1st term} \quad &= 2 \\
\text{2nd term} \quad &= 2 \times 3 \quad = 6 \\
\text{3rd term} \quad &= 6 \times 3 \quad = 2 \times (3^2) \quad = 18 \\
\text{4th term} \quad &= 18 \times 3 \quad = 2 \times (3^3) \quad = 54 \\
\text{5th term} \quad &= 54 \times 3 \quad = 2 \times (3^4) \quad = 162 \\
\text{6th term} \quad &= 162 \times 3 = 2 \times (3^5) \quad = 486 \\
\text{10th term} \quad & = 2 \times (3^9) \quad = 39\,366 \\
\text{Thus, the } n\text{th term} \quad & = 2 \times (3^{n-1})
\end{aligned}
$$

If the nth term is 13 122 we can say that $2 \times 3^{n-1} = 13\,122$

$$
\begin{aligned}
\text{i.e.} \qquad &3^{n-1} = 6561 \\
\text{Now} \qquad &3^8 \quad = 6561 \\
\text{thus} \qquad &n - 1 = 8 \\
\text{i.e.} \qquad &n \quad = 9
\end{aligned}
$$

Thus the 9th term is 13 122.

PRACTICE 12.2.3 Try these questions using a calculator where necessary

1 Find the 6th, 10th, 25th and nth terms of the following sequences:

  a 2, 5, 8, 11, ...
  b 1, 6, 11, 16, ...
  c 3, 6, 12, 24, ...
  d 20, 17, 14, 11, ...
  e 64, 32, 16, ...

2 Find the nth term of the sequence 1 5 9 13 ... .
How many terms of the sequence are needed to reach 85?

3 Find the nth term of the sequence 2 10 50 250 ... .
How many terms of the sequence are needed to reach 6250?

4 Find the nth term of the sequence 1 -2 4 -8 ... .
How many terms of the sequence are needed to reach -512?

Coordinates

Coordinates are used to locate points on a graph.
For example, the position of point P is written as the coordinates (4, 3).
This means that the point is 4 units in the direction of the x-axis and 3 units in the direction of the y-axis.

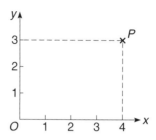

The horizontal line is usually called the **x-axis** and the vertical line is usually called the **y-axis,** although *any two variables can be used*.

The point where the two axes cross is called the **origin.**
The coordinates of the origin are (0, 0).

12.3 LINEAR GRAPHS

Extending the axes

We can see above how to fix the positions, or coordinates, of points on a graph. However, the axes can be extended both to the left and downwards in order to be able to *plot* the positions of points that have negative coordinates.
This is shown below:

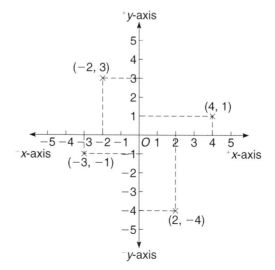

The points $(-2, 3)$, $(4, 1)$, $(-3, -1)$ and $(2, -4)$ are shown on the graph on page 325.

The 'x-coordinates' are -2, 4, -3 and 2.

The 'y-coordinates' are 3, 1, -1 and -4.

Functions and graphs

A **function** is another name given to an algebraic expression.

A functional graph shows us a *picture* of this expression which connects two variables.

Usually these are called x and y but any pair of letters can be used.

The horizontal, or x-axis, is called the *independent* axis.

The vertical, or y-axis, is called the *dependent*.

This is because the function is usually written in the form $y =$ (some expression in x) and the values of y *depend* on whatever values x takes.

It can also be written as $f(x) =$ (some expressions in x). $f(x)$ means 'a function of x'.

For example, in the function $y = 3x - 1$ we can substitute any values we like for x and find the corresponding y values. It can also be written as $f(x) =$ (some expressions in x). $f(x)$ means 'a function in x'.

When $x = -1$, $y = 3(-1) - 1 = -4$; when $x = 1$, $y = 3(1) - 1 = 2$; when $x = 3$, $y = 3(3) - 1 = 8$.

If we *plot* these points on a graph we get the following result:

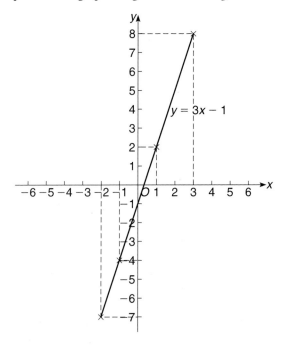

Notice that the points $(-1, -4)$, $(1, 2)$ and $(3, 8)$ all lie on a straight line. We can join these points up to get a straight lined graph, i.e. a *picture* of $y = 3x - 1$.

Looking at other points on the line, for example, $x = -2, y = -7; x = 0,$ $y = -1; x = 2.5, y = 6.5$, we can see that these values of x and y *fit* the equation $y = 3x - 1$ also.

In fact *every point on the line*, regardless of whether x and y are integers or not, *fits* or *satisfies* the equation of the graph $y = 3x - 1$.

NOTE

'Integer' means whole number.

Worked Examples

1   Does the point $(1, 6)$ lie on the straight line $y = 8x - 2$?

2   Does the point $(2, 3)$ lie on the straight line $f(x) = 3x + 1$?

3   The point $(-1, 2)$ lies on one of the straight lines $y = 2x - 3$ or $y = 6 + 4x$. Determine which line it lies on.

4   The x coordinates of two points on the straight line $f(x) = 3x - 1$ are $x = -2$ and $x = 4$. Find the y coordinates of these points.

1   When $x = 1, y = 8(1) - 2 = 8 - 2 = 6$. Yes, $(1, 6)$ does lie on the line $y = 8x - 2$.

2   When $x = 2, f(x) = 3(2) + 1 = 6 + 1 = 7$. No, $(2, 3)$ does not lie on the line $f(x) = 3x + 1$.

3   When $x = -1, y = 2(-1) - 3 = -5$. No, $(-1, 2)$ does not lie on $y = 2x - 3$.
     But $x = -1, y = 6 + 4(-1) = 2$, so $(-1, 2)$ does lie on $y = 2x - 3$.

4   When $x = -2, f(x) = 3(-2) - 1 = -7$. The y coordinate is -7.
     When $x = 4, f(x) = 3(4) - 1 = 11$. The y coordinate is 11.

PRACTICE 12.3.1   Try these questions without a calculator

1   Does the point $(-1, 1)$ lie on the straight line $y = 2 - 3x$?

2   Does the point $(2, -3)$ lie on the straight line $f(x) = 2x - 7$?

3   The point $(1, -4)$ lies on one of the lines $y = 3 - x, y = 2x - 6$ and $y = 4 + 3x$. Which line does it lie on?

4   a   The x coordinates of three points on the line $f(x) = 3 + 2x$ are given by $x = -3, x = 0$ and $x = 7$. Find the y coordinates.
     b   Plot these coordinates on a graph and show that all three points do indeed lie on a straight line.

Algebra

Drawing linear graphs

Some examples of linear equations are:

$$y = 3 \quad x = -4 \quad y = 2x - 9 \quad f(x) = 5 + 3x \quad 2x + 3y = 6$$

NOTE

Revise these skills on pages 292–297.

The last example does not look like the others, but using the skills learned at transposing formulae in Chapter 11 it can be made to look like the others, i.e.

$$2x + 3y = 6$$
$$\text{(subtract } 2x) \quad 3y = -2x + 6$$
$$\text{(divide by 3)} \quad y = -\tfrac{2}{3}x + 2$$

If we plotted all the points that *fitted* any of the above equations on a graph we would see that it was a straight line.

Linear graphs are just another way of saying *straight line graphs*.
We know if a graph is linear just by looking at the equation.

If the powers of x and y are both one then the graph is linear or straight.

To draw a linear graph we need to find the coordinates of any two points that fit its equation and then to plot them and draw a graph.

To make sure that we haven't made a mistake we usually plot three points and make sure that they lie on one straight line.

When we have plotted the points we can draw a straight line through them and continue it from one side of the graph paper to the other.

When calculating the coordinates of points it is best to *build up* the values in a table.

The following examples show how this is done.

Worked Examples

1 Draw the graph of $f(x) = 2x + 1$.
   Take any three values of x; say $x = -2, x = 0, x = 3$:

x	-2	0	3
$2x$	-4	0	6
$f(x) = 2x + 1$	-3	1	7

Plotting these points we get:

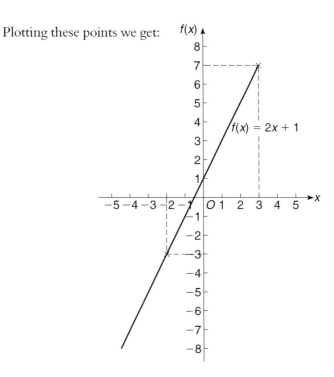

$f(x) = 2x + 1$

2   Plot the graph of $y = -3x + 6$.
Again, taking any three values
of x; say $x = -1$, $x = 0$, and
$x = 4$:

x	-1	0	4
$-3x$	3	0	-12
$y = -3x + 6$	9	6	-6

Plotting these points we get:

$y = -3x + 6$

3 Plot the graph of $2y + 3x = 4$.
We cannot immediately plot this as above.
We must first transpose the equation. Hence:

$$2y + 3x = 4$$

(subtract $3x$) $2y = -3x + 4$
(divide by 2) $y = -1.5x + 2$

Now taking three values of x; say $x = -4$, $x = 0$, and $x = 4$:

x	-4	0	4
$-1.5x$	6	0	-6
$y = -1.5x + 2$	8	2	-4

Plotting these points we get:

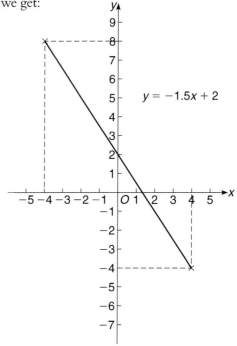

$y = -1.5x + 2$

PRACTICE 12.3.2a **Try these questions without a calculator**

1 Using any three values for x, calculate coordinates and draw the graphs of:

a $y = x$	**e** $y = x - 1$	**i** $y = 6 - \frac{1}{2}x$	**m** $4y + 3x = 12$
b $y = 3x$	**f** $y = 2x - 3$	**j** $y = -2x - 1$	**n** $2y + 5x = 8$
c $y = -2x$	**g** $y = 3x + 1$	**k** $y = 4 - 3x$	**o** $4x - 3y + 6 = 0$
d $y = x + 2$	**h** $y = \frac{1}{2}x + 4$	**l** $3y - 2x = 6$	**p** $3x + 4y + 5 = 0$

2 Elizabeth cooks her Christmas turkey at 15 minutes per pound weight followed by a final 20 minutes.

This can be represented by the equation $y = 15x + 20$ where y is the cooking time in minutes and x the weight of the turkey in pounds.

a Copy and complete the following table:

x	5	15	25
$15x$			
$y = 15x + 20$			

b Using x as the horizontal axis and y as the vertical axis plot the three points calculated above and draw the graph.

c Using the graph obtained find how long Elizabeth needs to cook:
   i an 8,   **ii** an 18,   **iii** a 23 pound turkey.

d Elizabeth puts her turkey into a pre-heated oven at 8:10 am and takes it out at 12 noon. If the turkey is perfectly cooked how heavy was it?

PRACTICE 12.3.2b   Try these questions with a calculator

1 When the gas supply industry was de-regulated in 1996 NEWGAZ offered its customers a choice of two tariffs:

   (A) An annual standing charge of £40 and gas supplied at 1.4 pence per unit, or

   (B) gas supplied at 1.6 pence per unit.

The cost of gas supplied under the two tariffs can be written as $C = 40 + 0.014n$ for tariff (A) and as $C = 0.016n$ for tariff (B), where C is the cost in £ and n the number of units.

a Copy and complete the following table:

n	10 000	25 000	55 000
$C = 40 + 0.014n$			
$C = 0.016n$			

b Using C as the vertical axis and n as the horizontal axis plot both of the graphs above *on the same grid*.

c Use the graphs obtained to find out the number of units where the cost would be the same under either tariff.

d Calculate which tariff should be used to obtain the cheapest gas if 14 000 units are used and what the saving would be.

e Calculate which tariff should be used to obtain the cheapest gas if 50 000 units are used and what the saving would be.

Solving simultaneous equations by using graphs

When we draw the graph of any straight line all the possible values of x and y which fit the equation of the graph must lie on the line.
Imagine two straight lines drawn on the same graph.
Unless the lines are parallel *they must cross (intersect) at one point.*
Therefore, since the coordinates of x and y must satisfy the equations of the lines, the single values of x and y *at the point of intersection of the two lines,* must be the solutions of the simultaneous equations.
For example, solving the simultaneous equations $x + y = 4$ and $2x - y = 5$, we get:

$$x + y = 4$$
$$2x - y = 5$$

(adding) $3x = 9$ i.e. $x = 3$
(substituting) $3 + y = 4$ i.e. $y = 1$

If we now draw the graphs of $x + y = 4$ (i.e. $y = 4 - x$) and $2x - y = 5$ (i.e. $y = 2x - 5$), we can see that they intersect at the point (3, 1).

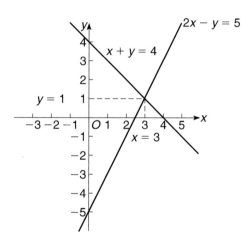

Therefore, we have an alternative method of solving a pair of simultaneous equations:

plot the graphs of the two equations and find the coordinates of the point of intersection.

PRACTICE 12.3.3

1 Solve the simultaneous equations by drawing the graphs of the equations and finding the points of intersection.

a $2a + 3b = 15$ **c** $5e + f = 3$ **e** $5j + 3k = -15$
      $a + 2b = 8$ $e + 2f = -3$ $3j - 2k = -9$
b $4c - 6d = -24$ **d** $3g + 4h = -29$ **f** $7m - 3n = 20$
      $3c + 3d = -3$ $4g - 3h = 3$ $3m - 5n = 3$

Gradient and intercept

As we saw in the last section, any linear (or straight line) graph, can be written $y = mx + c$, where m and c are *constants* for each individual line.

c is usually called the **intercept**. It is the place where the graph crosses the y-axis. From above we see that $y = 2x + 1$ crosses the y-axis at $(0, 1)$, that $y = -3x + 6$ crosses the y-axis at $(0, 6)$ and that $2y + 3x = 4$ crosses the y-axis at $(0, 2)$.

m is the coefficient of the x term. It is called the **gradient** of the line. It measures how *steep* the line is compared to the x-axis.

$$\text{Hence} \quad y = 2x + 1 \text{ has a gradient } m = 2$$
$$y = -3x + 6 \text{ has a gradient } m = -3$$
$$2y + 3x = 4 \text{ has a gradient } m = -1.5$$

If m is positive it means that the line slopes *upwards to the right*

i.e.

If m is negative it means that the line slopes *downwards to the right*

i.e.

To find the gradient of a straight line

There are two main methods for calculating the gradient of a straight line.

1 *From the equation of the line.*
As shown in the last section the gradient is the coefficient of the x term.
For example:

$y = 5x + 2$ has gradient $= 5$

$y = 3 - 4x$ has gradient $= -4$

$2y - 3x = 7$ must first be transposed:

$2y = 3x + 7$

$y = \frac{3}{2}x + \frac{7}{2}$ i.e. a gradient of $\frac{3}{2}$ or 1.5

2 *From a plotted graph.*

   a Choose *any two* convenient points on the line.

   b Calculate the vertical difference in *y* coordinates.

   c Calculate the horizontal difference in *x* coordinates.

   d The gradient $m = \dfrac{\text{the difference in } y \text{ coordinates}}{\text{the difference in } x \text{ coordinates}}$

Look along the line from left to right.
If the line slopes *upward*, both differences are positive
and the line has a positive gradient.

If the line slopes *downward* from left to right, the *x*
difference is positive and the *y* difference is negative
(i.e. it decreases). This means that the line has a negative
gradient.

For example:

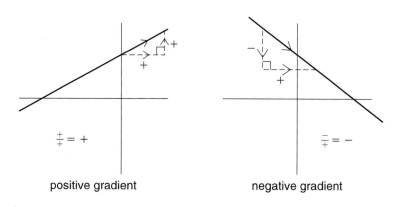

positive gradient   negative gradient

Worked Examples

1 Find the gradient of the line shown.

   y difference $= 10 - 4 = 6$

   x difference $= 5 - 2 = 3$

   gradient $= m = \dfrac{y \text{ difference}}{x \text{ difference}} = \dfrac{6}{3} = 2$

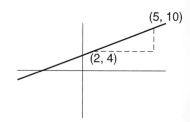

2 Find the gradient of the line shown.

   y difference $= 5 - -1 = 5 + 1 = 6$

   x difference $= 6 - -3 = 6 + 3 = 9$

   gradient $= m = \dfrac{y \text{ difference}}{x \text{ difference}} = \dfrac{6}{9} = \dfrac{2}{3}$

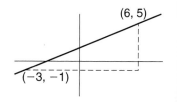

PRACTICE 12.4.2

1 Use your answers to Practice 12.4.1 **1a–f** to find:

    i the coordinates of the lowest, or highest, point,

    ii the equation of the line of symmetry,

    iii the solution of each quadratic expression $= 0$.

2 The average safe braking distance, d yds, for vehicles is given by the equation $d = \dfrac{v^2}{50} + \dfrac{v}{3}$, where v is the speed of the vehicle in mph.

    a Draw up a table of values for d. Let v take values from 0 to 80 in steps of 10.

    b Draw the graph of $d = \dfrac{v^2}{50} + \dfrac{v}{3}$ using v as the horizontal axis.

    c Use your graph to find the safe braking distance when the vehicle is travelling at:

        i 15 mph,   **ii** 45 mph,   **iii** 75 mph.

    d A driver suddenly sees an obstruction 50 yards ahead. She just stops in time. How fast was she travelling when she first saw it?

3 Amelia has a piece of pipe 40 cm long. She bends it into a rectangle of length x cm.

    a Show that the area of the rectangle is given by the equation $A = 20x - x^2$.

    b Draw up a table and draw the graph of $A = 20x - x^2$ for values of x from 0 to 20.

    c Use your graph to find:

        i the area when $x = 3.6$ cm,

        ii the length and breadth of the rectangle when the area is 98 cm^2,

        iii the maximum area of the rectangle,

        iv the equation of the line of symmetry on the graph,

        v the dimensions of the rectangle which has the maximum area.

4 Sam, the *human cannonball*, is fired from a gun to land on a platform 40 m high. The equation of his path is given by $h = x - \dfrac{x^2}{360}$, where x is the horizontal distance in metres.

    a Complete a table of values for h and x, for values of x from 0 to 60.

    b Draw the graph of h against x.

    c How far from the gun horizontally is the platform?

We often see, in papers and magazines, a lot of information in the form of graphs. These show a lot of data very easily and, with a little practice, we can find information very quickly.

The shape of a graph can often tell us a lot about what is happening in a real life situation. The following information will be useful.

Linear graphs

All linear graphs have no powers of x or y above 1 (see Topic 12.3). They are all straight lines. An example is the line $2y - 3x = 4$ (which can be rewritten as $y = 1.5x + 2$).

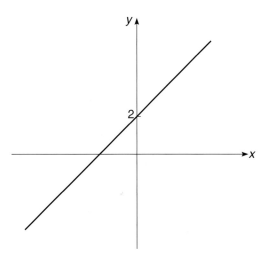

If the line is rising to the right then the values of y and x are both increasing. Some examples would be:

   i the distance that a car is from a particular point when travelling away from it at a constant speed,

  ii the speed of a car when accelerating at a steady rate,

 iii the height of water in a cylindrical jar when water is poured into it at a constant rate.

If the line is rising to the left then the value of y is decreasing while the value of x is increasing (and vice versa).

Some examples would be:

   i the distance that a car is from a particular point when travelling towards it at a constant speed,

  ii the speed of a car when decelerating at a steady rate,

 iii the height of water in a cylindrical jar when water is poured out of it at a constant rate.

If any rate of increase or decrease is not constant then the line would be curved and not straight – it would not be **linear**. An example would be the height of water in a conical jar when water is poured out of it at a constant rate as the example shows.

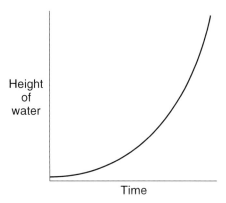

Quadratic graphs

Quadratic graphs, or parabolas, are graphs of the form $y = ax^2 + bx + c$, where a, b and c are fixed numbers (constants) (see Topic 12.5). If the value of a (i.e. the x^2 term) is positive, the graph is shaped as in example **i** below; if the value of a (i.e. the x^2 term) is negative, the graph is shaped as in example **ii** below.

i   ii

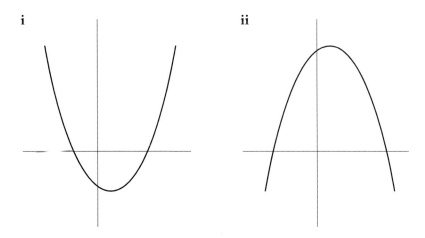

Worked Examples

1   Cornwall has declared itself independent.

Its unit of currency is an oval shaped coin called the *Pasty*.
The graph below shows how to convert from £ Sterling to the *Pasty*.

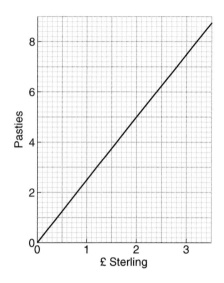

a How many *Pasties* do I get for £1?
b How much is 1 *Pasty* worth in pence?
c On holiday in Newquay I change a traveller's cheque for £25 into *Pasties*. How many do I get?
d After my holiday I find I have 76 *Pasties* left. Excluding commission, how much do I get back in £ sterling?

    a When £ = 1, *Pasties* = 2.5
    b 2.5 *Pasties* = £1, therefore 1 *Pasty* = $\frac{100}{2.5}$ = 40 pence
    c I get 25 × 2.5 = 62.5 *Pasties*
    d I get $\frac{76}{2.5}$ = £30.40.

2 The vertical height of an aeroplane after take-off is shown by the graph below.

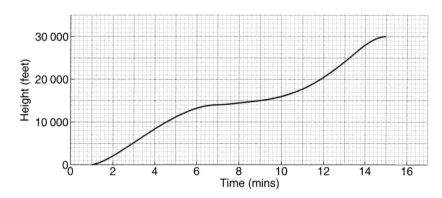

a How long does the plane taxi along the runway?
b When does the plane first reach maximum height?
c How high is the plane after: **i** 2 minutes, **ii** 7 minutes?
d When does the plane reach half its maximum height?

    a 1 minute   **c** **i** 2000 feet   **d** 8.5 minutes
    b 15 minutes   **ii** 14 000 feet

PRACTICE 12.5.1

1 The graph below shows the relationship between temperature measured in degrees fahrenheit (°F) and degrees celsius (°C).

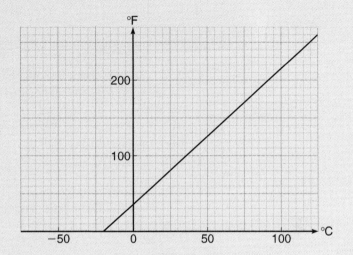

   a The freezing point of water is 0 °C. What is this in °F?
   b The boiling point of water is 212 °F. What is this in °C?
   c Normal body temperature is 98.6 °F. What is this in °C?
   d Alcohol boils at 85 °C. What is this in °F?

2 Bill walks Hugo, his dog. The distance they are from home is shown in the graph below.

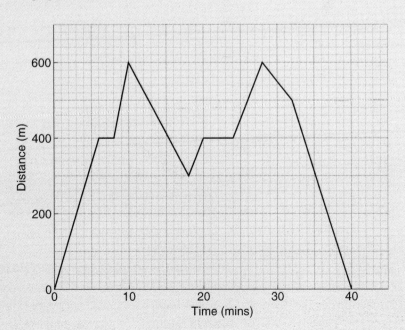

a How far are they from home after: **i** 5, **ii** 12, **iii** 27, **iv** 35 minutes?
b What is the furthest distance they get from home?
c After how long are they: **i** 200 metres, **ii** 550 metres from home?
d Bill stands and talks to a friend for 4 minutes. When did this happen?
e How long is it from the first to the second time that Bill and Hugo are 600 m from home?
f At one stage it began to rain. Bill and Hugo headed for home. When the shower stopped Bill decided to resume the walk.
   i When did this happen?
   ii How long did the shower last?
   iii How far did they walk towards home?
g How far did Bill and Hugo walk altogether?

3 The graph shows the journeys made by a van and a car starting from Oxford and travelling to Luton and back.

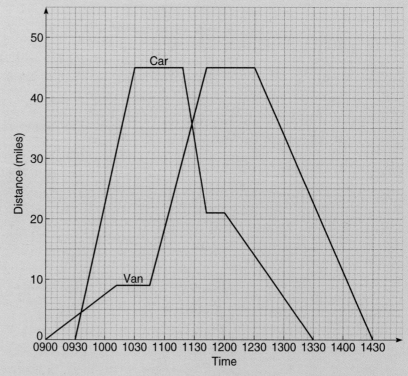

a How far had the car travelled when it met the van for the second time?
b Calculate, in mph, the average speed of the car between 0930 and 1030.
c During which period of time was the van travelling at its greatest speed? (SEG)

4   A firm making glasses makes a profit of £*y* from *x* glasses according to
    the graph below.

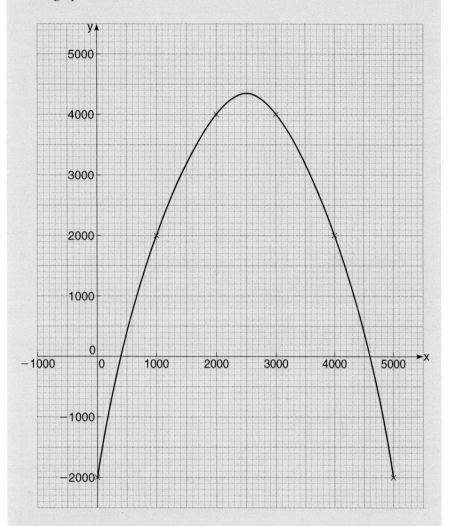

Find, from the graph:

a   the number of glasses the firm should produce in order to make the
    maximum profit,

b   the minimum number of glasses the firm should produce in order
    to make sure that it does not make a loss,

c   the range of values of *x* for which the profit is more than £3250.
    (SEG)

5   A swimming pool is in the shape of a prism with a trapezium-shaped
    cross-section. It has a 'shallow end' depth of 1 metre and a 'deep end'
    depth of 3 metres. Water is poured in at a steady rate. Draw a sketch
    graph showing how the depth of water rises over time.

6 Which of the graphs below illustrates the statement 'Credit card debt is now falling but by less each year'.

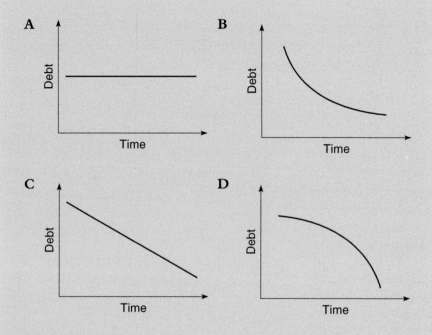

7 Water is poured at a steady rate into each of the following containers.

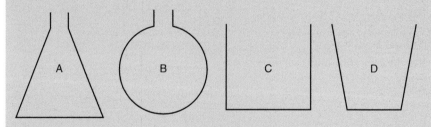

The graphs below show the comparison between the height of the water in the containers and the time after the start of pouring in the water.

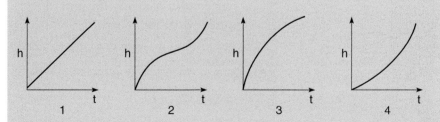

Write down which of the graphs 1, 2, 3 and 4 correspond to the containers A, B, C and D.   (SEG)

8 Draw sketch graphs of the depth of water against time elapsed when water flows at a constant rate into tanks which are rectangular prisms with the cross sections A, B, C and D shown:

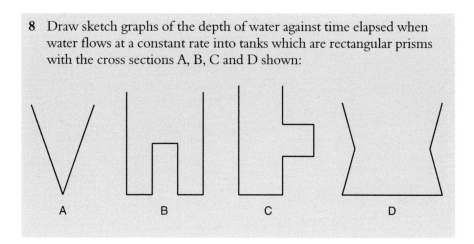

A   B   C   D

Graphs from experimental data

Graphs can be used to find relationships in experimental data.

In an experiment we sometimes suspect that the variables are connected by a linear, or straight line, relationship.

By plotting the points and then drawing the straight line that *best fits* the points we can find out the equation that connects those variables.

Worked Example

The temperatures of a cooling liquid are taken using two thermometers – one calibrated in degrees fahrenheit (°F), the other in degrees celsius (°C).

x (°C)	100	80	60	40	20	0
y (°F)	210	175	140	105	70	30

a Plot these points on graph paper.

b Draw the straight line that you think best fits the plotted points.

c Using your graph calculate:
   i the intercept on the fahrenheit axis,
   ii the gradient.

d Use your values from c above to write down the equation $y = mx + c$ and obtain an equation which converts °C to °F.

e Use your answer to d above to calculate the temperature, in fahrenheit, of:
   i 24 °C,
   ii 66 °C.

a, b

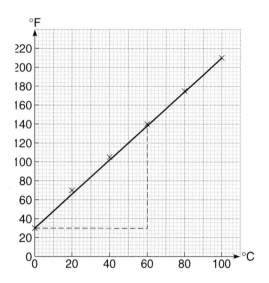

c From the graph
 i the intercept is 30,
 ii the gradient is $\frac{110}{60} = 1.83$ (3sf).

e Using the above equation
 i °F = 1.83 × 24 + 30 = 73.92
 ii °F = 1.83 × 66 + 30 = 150.78

d $y = mx + c$
 i.e. $y = 1.83x + 30$
 Hence °F = 1.83 °C + 30

PRACTICE 12.5.2

1 The table below shows the values of x and y connected by the equation $y = mx + c$.

x	2	5	8	11	14	17
y	14	24	34	44	55	65

 a Plot the points given and draw your line of best fit.
 b From your graph calculate the values for the gradient, m, and the y intercept, c.
 c Use your equation to estimate values of y when:
  i $x = 4$ and, ii $x = 10$.

2 The table below shows the values of x and y connected by the equation $y = mx + c$.

x	1	3	5	7	9	11	13	15	17
y	42	35	29	23	16	10	3	−3	−9

 a Plot the points given and draw your line of best fit.
 b From your graph calculate the values for the gradient, m, and the y intercept, c.
 c Use your equation to estimate values of y when:
  i $x = 2.54$, ii $x = 11.7$, iii $x = 14$.

3 Ohm's law states that the voltage (V volts), current (I amps) and resistance (R ohms) in part of an electrical circuit are connected by the formula $V = IR$.

The following table gives some experimental values obtained by a student.

V	0	2	4	6	8	10	12	14
I	0	0.25	0.55	0.82	1.01	1.28	1.60	1.80

a Plot these points, with I as the horizontal axis up to 2.6 and draw your line of best fit. Extend the line to $V = 20$.
b Measure the gradient of the line. What does it represent in the equation $V = IR$?
c Use your equation for $V = IR$ to find:
   i the current when the voltage is raised to 20 volts,
   ii the voltage that gives a current reading of 1.5 amps.

4 The recorded population of a village on 31st July over a period of time is shown below:

Year	1980	1984	1986	1989	1991	1994
Population	300	510	650	900	925	1050

a Plot the given points on a graph using the year as the horizontal axis, extended to the year 2000.
b One of the recorded figures is *clearly inaccurate*. Which year is this?
c Ignoring the inaccurate figure draw your line of best fit.
d From your graph, write down:
   i your estimate of the correct figure to replace the inaccurate one,
   ii your estimate of the population in the year 2000.

5 A second-hand car dealer estimates the resale value (£C) of a car is given by the formula $C = N - kD$, where N is the value of the car when new and D is the recorded mileage. On his forecourt there are six cars, all of the same make and model, having the same value when new. Their prices are as follows:

C	9700	9000	8750	8000	6500	5250
D	5000	16 500	25 000	42 400	68 000	93 500

a Plot these points on a graph using D as the horizontal axis and ranging from 0 to 100 000.
b Draw your line of best fit.
c Use your graph to calculate: **i** the value of the cars when new,
                                           ii the gradient of the line of best fit.
d Use your answer to **c** to write down the equation $C = N - kD$ inserting your values of N and k.
e Use your equation to calculate the resale value of a similar car when the mileage was **i** 10 000 miles and **ii** 100 000 miles.
f Mr Schumacher had £7500 to spend on a used car. What sort of mileage should it have done?

12.6

FURTHER GRAPHS

We now know how to draw quadratic graphs. We can extend our knowledge and draw other sorts of curved graphs. All we do is to build up the equation in the form of a table. Then we draw the graph as before.

Worked Examples

1 **a** Draw the graph of $y = \dfrac{24}{x} + 2x - 10$ for values of x from 1 to 8.

     b Use your graph to find:
         i the minimum value of y,   **iii** the value of x when $y = 10$.
         ii the value of y when $x = 7.5$,

a

x	1	2	3	4	5	6	7	8
$\dfrac{24}{x}$	24	12	8	6	4.8	4	3.43	3
$2x$	2	4	6	8	10	12	14	16
-10	-10	-10	-10	-10	-10	-10	-10	-10
y	16	6	4	4	4.8	6	7.43	9

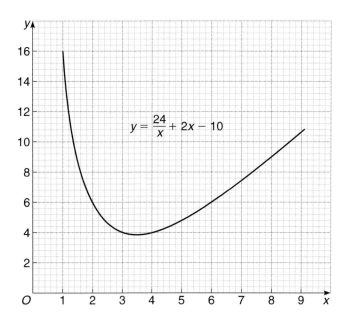

$$y = \frac{24}{x} + 2x - 10$$

     b   **i** Minimum value of $y = 3.46$.   **iii** When $y = 10$, $x = 1.4$.
         ii When $x = 7.5$, $y = 8.2$.

2 **a** Plot the graph of $y = \dfrac{10}{x}$ from $x = -4$ to -1 and from $x = 1$ to 4.
     b Look at what happens to y as x goes from -1 to 0 and from 0 to 1. Put this in on your graph.
     c Use your graph to find y when: **i** $x = -2.5$,   **ii** $x = 1.7$.
     d Draw the graph of $y = x$ on the same paper.
     e Use your graph to find $\sqrt{10}$ to an appropriate degree of accuracy. Explain your answer.

Functions and graphs

A *function* is another name given to an algebraic expression.
A functional graph shows us a picture of this expression which connects two variables.
Usually these are called x and y but any pair of letters can be used.
The horizontal, or x-axis, is called the independent axis.
The vertical, or y-axis, is called the dependent.
This is because the function is written in the form $y =$ (some expression in x) and the values of y depend on whatever values x takes.

Linear graphs

Linear graphs are just another way of saying straight line graphs.
We know if a graph is linear just by looking at the equation.
If the powers of x and y are both one then the graph is linear or straight.
To draw a linear graph we find the coordinates of any two points that fit its equation and then plot them.
To make sure that we haven't made a mistake we usually plot three points and make sure that they lie on one straight line.
When we have plotted the points we can draw a straight line through them.
When calculating the coordinates it is best to *build up* the values in a table.

Solving simultaneous equations by using graphs

When we draw the graph of any straight line all the possible values of x and y which fit the equation of the graph must lie on the line.
Therefore, to solve a pair of simultaneous equations graphically;
plot the graphs of the two equations and find the coordinates of the point of intersection.

Gradient and intercept

NOTE

You need to memorise (and understand) this formula.

Any linear (or straight line) graph, can be written as $y = mx + c$, where m and c are constants for each individual line.
c is called the *intercept*. It is the place where the graph crosses the y-axis.
m is the coefficient of the x term. It is the *gradient* of the line.
It measures how *steep* the line is compared to the x-axis.
If m is positive it means that the line slopes upward to the right.
If m is negative it means that the line slopes downwards to the right.

To find the gradient of a straight line

There are two main methods for calculating the gradient of a straight line.
From the equation of the line: the gradient is the coefficient of the x term.
From a plotted graph:

a Choose *any two* convenient points on the line.

b Calculate the vertical difference in y coordinates.

c Calculate the horizontal difference in x-coordinates.

d The gradient $m = \dfrac{\text{the difference in } y\text{-coordinates}}{\text{the difference in } x\text{-coordinates}}$.

If the line slopes upward, both differences are positive and the line has a positive gradient.
If the line slopes downward from left to right, the x difference is positive and the y difference is negative (i.e. it decreases).
This means that the line has a negative gradient.

Interpreting graphs

We often see, in papers and magazines, a large variety of information presented in graphical form.
These graphs show a lot of data very easily and, with a little practice, we can find information very quickly.

Graphs from experimental data

Graphs can be used to find relationships in experimental data.

In an experiment we sometimes suspect that the variables are connected by a linear, or straight line, relationship.

By plotting the points and then drawing the straight line that *best fits* the points we can find out the equation that connects those variables.

The plotted points will probably not lie on an exact straight line.
This is because of slight inaccuracies in the reading of the apparatus or of taking measurements.
In this case we draw the straight line that most closely *fits* the plotted points.

Quadratic graphs

We can draw curves for any quadratic expression of the form $ax^2 + bx + c$.
All are smooth curves called *parabolas*.
All are symmetrical (i.e. they look the same on both sides) about a line parallel to the y-axis through the lowest, or highest, point on the curve.

When drawing quadratic graphs it is best to follow a certain order:

1 Calculate the values of y for a number of values of x.
2 Draw axes on a graph. Use suitable scales to fit the values from your table.
3 Plot all your calculated points.
4 Draw a *smooth* curve through your plotted points.
   The curve will be smooth – so if you have mis-calculated any values of y it will be apparent.
   If the x^2 term is positive the graph points downwards.
   If the x^2 term is negative the graph points upwards.
5 Make sure the curve is labelled with its equation. This is very important if more than one curve is to be drawn on the same graph.

Solving quadratic equations by using quadratic graphs

Drawing quadratic graphs enables us to solve quadratic equations.
On any graph, $y = 0$ anywhere along the x-axis.
Hence, the solution of $ax^2 + bx + c = 0$ lies on the graph where the curve cuts the x-axis.

SECTION FOUR
Shape, space and measures (Module 5)

CONTENTS

CHAPTER 13
Properties of shape

In this chapter you will need to know that:

- a point measures the *position* of something
- a line can be curved or straight
- a straight line is the shortest distance between two points
- points on a line are marked as and are often marked with letters as shown
  A   B
- if two points, say A and B, are marked on a line, the part of the line marked AB is called the *line segment* AB.
- when two lines cross, or intersect, they meet at a point called a *vertex* (plural *vertices*)
- when two lines meet at an *angle*, the lines are called the *arms* of the angle
- an angle is measured by the amount of rotation that one arm has to turn through to coincide with the other; it has no connection with the lengths of the arms forming the angle

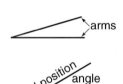

- a flat surface is called a plane
- shapes drawn in a plane are called *plane figures*
- the lines joining the vertices of plane figures are called its *sides*
- planes which form parts of three-dimensional figures are called *faces*
- in three-dimensional shapes, faces meet at edges and edges meet at vertices
- a *cube* is a solid containing six square faces
  All its edges are equal in length

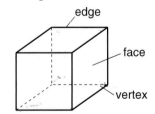

- a cuboid is a solid containing six rectangular faces
  It has a cross section which is also a rectangle

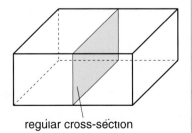

regular cross-section

▸ two lines which point in the same direction are called *parallel lines*; they are marked like this in diagrams:

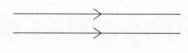

▸ when a line turns completely round until it points in the same direction we say it has turned through *1 turn* or *1 revolution*

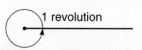

▸ 1 revolution is divided up into 360 small parts called *degrees* (°).

thus 1 revolution = 360°

▸ angles are usually measured to decimals of a degree, e.g. 22.3°

▸ if a line rotates half a turn, i.e. 180°, it is called a *straight angle*

▸ if a line rotates a quarter of a turn, i.e. 90°, it is called a *right angle*; right angles are marked like this:

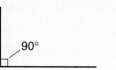

▸ two lines which intersect at right angles are called *perpendicular*

▸ an angle less than 90° is called an *acute angle*

▸ an angle between 90° and 180° is called an *obtuse angle*

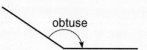

▸ an angle greater than 180° is called a *reflex angle*

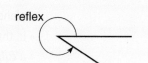

▸ if a number of lines all meet at a point, the sum of all the angles is 360° (*angles at a point*)

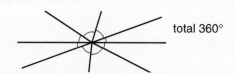

▸ two angles which add up to 90° are called *complementary angles*

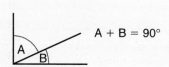

$A + B = 90°$

▸ two angles which add up to 180° are called *supplementary angles*

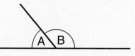

$A + B = 180°$

▸ angles next to one another, as shown in the last two examples, are said to be *adjacent angles*

▸ the hour hand of a clock turns through 1 revolution (360°) in 12 hours. Therefore it turns 30° each hour.
The minute hand of a clock turns through 1 revolution (360°) in 1 hour. Therefore it turns through 30° in 5 minutes or 6° every minute.

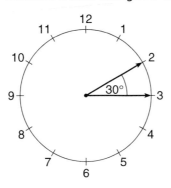 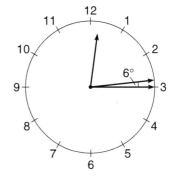

Bearings

▸ North has bearing 000°.
Due east has bearing 090°.
Due south has bearing 180°.
Due west has bearing 270°.
Bearings are measured from due north in a clockwise direction.

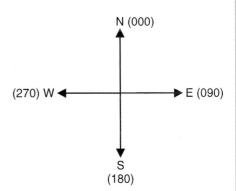

Parallel lines

A line crossing one or more parallel lines is called a *transversal*.

On either side of a transversal angles marked A are equal. They are called *alternate* angles, or Z angles. The angles marked B are also alternate (and equal).

The angles marked C are equal. They are called *corresponding* angles. The same is true for the angles marked D.

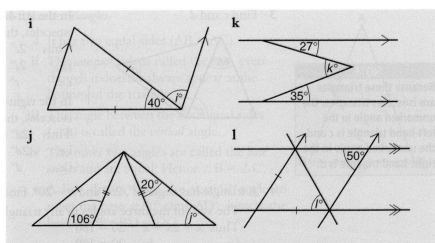

2 A triangle has angles x, $x + 30$, $x - 10$. Find the value of x.

3 An isosceles triangle has a vertical angle of 40°. How big are the base angles?

4 A triangle has sides of length 6 cm and 14 cm. The third side is also an integer number of cm. Find the minimum and maximum lengths of the third side.

5 Two angles of a triangle are $(3x - 10)°$ and $(4x + 20)°$. What is the value of the third angle?

Polygons

Polygon is the general name for a plane shape.
Some polygons have special names – square, rectangle, etc.

A 3-sided polygon is called a *triangle*
A 4-sided polygon is called a *quadrilateral*
A 5-sided polygon is called a *pentagon*
A 6-sided polygon is called a *hexagon*
A 8-sided polygon is called a *octagon*
A 10-sided polygon is called a *decagon*

The Eden Project is constructed using hexagons.

Just as any triangle contains 180°, there are fixed sums for the interior angles of other polygons. For example:

i *Quadrilateral*
As we can see a quadrilateral can be divided into two triangles; A and B.

Each triangle contains 180°.

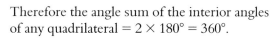

Therefore the angle sum of the interior angles of any quadrilateral = 2 × 180° = 360°.

ii *Pentagon*
As we can see a pentagon can be divided into three triangles; A, B and C.

Each triangle contains 180°.

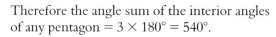

Therefore the angle sum of the interior angles of any pentagon = 3 × 180° = 540°.

iii *Any polygon*
A *quadrilateral* (4 sides) can be divided into two triangles.

A *pentagon* (5 sides) can be divided into three triangles.

Therefore a *hexagon* (6 sides) can be divided into four triangles, and so on.

Therefore a polygon (n sides) can be divided into n − 2 triangles.

Look at the polygon shown, with *n* sides.

The dotted side indicates that the number of sides is not fixed.

We can see that there are *n* − 2 triangles.

Each triangle contains 180°.

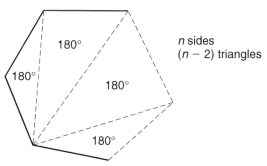

Therefore the angle sum of the interior angles of an n sided polygon is (n − 2) × 180°.

The exterior angle of a polygon

Extending (producing) the sides of a polygon gives us *n* exterior angles when there are *n* sides.

At *each* vertex the sum of the interior and exterior angles = 180°.

Therefore the total sum of all interior and exterior angles = 180° × *n*.

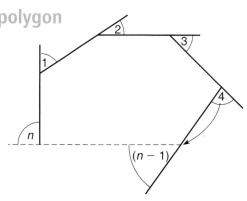

But we know that the sum of the interior angles $= (n - 2) \times 180°$
$$= 180n° - 360°.$$

Therefore the sum of the exterior angles $= 180n° - (180n° - 360°)$
$$= 180n° - 180n° + 360°$$
$$= 360°.$$

The sum of the exterior angles of any polygon $= 360°$.

Worked Examples

1   A polygon has 12 sides. What is its angle sum?

In this example $n = 12$.
Therefore the angle sum $= (12 - 2) \times 180° = 10 \times 180° = 1800°.$

2   In a pentagon, four of the exterior angles are 60°, 72°, 110° and 78°. How big is the fifth exterior angle?

The fifth angle is $360° - (60° + 72° + 110° + 78°) = 40°.$

Regular polygons

A regular polygon has all its sides and angles equal.
For example:

 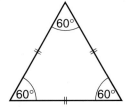 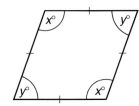

An equilateral triangle has 3 equal angles. All the sides and angles are equal for each triangle but the triangles can be of different sizes.

A rhombus has 4 equal sides. All the sides are equal but not the angles.

Since the angle sum of the interior angles is $(n - 2) \times 180°$, and there are n angles, we can say:

The size of the interior angle of a regular polygon $= \dfrac{(n - 2) \times 180°}{n}$

We know that the angle sum of the exterior angles $= 360°$

Therefore the size of the exterior angle of a regular polygon $= \dfrac{360°}{n}$

For example, if we know a regular polygon has 12 sides, we can say:

exterior angle $= \dfrac{360°}{12} = 30°$

thus interior angle $= 180° - 30° = 150°.$

Worked Examples

1 A regular polygon has exterior angles of 36°. How many sides does it have?

The exterior angle of a regular polygon $= \dfrac{360°}{n}$

Thus $36° = \dfrac{360°}{n}$

i.e. $n = \dfrac{360°}{36°} = 10$

The polygon has 10 sides.

2 Find the interior angle of a regular octagon.

For an octagon $n = 8$.

Thus interior angle $= (8 - 2) \times \dfrac{180°}{8} = \dfrac{1080°}{8} = 135°$.

(Alternatively, exterior angle $= \dfrac{360°}{8} = 45°$, interior $= 180° - 45° = 135°$.)

3 The interior angle of a regular polygon is 90°. How many sides does it have?

$(n - 2) \times \dfrac{180°}{n} = 90°$

i.e. $180n - 360 = 90n$

i.e. $90n = 360$

hence $n = 4$

The regular polygon has four sides and is a square.

PRACTICE 13.2.2   Try these questions without a calculator

1 Find the angle sum of polygons containing:

   a 7   b 11   c 22 sides

2 Find the number of sides of the regular polygons with the following exterior angles:

   a 72°   b 40°   c 24°   d 22.5°   e $11\frac{1}{4}°$

3 Find the number of sides of the regular polygons with the following interior angles:

   a 60°   b 108°   c 150°   d 165°   e 168°

4 Find the size of the interior and exterior angles of the regular polygons with the following numbers of sides:

   a 10   b 18   c 20   d 25   e 36

5 Find the interior angle of a regular hexagon.

6 In a pentagon, one angle is 100°. The other four angles are equal. How big is each one?

7 In a regular polygon each exterior angle is 120°. How many sides does it have?

8 In a regular polygon each interior angle is 100° more than the exterior angle. How many sides does the polygon have?

9 In a regular polygon each interior angle is four times the size of the exterior angle. How many sides does the polygon have?

10 One regular polygon has *n* sides. Another has 3*n* sides. The exterior angle of the first is 24° more than the exterior angle of the second. How many sides does each polygon have and what are the sizes of the interior and exterior angle in each case?

Quadrilaterals

A **quadrilateral** is a plane figure with four sides.
Different types of quadrilaterals have special names:

1   The regular quadrilateral is called a **square**.

2   The quadrilateral with both pairs of opposite sides parallel is called a **parallelogram**.

In every parallelogram:

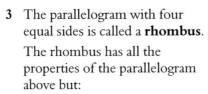

  a each pair of opposite sides is equal i.e. AB = DC, AD = BC,

  b opposite angles are equal i.e. ∠A = ∠C, ∠B = ∠D,

  c the diagonals bisect each other i.e. AO = OC, DO = OB.

3   The parallelogram with four equal sides is called a **rhombus**.

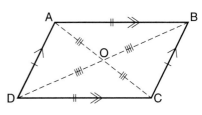

The rhombus has all the properties of the parallelogram above but:

all four sides are equal so the diagonals divide the rhombus up into four *identical* triangles,

therefore all the angles at O are equal,

thus: *the diagonals of a rhombus are perpendicular, and also bisect the angles,*

hence ∠DAO = ∠BAO = ∠DCO = ∠BCO

and ∠ABO = ∠CBO = ∠ADO = ∠CDO.

4 The parallelogram with all angles equal to 90° is called a **rectangle**.

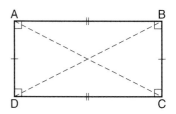

The rectangle has all the properties of the parallelogram stated above, but also, the diagonals are equal in length i.e. AC = BD.

Note that the square can also be thought of as a special case of a rectangle with all four sides equal – or as a special case of a rhombus with all angles equal.

5 The quadrilateral with *one* pair of opposite sides parallel but *not* equal is called a **trapezium**.

An isosceles trapezium is one which has its two non-parallel sides equal in length.

NOTE

'Adjacent' means next to.

6 The quadrilateral with both pairs of *adjacent* sides equal is called a **kite**.

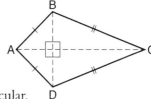

In every kite:

a ∠B = ∠D
b The diagonals AC and BD are perpendicular.

Worked Examples

1 Calculate the marked lengths and angles shown on the diagrams. Explain your answers.

$a = 4$ (opposite sides)

$y = 36°$ (opposite angles)

$p = 180° - (68° + 36°)$

$= 76°$ (angle sum of triangle)

$q = 68°$ (alternate angles)

Hence $x = 76° + 68° = 144°$.

NOTE

We could have said, more simply, that, using allied angles

$x = 180 - 36 = 144°$.

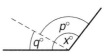

2   In the kite shown find angles *a*, *b* and *c*.

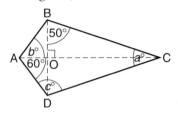

In triangle BOC

$\angle BCO = 180° - 90° - 50° = 40°$

Hence $a = 2 \times 40° = 80°$.

Since $\angle B = \angle D$ then $\angle ABO = \angle ADO = 30°$.

Thus $b = 180° - 90° - 30° = 60°$.

Clearly $c = 30° + 50° = 80°$.

PRACTICE 13.2.3   Try these questions without a calculator

1   Find the values of the marked angles in the following diagrams.

a

e

b

f

c

g

d

h

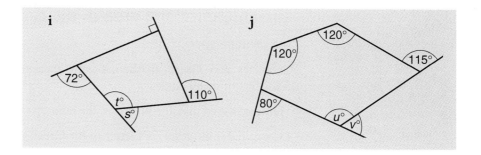

The circle

Reminder: We should already know the main terms associated with circles. The diagram illustrates them.

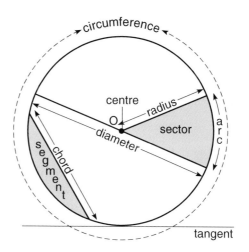

▶ The total perimeter is called the *circumference*.

▶ The distance from any point on the circumference to the centre is called the *radius*.

▶ Any straight line through the centre is twice the radius and is called the *diameter*.

▶ A *chord* is any straight line across the circle not passing through the centre.

▶ Part of the circumference is called an *arc*.

▶ Part of the area formed by two radii and an arc is called a *sector*.

▶ Part of the area formed by a chord and an arc is called a *segment*.

▶ A *tangent* is a straight line which touches a circle at one point only. It is perpendicular to the radius drawn to the point of contact of the tangent with the circle.

Circumference and area of the circle

The circumference

Centuries ago Greek mathematicians measured the circumferences and diameters of many circles.

They discovered that, for all circles, the ratio $\dfrac{C}{D}$ was a constant and just over 3.

They called it π. (π (pi) is a letter in the Greek alphabet.)

Hence: $\dfrac{C}{D} = \pi$ or $C = \pi D$ or $C = 2\pi r$ (r is the radius).

The exact value for π cannot be worked out – even by a computer, and it is an *irrational number*.

Most calculators now have a π button on them which gives $\pi = 3.141\,592\,654$ (depending on how many digits it has on its display).
In calculations we usually use $\pi = 3.14$ or else the π button on our calculators.
A good fractional equivalent is $\pi = \frac{22}{7}$.

The area

The area of the circle was also discovered by the Greeks – and it involves π !
The area for any circle, $A = \pi r^2$.
For example, the area of a circle of radius 3 m is $3.14 \times 3 \times 3 = 28.26$,
i.e. the area $= 28.3\ \text{m}^2$ (3 sf) or $\pi \times 3 \times 3 = 9\pi\ \text{m}^2$.

> **NOTE**
> We always square r first and then multiply by π.

> **NOTE**
> You need to memorise (and understand) these formulae:
> $C = \pi D$ or
> $C = 2\pi r$ and
> $A = \pi r^2$.

Worked Examples

1 Find the circumference of a circle of diameter 12.6 cm (take $\pi = 3.14$).

$D = 12.6$, therefore $r = 6.3$
$C = 2 \times 3.14 \times 6.3 = 39.564$, or using D, $C = 3.14 \times 12.6 = 39.564$
i.e. the circumference is 39.6 cm (3 sf) or $2 \times \pi \times 6.3 = 12.6\pi\ \text{cm}^2$.

2 Find the area of a circle of diameter 10.4 m.

$D = 10.4$, therefore $r = 5.2$
$A = 3.14 \times 5.2^2 = 3.14 \times 27.04 = 84.9056$
i.e. the area is $84.9\ \text{m}^2$ (3 sf) or $\pi \times 5.2^2 = 27.04\pi\ \text{m}^2$.

3 A circle has a circumference of 1 m. Find its area.

$C = \pi \times D$

i.e. $D = \dfrac{100}{3.14} = 31.85$ cm (1 m = 100 cm) or $\dfrac{100}{\pi}$.

Hence $r = \dfrac{31.85}{2} = 15.925$ cm   or $\dfrac{50}{\pi}$.

Thus area, $A = 3.14 \times 15.925^2$ or $\pi \times \left(\dfrac{50}{\pi}\right)^2$
$= 796.32$

$= 796\ \text{cm}^2$ (3 sf) $= \dfrac{2500}{\pi}\ \text{cm}^2$.

Using π

In examinations you may be asked to wite your answer to, say, 3 significant figures, or 2 decimal places, etc.

If the accuracy is not specified, it is quite permissible to leave your answer in terms of π. In fact, leaving it in terms of π is **more** accurate than rounding to a specified number of figures. So the answers to the calculations above would be 9π, 12.6π, 27.04π and $\dfrac{2500}{\pi}$ as shown.

PRACTICE 13.2.4   Try these questions with a calculator

Take $\pi = 3.14$ or use the π button on your calculator.

1   Find:

    a the circumference of circles of diameter
        i 5 cm   **ii** 12 cm   **iii** 21 cm   **iv** 8.9 cm   **v** 26.7 ft

    b the area of circles of radius
        i 4.3 in   **ii** 6 cm   **iii** 24 m   **iv** 4.3 in   **v** 25.6 ft

    c the complete perimeter of a semicircle of radius 14.6 ft.

2   The tile shown has the shape of a *quadrant* (quarter) of a circle of radius 10 cm.
    a Find its area.
    b Calculate the perimeter.

3   The washer shown has an outer radius of 3.6 cm and a hole of radius 0.4 cm.

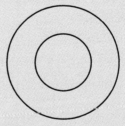

Calculate the area of the face of the washer. Write your answers
i in terms of π and **ii** correct to 3 sf.

4   Calculate the shaded area in each diagram.

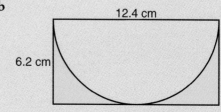

    a 5 m   5 m   **b** 12.4 cm   6.2 cm

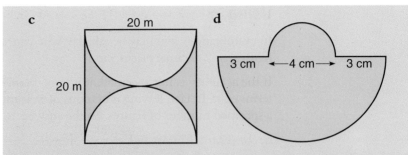

Write your answers in **i** terms of π and **ii** correct to 3 sf.

5   Three thin silver discs, of radii 4 cm, 7 cm and 10 cm are melted down
    and recast into another disc of the same thickness.
    Find the radius of this disc (ignore the thickness of the discs).

6   DJ Coxy's 12 in. record turns at $33\frac{1}{3}$ revolutions per minute.
    a   Find the circumference of the disc.
    b   Calculate how far a point on the rim of the disc travels in 1 minute.
    c   Hence calculate the speed of the point on the rim in inches per sec.

7   A reel contains 30 m of garden hose. The reel has a diameter of 20 cm.
    Ignoring the thickness of the hose, calculate the number of times the
    reel rotates when the complete length of the hose is unwound.

Nets

A **net** is a pattern which can be cut out and then folded into a solid shape.
For example, suppose we want to make the cuboid shown.

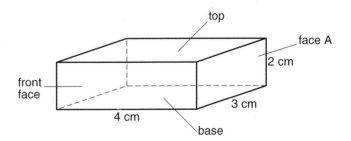

If all the faces are opened out we would have a *net* shaped like this:

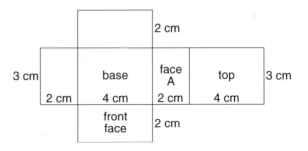

If this *net* is cut out and folded the cuboid can be made.

It is often possible to make more than one net for a given solid.

The cuboid above could also be constructed from this net:

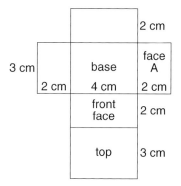

Worked Examples

1 Draw the net for the closed cylinder shown.

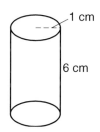

The curved sides, when opened out, would be a rectangle in which one side was the height of the cylinder and the other side the circumference of the circular ends.

Using $C = 2\pi r$ we get $C = 2 \times 3.14 \times 1 = 6.28$ cm.

Hence the required net is:

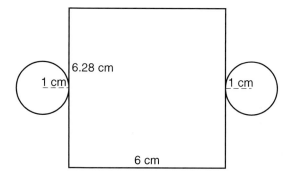

2 Illustrate the solid figure formed
   when the net shown is folded into
   a three-dimensional shape.

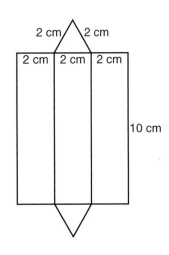

We can see that the final shape has
3 rectangular faces and 2 ends
which are equilateral triangles.

Hence we can see that the final
figure is a triangular prism.

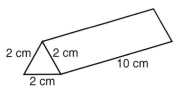

PRACTICE 13.2.5

1 The diagram shows a net.

   a What mathematical name is
      given to the solid formed
      when the net is folded?

   b Name the pairs of points
      that will *meet* when the solid
      is made.

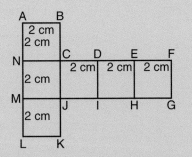

2 The diagrams below show some nets. Name the ones which would
   form cubes.

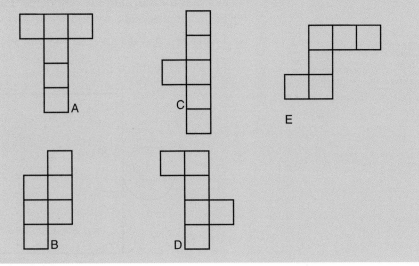

3 What solids are formed by the following nets?

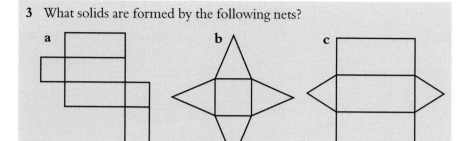

a   b   c

4 Draw accurate nets for the following solids.

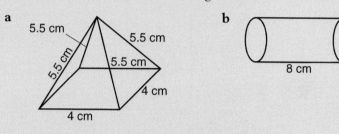

a
5.5 cm
5.5 cm
5.5 cm
5.5 cm
4 cm
4 cm

b
4 cm
8 cm

c A cuboid, 3 cm long, 2 cm wide and 1 cm high.
d A tetrahedron with the base an equilateral triangle of side 4 cm and each sloping face having a slant height of 6 cm.

Representing 3-dimensional objects in 2 dimensions

Three-dimensional objects can be represented in two dimensions using dotted or lined paper which is set out in equilateral triangles. This is known as *isometric paper*.

Worked Example

Illustrate the cuboid shown on isometric paper.

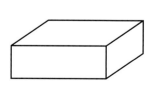

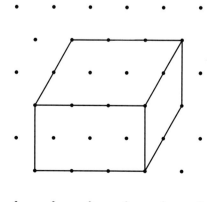

PRACTICE 13.2.6

1 Represent the following three-dimensional objects on isometric paper.

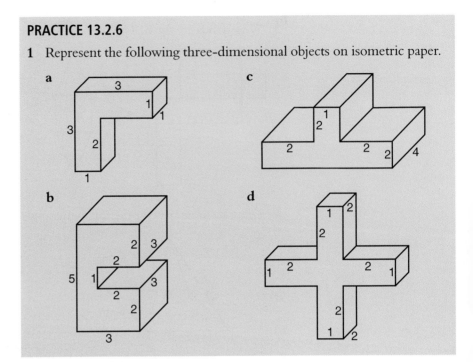

a

b

c

d

Plans and elevations

Plans and elevations are views we get when we look at objects. The plan is the view of the object when we look down on it from the top. An elevation is any side view. Looking at the shapes drawn in Practice 13.2.6 above, the diagram below shows

   i each plan view,
 ii each elevation viewed from the front, and
iii each elevation viewed from the right-hand side.

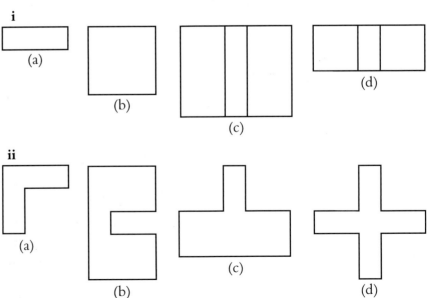

i

(a)

(b)

(c)

(d)

ii

(a)

(b)

(c)

(d)

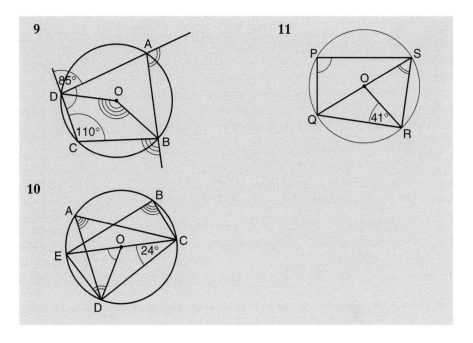

There are three types of symmetry.
2-dimensional shapes can have either **line symmetry** (reflection) or **rotational symmetry**.
3-dimensional solids can have **plane symmetry**.

Line symmetry

If a shape is identical on each side of a line drawn through it then it has *line symmetry*.
The kite shown has one line of symmetry along its longer diagonal.

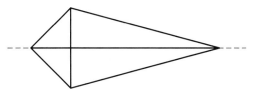

Each side of a line of symmetry is called the *mirror image* of the other.

We can show that a shape has line symmetry by placing a mirror along the mirror line and seeing that the reflected half is identical to the part of the shape behind the mirror.

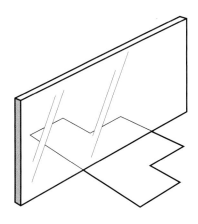

We can also show a shape possesses line symmetry by *tracing* the shape onto tracing paper and then folding it to show two identical halves.

Some shapes have no line symmetry. The parallelogram, for example, has none.

Others have several lines of symmetry, for example, the square has four lines of symmetry:

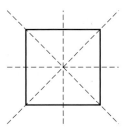

Rotational symmetry

As stated above, the parallelogram has no lines, or axes, of symmetry.

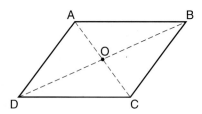

However, if we rotate any parallelogram through 180° about the centre O, it will look identical to its original position.

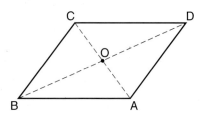

This is known as *rotational*, or *point, symmetry*.
The point about which the shape rotates is called the *centre*, or *point, of symmetry*.
Because there are two identical positions for a parallelogram, it is said to have *rotational symmetry of order 2*.
Different shapes have different orders of symmetry.
The equilateral triangle has rotational symmetry of order 3:

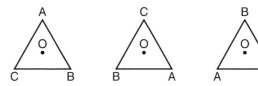

The square has rotational symmetry of order 4.

Plane symmetry

If a three-dimensional solid can be cut into two identical halves the solid has *plane symmetry*.

If we imagine the plane of symmetry was a mirror, the reflection together with the intact half would look just like the complete solid.
The cuboid, for example, has three planes of symmetry:

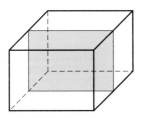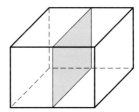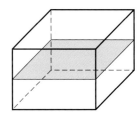

PRACTICE 13.3.1

1 Copy the following shapes and draw in the axes of symmetry.

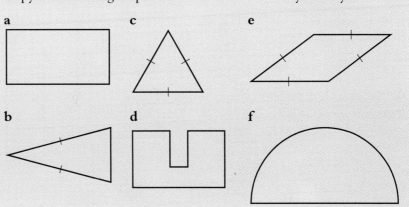

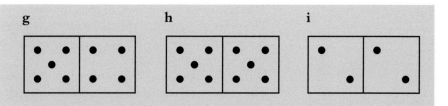

2 Write down a capital letter from the alphabet which could have

   a 2 lines of symmetry,

   b 4 lines of symmetry,

   c an infinite number of lines of symmetry,

   d rotational symmetry of order 2,

   e rotational symmetry of order 4,

   f infinite rotational symmetry,

   g rotational symmetry of order 2 but no line symmetry.

3 Copy and complete the following diagrams so that each figure is
   symmetrical about all the marked lines:

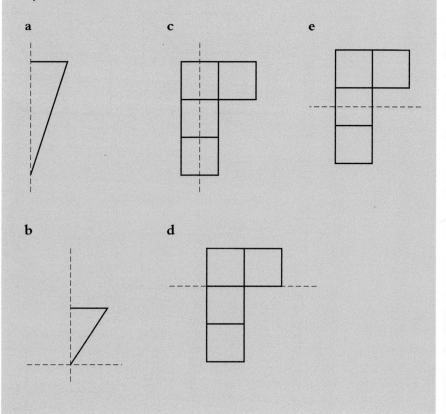

4 Copy and complete the following diagrams so that they have rotational symmetry. O is the centre of symmetry in each case.

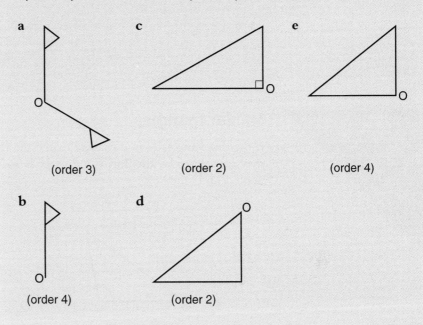

a

(order 3)

c

(order 2)

e

(order 4)

b

(order 4)

d

(order 2)

5 State the number of axes of symmetry and/or the order of rotational symmetry of the following:

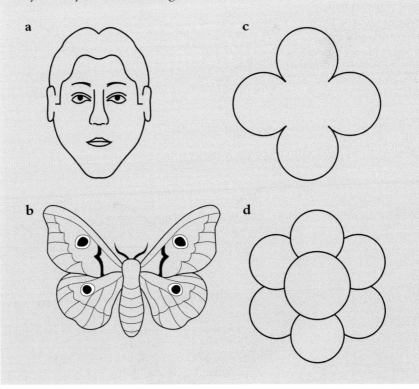

a

c

b

d

6 **a** How many planes of symmetry does a sphere have?
  b A cube has 12 planes of symmetry. Illustrate these by means of sketch diagrams.
  c Draw diagrams to show all the planes of symmetry of a prism with a cross sectional area of an equilateral triangle.

13.4

SIMILARITY AND CONGRUENCE

Similar triangles

If the three angles of one triangle match the three angles of another triangle, they are said to be **similar**. (One shape is an 'enlargement' of the other, see Topic 14.6.)

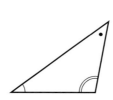 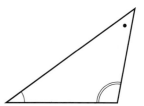

However, another thing is true about them – *corresponding sides are in the same ratio*.

Hence, if 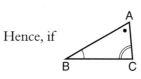 and 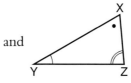 are similar

then $\dfrac{AB}{XY} = \dfrac{AC}{XZ} = \dfrac{BC}{YZ}$ or $\dfrac{XY}{AB} = \dfrac{XZ}{AC} = \dfrac{YZ}{BC}$

Worked Examples

1 Find x and y.

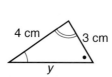 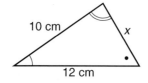

The triangles are similar, hence $\dfrac{4}{10} = \dfrac{3}{x} = \dfrac{y}{12}$

Since $\dfrac{4}{10} = \dfrac{3}{x}$ then $x = 3 \times \dfrac{10}{4} = 7.5$ cm.

Since $\dfrac{4}{10} = \dfrac{y}{12}$ then $y = 4 \times \dfrac{12}{10} = 4.8$ cm.

2 Prove that triangles OAB and ODC are similar.
   Hence find the values of p, q and r.

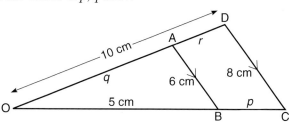

$\angle$O is common to both triangles.

$\angle$OAB = $\angle$ODC and $\angle$OBA = $\angle$OCD (corresponding angles)

Hence the triangles are similar.

Since the triangles are similar then $\dfrac{8}{6} = \dfrac{10}{q} = \dfrac{5+p}{5}$

i.e. $\dfrac{8}{6} = \dfrac{10}{q}$

i.e. $8 \times q = 10 \times 6$
       $8q = 60$
       $q = 7\tfrac{1}{2}\ \text{cm}$

Similarly $\dfrac{8}{6} = \dfrac{5+p}{5}$

i.e. $8 \times 5 = 6 \times (5 + p)$
       $40 = 30 + 6p$
       $10 = 6p$
       $1\tfrac{2}{3}\ \text{cm} = p$

Finally, since $q + r = 10$
       $7.5 + r = 10$
       $r = 2.5\ \text{cm}$

PRACTICE 13.4.1   Try these questions without a calculator

1 Find a and b.

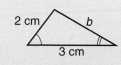
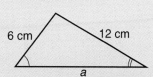

2 Find p and q.

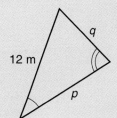

3 Find *c* and *d*.

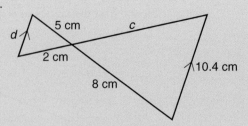

4 Find *r* and *s*.

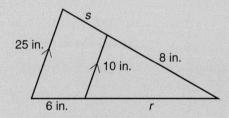

5 Find *d*, *e* and *f*.

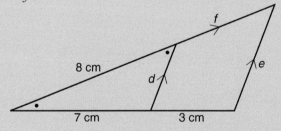

6 Find *g* and *h*.

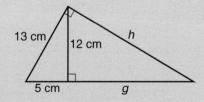

7 Find two similar triangles.
Hence find *m* and *n*.

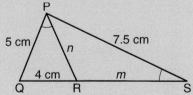

8 Tinky Winky is standing beside Po. Tinky Winky is 1.5 m tall and casts
a shadow 85 cm long. Po is 1.2 m tall. How long is Po's shadow?

8   A chord, AB, is drawn in a circle of radius 10 cm.

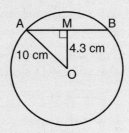

The centre is 4.3 cm from M, the centre of the chord.

How long is the chord?

9   A road has a gradient of 1 in 10 as shown in the diagram.

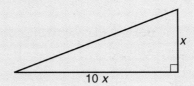

Alicia drives up the hill rising 200 yds vertically. How far:
a   has Alicia travelled horizontally,
b   has Alicia driven?

10   Find the distances between:
a $(0, 0)$ and $(4, 2)$ **c** $(^-3, 2)$ and $(5, 9)$
b $(2, 3)$ and $(6, 7)$ **d** $(^-4, ^-5)$ and $(4, ^-1)$

on a piece of graph paper with a unit distance of 1 cm.
Write your answer: **i** in surd form, **ii** to 3 sf.

11   In the diagram M is the mid-point of AB, AC = 17.5 cm and
BC = 11.4 cm. Calculate the length of MC.

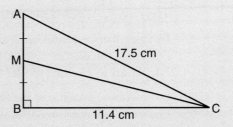

12   A semicircle is drawn with diameter AB = 28.6 m. A point C is marked
on the circumference and the triangle ABC drawn, where AC = 17.3 m.
Find the length of BC.

13.6 TRIGONOMETRY

Trigonometry is the name given to the mathematics of triangles – it literally means *triangle measurement*.

We use trigonometry with similar right-angled triangles to calculate sides and angles.

For example, suppose a post casts a shadow of 9 m and at the same time a man, 2 m tall, casts a shadow 1.5 m long.

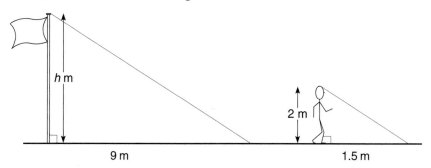

Because the two triangles are similar we can find the height of the post by writing:

$$\frac{h}{9} = \frac{2}{1.5}$$

Hence $\quad h = \frac{2 \times 9}{1.5}$

$\quad\quad\quad h = 12$ m.

NOTE
Revise your work on similar triangles before reading this. See page 400.

Using this ratio, $\frac{O}{A}$, we can calculate the height of any object if we know the length of its shadow at this time. But, as the angle of the sun changes, the ratio changes.

However, if we know the ratio $\frac{O}{A}$ for different angles

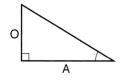

of the sun we could do any calculation we needed at any time.

The tan ratio

The ratio $\frac{O}{A}$ is called the **tangent ratio** or **tan ratio**.

Its value can be found on a scientific calculator, using the key marked TAN. Different calculators have different logic so we need to refer to our own calculators to see how to find the tan ratio for a particular angle.

For instance, imagine in the above example that the angle was now 58° and the length of the shadow of another pole was 10 m. We would write:

$$\tan 58° = \frac{h}{10}$$

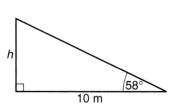

Using our calculators we find that the tan ratio for 58° is 1.600 (4 sf).

Hence we would write: $1.600 = \dfrac{h}{10}$

i.e. $10 \times 1.600 = h$

Hence the height of the object is 16.0 m (3sf).

The three trigonometrical ratios

When we look at one particular angle in a right-angled triangle the side opposite the angle is called the **opposite** (O). The side next to the angle is called the **adjacent** (A). Remember that the side opposite the right angle is called the **hypotenuse** (H).

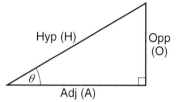

We already know from the previous section that the tan ratio is $\dfrac{O}{A}$.

i.e. we could write $\tan \theta = \dfrac{\text{opposite side}}{\text{adjacent side}}$

There are two more ratios in common use and on your calculator:

the sin ratio is $\dfrac{O}{H}$, i.e. $\sin \theta = \dfrac{\text{opposite side}}{\text{hypotenuse}}$

the cos ratio is $\dfrac{A}{H}$, i.e. $\cos \theta = \dfrac{\text{adjacent side}}{\text{hypotenuse}}$

These ratios are really called sine, cosine and tangent, but we always use sin, cos and tan for short.

NOTE
The ratios *only apply* to right-angled triangles.

An easy way to remember these ratios is the made up word:

SOHCAHTOA

i.e. $\sin \theta = \dfrac{O}{H}$ $\cos \theta = \dfrac{A}{H}$ $\tan \theta = \dfrac{O}{A}$

All three ratios can be found, for any particular angle, using the sin, cos and tan buttons on a scientific calculator.

Worked Examples

1   Find the sin, cos and tan ratios of: **a** 27°,   **b** 73.8°.

2   Find the angle whose: **a** sine is 0.361,   **b** cosine is 0.243   **c** tangent is 1.75.

Using our calculators we should obtain the following results:

1 a   sin 27° = 0.4540 (4 sf)   **b**   sin 73.8° = 0.9603 (4 sf)
cos 27° = 0.8910 (4 sf)   cos 73.8° = 0.2790 (4 sf)
tan 27° = 0.5095 (4 sf)   tan 73.8° = 3.442 (4 sf)

2 There is an *inverse* key on our calculators which enables us to use them *in reverse* to find the angles with a particular value of the sin, cos or tan ratio.

Using this inverse key we should obtain these results:

a The angle whose sine is 0.361 is 21.2° (to the nearest 0.1°).
b The angle whose cosine is 0.243 is 75.9° (to the nearest 0.1°).
c The angle whose tangent is 1.75 is 60.3° (to the nearest 0.1°).

Using the trigonometrical ratios to solve problems in right-angled triangles

Using our calculators we can now find any of the ratios we require and solve problems.

Be careful to:

i draw a diagram and mark the sides O, A and H on it,
ii write on the diagram what information is known,
iii mark on the diagram what information is needed,
iv pick the right ratio,
v write down the correct equation(s) and solve it/them.

The following worked examples show how to do it.

Worked Examples

1 Find p and q using the values shown and without using a calculator.

$\sin 26 = 0.4384$
$\cos 26 = 0.8988$
$\tan 26 = 0.4877$

Copy the diagram and add H, O and A.

We need p and know $H = 10$ cm;

Opp and Hyp are connected by sin as $\sin \theta = \dfrac{O}{H}$

hence $\sin 26° = \dfrac{p}{10}$

(multiply by 10) $\sin 26° \times 10 = p$
(obtain sin 26° from above) $0.4384 \times 10 = p$
(multiplying out) $4.38 \text{ cm} = p$

We need q and know H = 10;

Adj and Hyp are connected by cos as $\qquad \cos \theta = \dfrac{A}{H}$

hence $\cos 26° = \dfrac{q}{10}$

(multiply by 10) $\qquad\qquad\qquad \cos 26° \times 10 = q$

(obtain cos 26° from above) $\qquad\quad 0.8988 \times 10 = q$

(multiplying out) $\qquad\qquad\qquad\quad 8.99 \text{ cm} = q$

2 Find r and s using a calculator.

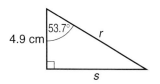

Copy the diagram and
add H, O and A.

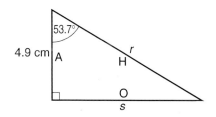

We need r and know A = 4.9 cm;

Adj and Hyp are connected by cos as $\qquad \cos \theta = \dfrac{A}{H}$

hence $\cos 53.7° = \dfrac{4.9}{r}$

(multiply by r) $\qquad\qquad\qquad \cos 53.7° \times r = 4.9$

(divide by cos 53.7°) $\qquad\qquad\qquad r = \dfrac{4.9}{\cos 53.7°}$

(obtain cos 53.7° from calculator) $\qquad r = \dfrac{4.9}{0.5920}$

(divide) $\qquad\qquad\qquad\qquad r = 8.28 \text{ cm (3 sf)}$

We need s and know A = 4.9 cm;

Adj and Opp are connected by tan as $\qquad \tan \theta = \dfrac{O}{A}$

hence $\tan 53.7° = \dfrac{s}{4.9}$

(multiply by 4.9) $\qquad\qquad\quad \tan 53.7° \times 4.9 = s$

(obtain tan 53.7° from calculator) $\quad 1.3613 \times 4.9 = s$

(multiplying out) $\qquad\qquad\qquad\qquad s = 6.67 \text{ cm (3 sf)}$

3 Find angle θ and t.

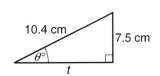

Copy the diagram and
add H, O and A.

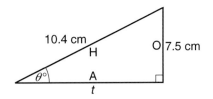

We need $\theta°$ and know H = 10.4 cm and O = 7.5 cm;

Opp and Hyp are connected by sin as $\sin \theta° = \dfrac{O}{H}$

$$\text{hence } \sin \theta° = \frac{7.5}{10.4}$$

$$\sin \theta° = 0.7212$$

Hence $\theta°$ = the angle whose sin is 0.7212
= 46.15 (we need more accuracy for
subsequent working)

i.e. $\theta°$ = 46.1° (nearest 0.1°)

We need t and know H = 10.4 cm;

Adj and Hyp are connected by cos as $\cos \theta° = \dfrac{A}{H}$

$$\text{hence } \cos 46.15° = \frac{t}{10.4}$$

(multiply by 10.4) $\cos 46.15° \times 10.4 = t$
(obtain cos 46.15° from calculator) $0.6928 \times 10.4 = t$

i.e. t = 7.20 cm (3 sf)

It is important to use enough figures in your working to ensure that your
answer is accurate enough. A good *rule of thumb* is to use *at least* 4 figures in
working (our calculators give us more than that), and to write answers to
3 figure accuracy.

PRACTICE 13.6.1a   Try this question without using a calculator

1 A ladder, 7 m long, rests on horizontal ground against a vertical wall. The
angle between the ladder and the ground is 75°. How far up the wall
does the ladder reach? Use one of the values given below to help you.

sin 75 = 0.9659   cos 75 = 0.2588   tan 75 = 3.7321

PRACTICE 13.6.1b Try these questions using a calculator

1 Use a calculator to find the value of:

  a sin 26°   **d** sin 71.23°

  b cos 33°   **e** cos 6.14°

  c tan 42°   **f** tan 88.41°

2 Find the angle:

  a whose sin is 0.5,   **d** whose sin is 1,

  b whose cos is 0.8660,   **e** whose cos is 1,

  c whose tan is 3.142,   **f** whose tan is 3.

3 Find the marked sides in the following diagrams:

a 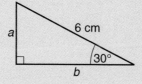   **e**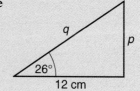

b 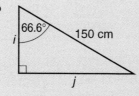   **f**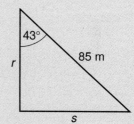

c 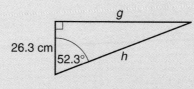   **g**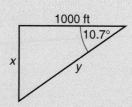

d 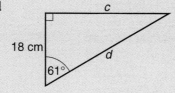   **h**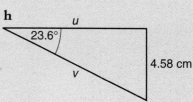

4 Find the marked sides in the following diagrams:

a

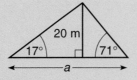

c

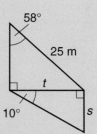

b

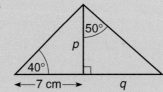

d

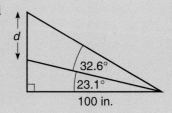

5 Find the marked angles in the following diagrams:

a

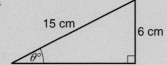

c

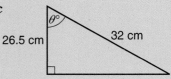

b

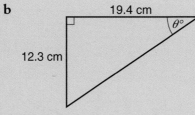

d

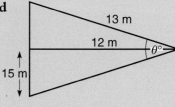

6 In the isosceles triangle shown calculate the length of the base AB and the vertical height ON.

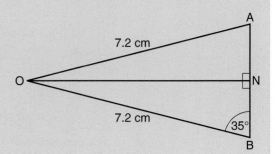

Bearings

Directions are given by using **bearings**.

Bearings are angles measuring the direction of an object *from due north and in a clockwise direction*. They are usually given as three figures before the decimal point.

Some examples are:

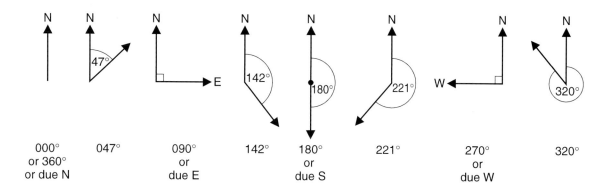

| 000° or 360° or due N | 047° | 090° or due E | 142° | 180° or due S | 221° | 270° or due W | 320° |

Worked Example

Shaheed walks 8 km on a bearing of 141°. How far south is he from his starting point?

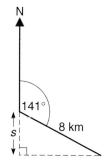

The angle in the triangle shown
= 180° − 141°
= 39°.

We need *s* and know H = 8 km.

Adj and Hyp are connected by cos.

Hence $\cos 39° = \dfrac{s}{8}$

$\cos 39° \times 8 = s$

i.e. *s* = 6.22 km (3 sf)

Thus Shaheed is 6.22 km south of his starting point.

Angles of elevation and depression

Angles measured from the horizontal upwards are called angles of elevation and if measured downwards angles of depression.

Worked Examples

1 Douglas is standing on a cliff top and sees a yacht out to sea at an angle of depression of 35°. The cliff is 250 m high. How far is the yacht from the base of the cliff? Ignore Douglas's height.

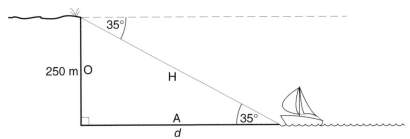

Using alternate angles in parallel lines we can see that the angle in the triangle is also 35°.

We need d and we know Opp = 250 m.
Opp and Adj are connected by tan.

Hence $\tan 35° = \dfrac{250}{d}$

$\tan 35° \times d = 250$

$d = \dfrac{250}{\tan 35°}$

$= \dfrac{250}{0.7002}$

$d = 357.037$ m (3 sf)

The yacht is 357 m from the base of the cliff.

2 Marconi is looking at the top of a vertical radio mast. The angle of elevation of the top of the mast is 51.7° and Marconi is standing 200 ft from the base of the mast on horizontal ground. Marconi's eyes are 6 ft above ground level. Find the height of the mast.

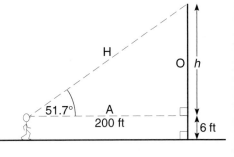

We need h and we know Adj = 200 ft.
Opp and Adj are connected by tan.

Hence $\tan 51.7° = \dfrac{h}{200}$

$\tan 51.7° \times 200 = h$

$1.2662 \times 200 = h$

$253.24 \text{ ft} = h$

But Marconi's eyes are 6 ft above ground level, i.e the height of the mast is $253 + 6 = 259$ ft (3 sf).

PRACTICE 13.6.2   Try these questions with a calculator

1 A TV mast, 1000 ft high, is held in place by ropes attached to the top of the mast and at an angle of elevation from the ground of 76.1°. How long are the ropes and how far from the base of the mast are they secured to the ground?

2 A plane flying at 30 000 ft is 10 miles horizontally from the airport. What is the angle of depression of the airport from the plane?

3 Matthew has a shadow 191 cm long. The sun is at an angle of elevation from the ground of 40°. How tall is Matthew?

4 At a skating rink a bank of seats measures 100 ft from front to back and rises 15 ft vertically.

At what angle, θ, to the horizontal does the bank of seats slope?

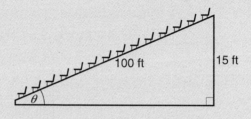

5 A mountain is 3500 m high. Find the angle of elevation of the top of the mountain from a point level with the base of the mountain and 10 miles from the centre. (Take 1 mile as 1.6 km.)

6 Hannah is holding a kite string of length 100 feet. The angle of elevation of the kite from Hannah's eyes is 65.2°. Hannah's eyes are 5 ft above ground level. How high is the kite above ground level?

7 An isosceles triangle has two sides of length 10.4 cm and a base of 7.25 cm. Find the vertical angle of the triangle.

NOTE
Vertical angle means the angle at the top of the triangle.

8 The diagram shows a triangular yacht course from Harbour P, round buoys Q and R and back to the harbour again.

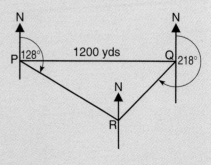

Q is 1200 yds due east of P, and R is on a bearing of 218° from Q and on a bearing of 128° from P.

Find the total length of the course.

9 The diagram shows the cross section of a shed attached to the wall of a house.

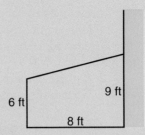

At what angle to the horizontal does the roof slope?

10 Ethan is orienteering on the moors. He hikes for 10 km on a bearing of 021° and then 5 km on a bearing of 111°. Calculate the distance and bearing that Ethan now is from his starting position.

11 The diagram shows a crane with a load on it.

How high is the top of the crane above the ground? Ignore its width.

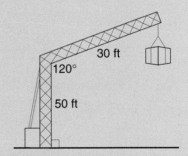

12 The angles of elevation of the top and bottom of a hot air balloon are 65.5° and 37.1° respectively from an observation post O. The balloon is 16 ft horizontally from O. Calculate the height, h, of the balloon and basket.

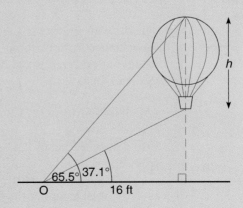

The circle

The total perimeter is called the *circumference*.
The distance from any point on the circumference to the centre is called the *radius* (plural radii).
Any straight line through the centre is twice the radius and is called the *diameter*.
A *chord* is any straight line across the circle not passing through the centre.
Part of the circumference is called an *arc*.
Part of the area formed by two radii and an arc is called a *sector*.
Part of the area formed by a chord and an arc is called a *segment*.
A *tangent* is a straight line which touches a circle at one point only. It is perpendicular to the radius drawn to the point of contact of the tangent with the circle.
In any circle the line bisecting any chord at right angles, passes through the centre of the circle.
This line also divides the triangle formed by the chord and the two radii at the ends of the chord into two identical (congruent) right-angled triangles.
In any circle the triangle formed by a diameter joined to any other point on the circumference is right-angled.

Circumference and area of the circle

The circumference for any circle, $C = 2\pi r$ (r is the radius).
The exact value for π cannot be worked out.
Most calculators now have a π button on them which gives $\pi = 3.141\,592\,654$.
In calculations we usually use $\pi = 3.14$ or else the π button on our calculators.
A good fractional equivalent is $\pi = \frac{22}{7}$.
The area for any circle, $A = \pi r^2$.
We always square r first and then multiply by π.

Nets

A *net* is a pattern which can be cut out and then folded into a solid shape.
If all the faces are opened out we have a net shape.
It is often possible to make more than one net for a given solid.

Representing 3-dimensional objects in 2 dimensions

Three-dimensional objects can be represented in two dimensions using dotted or lined paper which is set out in equilateral triangles.
This is known as *isometric paper*.

Symmetry

There are three types of symmetry.
2-dimensional shapes can have either *line* (reflection) or *rotational symmetry*.
3-dimensional solids can have *plane symmetry*.

Line symmetry

If a shape is identical on each side of a line drawn through it then it is has *line symmetry*.
A line of symmetry is also called an *axis of symmetry*, or a *mirror line*.
Each side of a line of symmetry is called the *mirror image* of the other.
We can show that a shape has line symmetry by placing a mirror along the mirror line and seeing that the reflected half is identical to the part of the shape behind the mirror.
We can also show a shape possesses line symmetry by *tracing* the shape onto tracing paper and then folding it to show two identical halves.
Some shapes have no symmetry, others have several lines.

Rotational symmetry

The parallelogram has no lines, or axes, of symmetry. However, if we rotate any parallelogram through 180° about the centre O, it will look identical to its original position.
This is known as *rotational*, or *point, symmetry*.
The point about which the shape rotates is called the *centre*, or *point*, *of symmetry*.
Because there are two identical positions for a parallelogram, it has *rotational symmetry of order 2*.
Different shapes have different orders of symmetry.
The equilateral triangle has rotational symmetry of order 3; the square has rotational symmetry of order 4.

Plane symmetry

If a three-dimensional solid can be cut into two identical halves the solid has *plane symmetry*.
If we imagine the plane of symmetry was a mirror, the reflection together with the intact half would look just like the complete solid.

Similar triangles

If the three angles of one triangle match the three angles of another triangle, they are said to be *similar*.
Another thing is true about them – *corresponding sides are in the same ratio*.
To prove two triangles are similar, we only need to prove that *two* pairs of angles are equal.

Other similar shapes

Shapes other than triangles are similar if:

a the angles in one shape are equal to corresponding angles in the other,
b all pairs of corresponding sides are in the same ratio.

For triangles, *one* of the above statements implies that the other is true.
For other shapes this is not so.

Pythagoras' theorem

The square on the hypotenuse is equal to the sum of the squares on the other two sides.
We can use Pythagoras' theorem to find the length of any side in a right-angled triangle if we know the lengths of the other two.
Also, if we know all three sides of the triangle and they fit Pythagoras' theorem, then it proves that the triangle is right-angled.

Pythagorean triples

There are some well known right-angled triangles that have lengths of sides that are whole numbers (integers). These are called *Pythagorean triples*.
The most well known of all is the 3, 4, 5 triangle since $3^2 + 4^2 = 5^2$.
Some other well known triples are:

5, 12, 13 since $5^2 + 12^2 = 13^2$ i.e. $25 + 144 = 169$
8, 15, 17 since $8^2 + 15^2 = 17^2$ i.e. $64 + 225 = 289$
7, 24, 25 since $7^2 + 24^2 = 25^2$ i.e. $49 + 576 = 625$, etc.

Any multiples of the above are also Pythagorean triples and thus sides of right-angled triangles.

Trigonometry

Trigonometry is the name given to the mathematics of triangles.
We use trigonometry with similar right-angled triangles to calculate sides and angles.

The three trigonometrical ratios

When we consider a particular angle in a right-angled triangle the side opposite the angle is called the *opposite* (O).
The side next to the angle is called the *adjacent* (A).
The side opposite the right angle is called the *hypotenuse* (H).

The tan ratio is $\dfrac{O}{A}$.

The sin ratio is $\dfrac{O}{H}$.

The cos ratio is $\dfrac{A}{H}$.

An easy way to remember these ratios is the made up word: SOHCAHTOA.

All three ratios can be found for any particular angle using the sin, cos and tan buttons on a scientific calculator.

The above ratios *only apply* to right-angled triangles.

Using the trigonometrical ratios to solve problems in right-angled triangles

Using our calculators we can now find any of the ratios we require and solve problems. Be careful to:
1 Draw a diagram and mark the sides O, A and H on it.
2 Write on the diagram what information is known.
3 Mark on the diagram what information is needed.
4 Pick the right ratio.
5 Write down the correct equation(s) and solve it/them.

Bearings

Directions are given by using *bearings*.

Bearings are angles measuring the direction of an object *from due north and in a clockwise direction*. They are usually given as three figures before the decimal point.

Angles of elevation and depression

Angles measured from the horizontal upwards are called *angles of elevation* and if measured downwards *angles of depression*.

CHAPTER 14

Transformations

14.1 RECAP

In this chapter you will need to:
- ▸ be able to plot points on graphs by using coordinates (see Topic 12.1)
- ▸ know about coordinates in all four quadrants (see Topic 12.3)
- ▸ know about bearings (see Topic 13.6)

14.2 VECTORS

Vectors are quantities that have both a size *and* a direction, for example, a speed of 20 km/h due north.

Three examples of vector quantities are: acceleration, speed (velocity) and displacement. (Displacement means distance in a particular direction.)

For example, we could say that Town B was 3 miles due east and 4 miles due north of Town A.

This displacement vector is represented as $AB = \begin{pmatrix} 3 \\ 4 \end{pmatrix}$.

This is called a column vector.

By Pythagoras, we know that the distance AB is 5 miles, and trigonometry tells us that the angle $\theta°$ is 36.9°.

Thus, the size, or length, of the vector is 5 miles.

The **direction** of the vector is 036.9° (in this example, the direction of the vector is a bearing).

This is shown diagrammatically as:

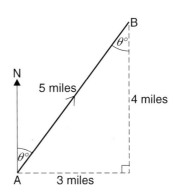

Transformations

The word **transformation** means *change*.
All transformations change a diagram - by altering its position, size or shape.
In the GCSE syllabus we have to know about four types of transformation:

▶ Translation

▶ Reflection

▶ Rotation

▶ Enlargement

14.3 TRANSLATION

Translation is the simplest of the four transformations.
In a translation every point on a shape is moved by the same displacement – i.e. by equal distances and in the same direction.
We can think of a translation as *sliding* the shape from its **object** position to its **image** position.

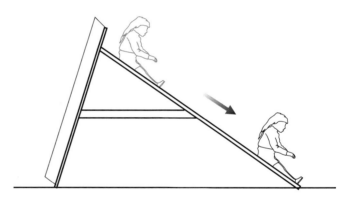

A translation is written as a column vector.
For example, if the rectangle A(1, 3), B(4, 3), C(4, 2), D(1, 2) has the translation vector $\begin{pmatrix} 5 \\ 3 \end{pmatrix}$ applied to it we can calculate its image position $A_1B_1C_1D_1$ as

$$A_1 = \begin{pmatrix} 1 \\ 3 \end{pmatrix} + \begin{pmatrix} 5 \\ 3 \end{pmatrix} = \begin{pmatrix} 6 \\ 6 \end{pmatrix}$$

$$B_1 = \begin{pmatrix} 4 \\ 3 \end{pmatrix} + \begin{pmatrix} 5 \\ 3 \end{pmatrix} = \begin{pmatrix} 9 \\ 6 \end{pmatrix}$$

$$C_1 = \begin{pmatrix} 4 \\ 2 \end{pmatrix} + \begin{pmatrix} 5 \\ 3 \end{pmatrix} = \begin{pmatrix} 9 \\ 5 \end{pmatrix}$$

$$D_1 = \begin{pmatrix} 1 \\ 2 \end{pmatrix} + \begin{pmatrix} 5 \\ 3 \end{pmatrix} = \begin{pmatrix} 6 \\ 5 \end{pmatrix}$$

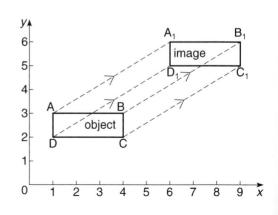

Translation facts

1 Translations are usually written as the vector $\begin{pmatrix} x \\ y \end{pmatrix}$.

2 This means that the number in the top row is the translation in the x-direction and the number in the bottom row is the translation in the y-direction.

For example, $\begin{pmatrix} 4 \\ 3 \end{pmatrix}$ means an increase of 4 units to the right (or in the positive x-direction) and 3 units upwards (or in the positive y-direction).

$\begin{pmatrix} -2 \\ -7 \end{pmatrix}$ means an increase of 2 units to the left (or in the negative x-direction) and 7 units downwards (or in the negative y-direction).

3 Translation does not affect the size or shape of the object. It only changes the position.

4 *All* the lines drawn between any pair of corresponding object and image points are equal and parallel (for example $AA_1 = BB_1 = CC_1 = DD_1$).

5 Any image point is found by adding the translation vector to the corresponding object point.

Worked Examples

Calculate and draw the image points obtained by applying the translations given to the object shape shown.

a $\begin{pmatrix} 4 \\ 6 \end{pmatrix}$ b $\begin{pmatrix} 5 \\ -6 \end{pmatrix}$ c $\begin{pmatrix} -7 \\ 2 \end{pmatrix}$ d $\begin{pmatrix} -3 \\ -5 \end{pmatrix}$

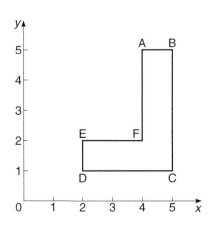

7 Calculate the translation vectors for the translations shown below, A_1 to A_2, etc.:

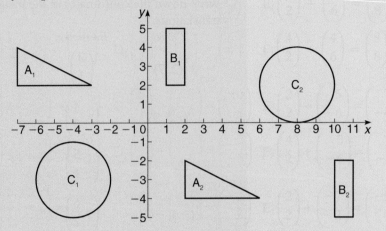

8 Point A(3, 5) is mapped onto point A_1(8, 4). Find the image of point (2, −1) under the same translation.

We first met the idea of **reflection** when we studied symmetry (see Topic 13.3). Reflection happens when a shape has a line of symmetry – one half of the shape can be *reflected* or *folded* along the mirror line on to the other half. Each half is called the *mirror image* of the other.

Reflection facts

1 Reflection does not affect the size and shape of the object. It only changes the position.

2 The image is where the object is *folded* over a mirror line.

3 The image of any point is the same distance behind the mirror line that the corresponding object point is in front.

4 The mirror line cuts the line joining the object and image points in half at right angles to it. This is called the perpendicular bisector of the line. (For more on perpendicular bisectors see Topic 14.8 later.)

NOTE

When finding the image of object shapes on graph paper the mirror line is often written as an equation. (To revise equations of straight lines see Topic 11.4.)

5 If an object point lies on the mirror line the image is the same point.

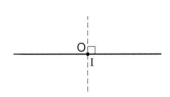

6 Reflections can easily be shown using tracing paper. One side of the mirror line is drawn and, when turned over, it can easily be seen to *fit* the other side of the mirror line.

i   **ii**

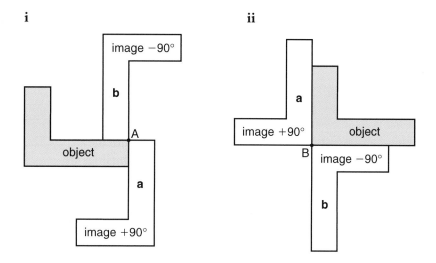

2   Rotate the given shape, about the origin, by

    a   +90°   **b**   −90°   **c**   180°

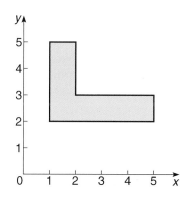

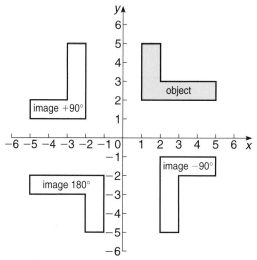

To find the angle of rotation

If the positions of the object and image are known the angle of rotation can be found.

Method one

Produce two corresponding lines on the diagrams back until they intersect. (Corresponding lines are lines that are in the *same place* in each diagram.)

The angle between them is the angle of rotation, $\theta°$.

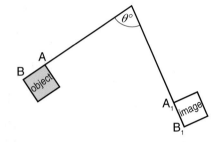

Method two

Draw lines from any two corresponding points on the object and image back to the centre of rotation.

The angle between them is the angle of rotation, $\theta°$.

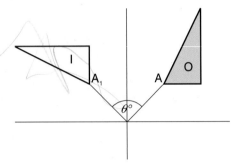

To find the centre of rotation

  i Draw a line between any pair of corresponding points.

  ii Draw the perpendicular bisector of this line.

  iii Repeat **i** and **ii** for another pair of corresponding points.

  iv The centre of rotation is the point where these two lines intersect.

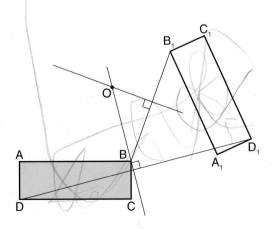

PRACTICE 14.5.1

1 Copy the following diagrams onto squared paper. In each case draw the image obtained by rotating the shape:

    a 90° anticlockwise, about the given point,

    b 90° clockwise, about the given point.

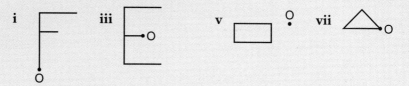

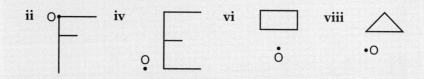

2 Find the images of the given shape after rotations about the origin of:

    a   +90°,   **b** −90°,   **c** $\frac{3}{4}$ of a turn anticlockwise.

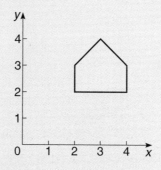

3 Join the following points to draw a flag and pole: A(2, ⁻6), B(2, ⁻3), C(2, ⁻2), D(4, ⁻2) and E(4, ⁻3).

    Find the images of the diagram after the following rotations about the origin:

    a 180°,   **b** $\frac{3}{4}$ of a turn clockwise,   **c** +90°.

4 A square is formed by the points A(2, 2), B(4, 2), C(4, 4) and D(2, 4).

    a Rotate this square through +90° about the origin.

    b Apply the translation vector $\begin{pmatrix} -6 \\ 0 \end{pmatrix}$ to the original square.

    c Are the solutions to **a** and **b** the same? Explain your answer.

5 Find the angles of rotation in the following diagrams:

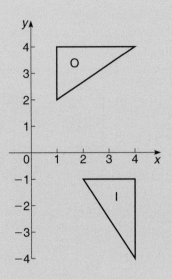
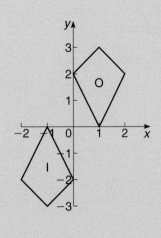

6 Find the centre of rotation and measure its angle.

7 Redraw the diagram in question **2**. Repeat the same three rotations as in the question but about the following centres of rotation.

a (1, 2)   **b** (2, 1)   **c** (2, ⁻1)   **d** (⁻1, 1)   **c** (⁻1, ⁻1)

8 a Draw the triangle with the following coordinates:
(⁻2, 2), (3, 2), (3, 3).

b Rotate this triangle by ⁻90° about (4,1).

c Rotate your answer to **b** by 180° about (⁻2, 1).

d Rotate your answer to **c** by ⁻90° about (⁻3, ⁻2).

e Write down the final coordinates.

The word **enlargement** is used when the size of an object is changed. For example:

Enlargement facts

1 Enlargement affects both the position and the size of the object.

2 Enlargement does not affect the shape. The image is exactly the same shape as the object but is different in size. Such figures are called *similar figures*, i.e. exactly the same shape but differing in size (see Topic 13.4).

3 Any pair of corresponding lengths on the object and image are *in the same ratio*. This ratio is called the *scale factor* of the enlargement.

4 If the scale factor is greater than one, the image is larger than the object. If it is less than one, it is smaller than the object.

5 If a shape is enlarged by scale factor K then each side of the image is K times its corresponding length on the object. Therefore the perimeter of the image is K times the length of the perimeter of the object.

Worked Examples

1 Draw an enlargement of the given shape with a scale factor 3.

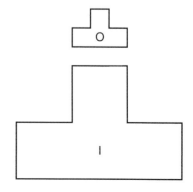

Each corresponding side on the image is 3 times the corresponding length on the object.

2 Shape A is mapped onto shape B.
   Calculate the scale factor of this enlargement.

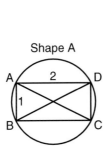
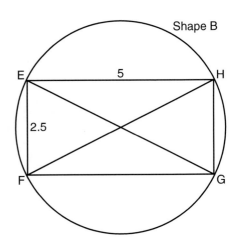

Comparing some of the corresponding sides, we get:

$$\frac{FG}{BC} = \frac{5}{2} = 2.5 \qquad \frac{EF}{AB} = \frac{2.5}{1} = 2.5, \text{ etc.}$$

Hence the scale factor is 2.5.

(Any pair of corresponding sides can be used – note the radii of the

circles are 1.1 and 2.75 ; and $\frac{2.75}{1.1} = 2.5$.)

Constructing enlargements

Enlargements are constructed *from a particular point.*
This point is called the *centre of enlargement.*
It can be either inside or outside the shape.

The method is as follows:

i Draw straight lines from the centre of enlargement (O) through each vertex of the object.

ii Measure the distance from O to each vertex.

iii Multiply each of these distances by the scale factor for the enlargement.

iv Mark off these new distances from O through each vertex.

v Join up these points to form the image.

Worked Examples

Construct enlargements of the given shapes with given scale factors from the centres marked O.

a

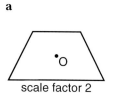

scale factor 2

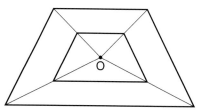

b

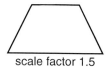

scale factor 1.5

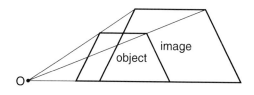

PRACTICE 14.6.1

1 Use squared paper to draw enlargements of the following shapes with the given scale factors.

a

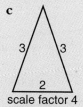

scale factor 3

c

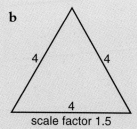

scale factor 4

b

scale factor 1.5

d

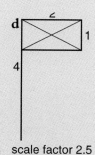

scale factor 2.5

2 Find the scale factors in each of the following enlargements:

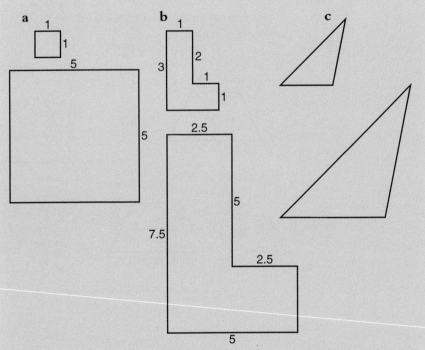

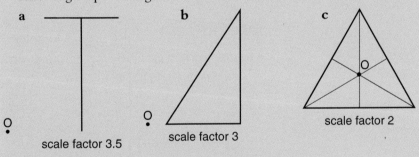

3 Use squared paper to copy and construct enlargements for each of the following shapes with given scale factors and from the marked centres:

a scale factor 3.5   **b** scale factor 3   **c** scale factor 2

4 Enlarge the given shape from centre O with scale factor $\frac{1}{2}$:

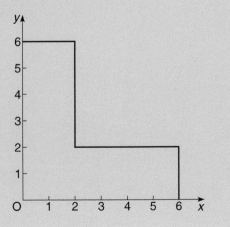

5 Find the centre of enlargement and scale factor of the following enlargements:

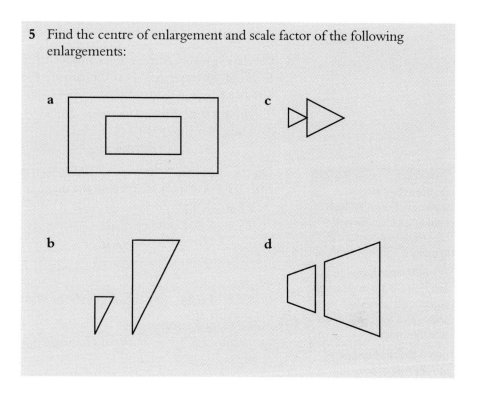

Maps and scales

Enlargement is used in map drawing.

A map is a scale drawing of a geographical area.

The *scale factor* is the ratio between a given distance on the map and the same distance on the ground.

The map scale is shown in one of two ways:

  i A ratio, for example, 1 : 25 000.

    This means that one unit on the map represents 25 000 equal units on the ground.

    Note that   1 cm : 25 000 cm works out at 1 cm : $\frac{1}{4}$ km and

                1 in. : 25 000 in. works out at 1 in. : 0.4 mile approx.

 ii A map scale, for example, 5 in. = 1 mile.

    This means that 1 inch on the map represents 0.2 mile or 352 yds.

    The scale is often shown as a diagram, for example,

Worked Examples

1 On the Ordnance Survey Travelmaster 1 : 250 000 map of Northern
Scotland, Inverness and Fort William are 14 inches apart. What is the real
distance between the towns?

> On this scale 1 inch represents 4 miles.
> Thus 14 inches = 14 × 4
> $$= 56 \text{ miles.}$$

2 On the same map Montrose and Aberdeen are marked as being 38 miles
apart. How far apart are they on the map?

> 4 miles = 1 in.
> Therefore 38 miles = $\frac{38}{4}$ in.
> $$= 9.5 \text{ in.}$$

PRACTICE 14.6.2a   Try these questions without a calculator

1 On a map, the scale is 1 in. = 4 miles.
  a Stafford is 4.2 in. north of Wolverhampton. How far is Stafford
    from Wolverhampton?
  b Bristol airport is 2.2 in. from Bristol (Temple Meads) station on the
    map. How far will a taxi take Jim and Dot on this journey?

2 On a map, the scale is 1 cm = 2.5 km.
  a From Manchester to Stockport is 10 km. How far apart are they on
    the map?
  b Cambridge is 88 km from London. How far apart are they on the map?

3 On a map of Europe, the scale is 1 in. = 20 miles. The Newhaven to
  Dieppe ferry route is 3.9 in. How far is Dieppe from Newhaven?

PRACTICE 14.6.2b   Try these questions with a calculator

1 On a map of Europe, the scale is 1 cm = 12.5 km. The Dover to Calais
  ferry route is marked as 41 km. How far is this on the map?

2 A set of town maps have a scale of 1 in. = $\frac{1}{4}$ mile.
  a The map is quoted as having a scale of 1 : x. Find the value of x,
    writing your answer to 2 significant figures.
  b In Cardiff, the Millennium Stadium is $1\frac{1}{4}$ in. from the station. How
    many yards is this?
  c In Edinburgh, St. Andrew's square is 1500 yards from the Albert
    Memorial. How far apart are they on the map?

3 A street map of London has a scale of 1 : 14 000.
  a On the map Nelson's Column is 8.6 cm from Buckingham Palace.
    How many metres apart are they?
  b Great Ormond Street Childrens' Hospital is 2.5 km from St.
    Thomas' Hospital. How far apart are they on the map?

14.7 COMBINED TRANSFORMATIONS

A combined transformation happens when one transformation is followed by another. Repeated transformations can often lead to interesting patterns. For example, the pattern below is made by repeated rotations:

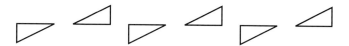

Often, two transformations which follow one another can be replaced by a single transformation.

For example, a reflection in the *y*-axis followed by a reflection in the *x*-axis is exactly the same as a single rotation of 180° about (0, 0).

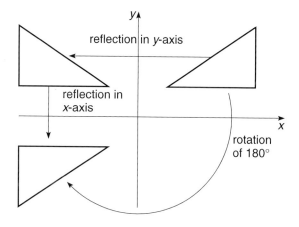

reflection in *y*-axis

reflection in *x*-axis

rotation of 180°

Worked Example

Triangle T, on the axes shown, can be transformed onto triangle S, by a combination of two transformations.

a Describe each transformation fully.

b Write down the *single* transformation which would replace the two original transformations.

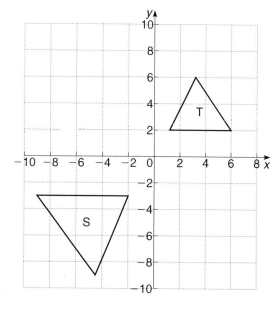

a i Rotation of 180° about (0, 0).

   ii Enlargement scale factor 1.5 centre (0, 0).

b The single transformation would be: enlargement scale factor −1.5 centre (0, 0).

The following questions give examination practice in both general and combined transformations.

PRACTICE 14.7.1

1 A pentagon ABCDE is shown.

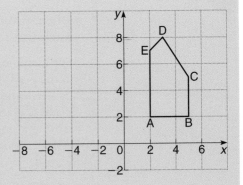

   a ABCDE is transformed into $A_1B_1C_1D_1E_1$ by the translation $\begin{pmatrix} 5 \\ -2 \end{pmatrix}$.

   On graph paper, draw and label the resulting pentagon.

   b ABCDE is transformed into $A_2B_2C_2D_2E_2$ by a rotation of 90° anticlockwise about $(0, 0)$.

   Draw and label the resulting pentagon on the diagram.

2 Draw and label axes for values of x and y between -16 and 16.
   a On the graph draw a letter F by plotting and joining the points $A(2, 1)$, $B(2, 3)$, $C(2, 5)$, $D(3, 3)$ and $E(4, 5)$.
   b Enlarge the letter by a scale factor 3 centre $(0, 0)$.
   c Rotate your enlargement by $+90°$ about $(0, 0)$.
   d The F drawn in **a** may be transformed into another F by a translation of $\begin{pmatrix} 6 \\ -8 \end{pmatrix}$.

   Draw the resulting image on your graph.

3 A flag is represented on graph paper by the points $A(1, 0)$, $B(1, 2)$, $C(1, 4)$ and $D(4, 3)$.
   a Taking axes for x from -8 to 8 and for y from -10 to 10, plot the above points and join with straight lines AC, CD and DB.
   b Enlarge the flag by scale factor 2 centre $(0, 0)$.
   c Rotate the resulting enlargement by $-180°$ about $(0, 0)$.

4 a Reflect the given figure in the x-axis, followed by a rotation of 90° about $(0, 0)$.
   b Which single transformation is the equivalent of this?

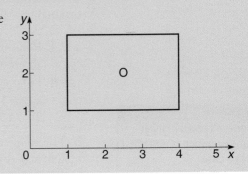

5 **a** Rotate the given figure by
180° about (0, 0), followed
by a rotation of −90° about
(0, 0).

  b Which single transformation
is the equivalent of this?

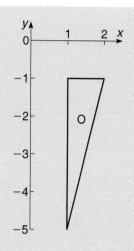

6 **a** Reflect the given figure in
the line $y = x$, followed by a
reflection in the line $y = -x$.

  b Which single transformation
is the equivalent of this?

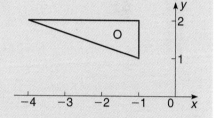

7 **a** Reflect the given figure
in the y-axis followed by a
rotation of 180° about (0, 0).

  b Which single transformation
is the equivalent of this?

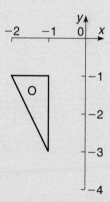

8 **a** Rotate the given figure by
−90° about (0, 0) followed by
a reflection in the x-axis.

  b Which single transformation
is the equivalent of this?

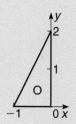

Tessellations

We can use transformations, polygons and symmetry to devise tessellations. A **tessellation** is a *tiling pattern*.

It is the arrangement of one or more shapes to completely fill a space, for example:

Tesellation can also be seen in the interesting construction of The Eden Project (see page 374).

Tessellation rules

1   There must be no gaps between the *tiles*.

2   No shape must overlap another shape.

3   At any vertex (point where shapes touch), all the angles must add up to 360°.

PRACTICE 14.7.2

1   The only regular polygons that tessellate on their own are those whose interior angles divide exactly into 360°.
    Use the information in Topic 13.2 to find which regular polygons tessellate on their own.

2   Will *any* parallelogram tessellate? Explain your answer.

3   Will *any* rhombus tessellate? Explain your answer.

4   *Investigation*
    Investigate, as an assignment, the use of tessellations that occur in one of the following areas:

    a nature,   **b** wallpaper and floor coverings,   **c** advertising.

14.8 CONSTRUCTIONS AND LOCI

Constructions

Sometimes we have to make accurate drawings so we have to be able to use drawing instruments.

Lines and angles

There are a number of sensible 'rules' to remember when we are drawing and measuring lines:

a Make your drawings as accurate as possible. This means:

  i Hold your ruler firmly on the paper so that it doesn't slip.

  ii Make sure your pencil is SHARP! – an HB is usually best to use.

  iii Draw firm lines but do not press too hard on the paper.

  iv Make sure any compasses you use are not too loose. They need to be firm so that the radius you are using stays the same.

  v If you are drawing an angle make sure you hold your protractor or angle measurer correctly.

  vi When you are drawing an angle make sure you are using the correct part of the instrument. An acute angle is less than 90° and an obtuse one between 90° and 180°.

b When drawing and, especially, measuring lines:

  i Use the correct unit for the situation. You wouldn't give the distance from the Earth to the Moon in cm, or you wouldn't measure the length of your little finger in m.

  ii Remember that any line measurement can never be exactly accurate no matter how carefully you draw it.
    Any measurement is only accurate to $\pm\frac{1}{2}$ the unit in which it is measured.
    If you draw a line, say of 5.7 cm you can only be really sure that it is somewhere between 5.65 cm and 5.75 cm. This is because the measurement units are to the nearest 0.1 cm.
    If you measured a line that you said was 84 cm long, you can only be really sure that its true length is between 83.5 cm and 84.5 cm. This is because the measurement units are to the nearest 1 cm.

  iii Measure angles to the nearest degree. Angles, both drawn and measured, are then accurate to $\pm\frac{1}{2}$ of one degree either way.

PRACTICE 14.8.1

1 Draw the following straight lines and write down the possible range of answers in which the true lengths lie:

  a 10 cm,   **b** 7.8 cm,   **c** 134 mm,   **d** 7 in.,   **e** 15.2 in.

Ask a friend to check and confirm your accuracy.

2 Draw the following angles and write down the possible range of answers in which the true angles lie:

   a 25°,   **b** 48°,   **c** 74°,   **d** 123°,   **e** 153°.

Ask a friend to check and confirm your accuracy.

3 Measure the following angles and write down the possible range of answers in which the true angles lie:

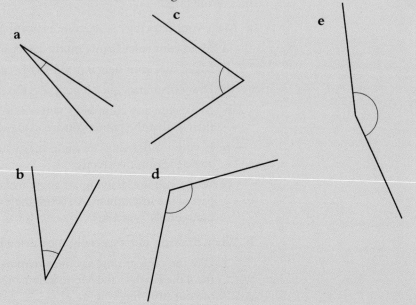

4 On graph paper, draw scales from 0 to 10 on the *x*-axis and from 0 to 12 on the *y*-axis. Plot the following sets of three points and draw the triangles formed. Measure the angles and add them together to see how close you get to the angle sum of a triangle (180°):

   a $(0, 0), (5, 0), (5, 12)$ **d** $(1, 10), (9, 8), (3, 4)$

   b $(1, 1), (7, 1), (7, 9)$ **e** $(0, 0), (5, 0), (9, 12)$

   c $(1, 2), (10, 4), (5, 11)$ **f** $(1, 3), (5, 8), (10, 2)$

5 On graph paper, draw scales from 0 to 10 on the *x*-axis and from 0 to 12 on the *y*-axis. Plot the following sets of four points and draw the quadrilaterals formed. Measure the angles and add them together to see how close you get to the angle sum of a quadrilateral (360°):

   a $(0, 0), (9, 0), (9, 12), (0, 12)$ **d** $(1, 4), (8, 2), (3, 11), (10, 9)$

   b $(1, 1), (9, 1), (7, 12), (4, 12)$ **e** $(2, 3), (8, 1), (7, 9), (5, 11)$

   c $(2, 2), (7, 2), (10, 6), (5, 6)$ **f** $(1, 3), (5, 2), (9, 11), (2, 5)$

6 Draw any pentagon, making it large enough to measure the angles easily. Measure them and see how close you get to the angle sum of a pentagon (540°).

7 Draw any octagon, making it large enough to measure the angles easily. Measure them and see how close you get to the angle sum of an octagon (1080°).

8 Draw a horizontal line 55 mm long. At the right hand end draw an angle of 108° and draw another line of 55 mm. Repeat this 3 more times. What should have happened? Has it?

9 Draw a vertical line PN. PN lies due north. Draw lines, from P, each 45 mm long, in directions giving the bearings:

a 021°	**c** 119°	**e** 202°	**g** 311°	**i** SE
b 072°	**d** 157°	**f** 256°	**h** 347°	**j** SW

10 Stating and using a suitable scale, draw accurate diagrams to show the following situations:

    a The line PQ where Q is 5 km from P and on a bearing of 026°.

    b The line MN where N is 8 miles from M and on a bearing of 144°.

    c The line RS where S is 13 m from R and on a bearing of 234°.

    d The line YZ where Z is 6.8 ft from Y and on a bearing of 333°.

11 Stating and using a suitable scale, draw accurate diagrams to show the following situations:

    a B is 3 km from A on a bearing of 035°. C is 4 km from B on a bearing of 053°. Measure and state the distance and bearing of C from A.

    b Q is 7 miles from P on a bearing of 156°. R is 4.5 miles from Q on a bearing of 038°. Measure and state the distance and bearing of R from P.

    c G is 8 km from F on a bearing of 040°. H is 15 km from G on a bearing of 220°. Measure and state the distance and bearing of H from F.

    d Y is 3.1 in. from X on a bearing of 252°. Z is 4.9 in. from Y on a bearing of 330°. Measure and state the distance and bearing of Z from X.

Constructions

a To bisect (cut in half) a line AB:

    i Open a pair of compasses to more than half AB.

    ii With centre at A draw an arc P.

    iii With the compasses at the same setting and with centre B draw an arc Q to cut (intersect) arc P.

    iv Draw the line joining the points where the two arcs intersect.

    This line bisects AB at right angles. It is called the *perpendicular bisector* of AB. M is the mid-point of the line AB.

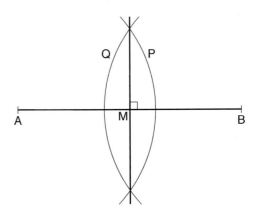

b To bisect an angle ABC:

    i With centre at B and any suitable radius, draw an arc intersecting the arms of the angle at P and Q.

    ii With centres P and Q and a radius more than half PQ, draw two arcs to intersect at R.

    iii Join RB. This line bisects ∠ABC.

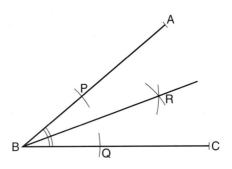

c To construct the perpendicular at a point on a line, use the same method as bisecting an angle, where ∠ABC is 180°. We bisect it to get 90°.

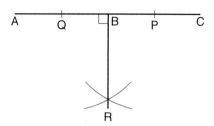

d To construct the perpendicular from a point, P, to a line XY.
   i With centre P draw an arc to cut (intersect) the line XY in two places, A and C.
   ii With centres A and C, draw two arcs to cut (intersect) at Q.
   iii Join PQ and mark point B where this line cuts AC.
   iv The perpendicular from P meets the line XY at point B.

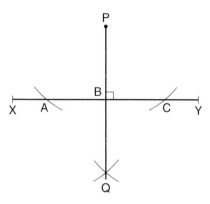

Worked Examples

1 Construct the triangle with sides 4 cm, 6 cm and 8 cm. Measure the largest angle.
   i Draw a line and mark A and B on it 8 cm apart.
   ii With radius 6 cm and centre A, (or B), draw arc P.
   iii With radius 4 cm and centre B, (or A), draw arc Q to intersect arc P. This is point C.
   iv Complete the triangle ABC.
   v Using a protractor measure the required angle, ∠C = 104°.

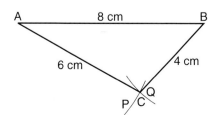

2 Construct the triangle where BC = 6 cm, ∠B = 47° and ∠C = 63°.
   Bisect ∠A and mark the point where this line intersects BC as D.
   Measure BD.

    i Draw a line and mark B and C on it 6 cm apart.
   ii Using a protractor draw a straight line at B at 47° to BC.
  iii Using a protractor draw a straight line at C at 63° to BC.
  iv Mark the point where these lines intersect as A.
   v Using compasses bisect ∠A and mark D on BC.
  vi Measure BD.

The length BD was measured as 3.3 cm (2 sf).

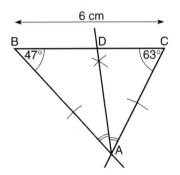

PRACTICE 14.8.2

1 Construct the following triangles:

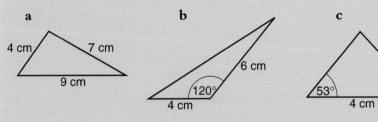

2 Draw a line and mark AB = 5 cm on it.
   Construct a perpendicular to the line at B and mark C on this line
   where BC = 4 cm.
   Complete triangle ABC.
   Measure and record the length AC.

3 Construct an isosceles triangle with sides 8 cm, 8 cm and 6 cm.
   Bisect the vertical angle.
   Show that it perpendicularly bisects the base.

4 Draw any triangle.
   Bisect all three angles and show that the three bisectors all pass through
   one point.

5 Draw any triangle.
Draw all three medians (lines joining any vertex to the mid-point of the opposite side). Show that the three medians all pass through one point. (This point is called the *centre of gravity* of the triangle.)

6 Draw any triangle.
Construct the perpendicular bisectors of all three sides.
Show that the three bisectors all pass through one point.
Using this point as the centre, draw the circle that passes through the three vertices. Explain why this is so.

7 Draw any triangle with acute angles. Construct the perpendicular lines from each of the three vertices to the opposite sides. (These are called altitudes.) Show that these altitudes all pass through one point.

Locus

The word **locus** means *path*. A locus is the path traced out by a point when it moves to obey a given law or laws.

For example, the locus of a point which is always 2 cm from a fixed point O, is the circumference of a circle, centre O, radius 2 cm:

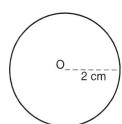

When drawing a locus we sometimes have to experiment by marking some points on a diagram that obey the given law.

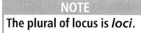

NOTE
The plural of locus is *loci*.

When we can see what the locus looks like we can complete the diagram.

A locus can sometimes be an area.

For instance, in the example above, the locus of points P such that OP < 2 cm, would be the total area inside the circle (not including the circumference). If OP ≤ 2 it would include the circumference.

Some common loci

1 The locus of a point which moves such that it is a fixed distance from a given point is the circumference of a circle.

2 The locus of a point which moves such that it is a fixed distance from a given line is a pair of lines parallel to the given line and the fixed distance d from it.

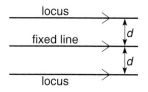

3 The locus of a point which moves such that it is always the same distance from two fixed points A and B is the perpendicular bisector of AB.

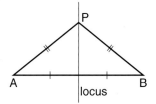

4 The locus of a point which moves such that it is always the same distance from two fixed straight lines is the angle bisector of the lines.

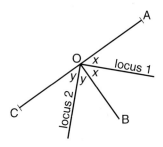

In the diagram shown, OA and OB are the fixed straight lines and locus 1 bisects the angle.

However, if (as here) AO is produced the exterior $\angle$COB is formed and locus 2 bisects that angle.

Also, since AOC is a straight angle, i.e. 180°, then $2x + 2y = 180°$, so $x + y = 90°$.

But, $x + y$ is the angle between the two loci. Thus:

the bisectors of the interior and exterior angles formed by two straight lines are perpendicular.

Worked Examples

1 A and B are fixed points 8 inches apart.
Find the locus of a point which moves such that it is always equidistant from A and B and never further than 5 inches from either point.

As shown before the initial locus is the perpendicular bisector of AB, but, using Pythagoras, we can see that it can only extend for 3 inches on each side of the line AB.

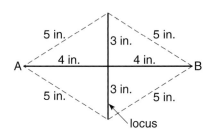

2   A goat is tethered to one corner of a square
    shed of side 2 m in the middle of one wall
    of a large field. Its rope is 5 m long.
    Indicate the locus of the grass from which
    the goat can feed.

    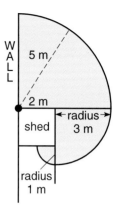

    At first the goat can feed within a circle of
    radius 5 m, but after turning the first corner
    the radius becomes 3 m and then 1 m after
    it turns the second corner.

    The diagram shows the area that
    is available to it.

PRACTICE 14.8.3

1   ∠ABC is 90° and BC = 10 cm. Find the locus of points which are
    equidistant from:

    a   B and C,

    b   AB and BC.

    Mark the point D which lies on both loci and measure the length DB.

2   AB is a line 5 cm long and is the hypotenuse of a right-angled triangle
    ABC. Draw the locus of point C. (Remember your circle theorems!)

3   A rectangular room 6 m by 4 m has power points at both ends of one of
    the longer sides. Truda has a vacuum cleaner of combined length, with
    cable, of 4.5 m.
    Show the locus of all points in the room which Truda cannot reach.

4   AC is the hypotenuse of a right-angled triangle ABC. AB = 5 cm and
    BC = 12 cm.
    Show the locus of all points inside the triangle which are closer to A
    than B but less than 10 cm from C.

5   In triangle ABC, AC = 4 in., BC = 8 in. and ∠ACB = 64°. Draw the
    following loci:

    a   the locus of all points the same distance from AC and BC,

    b   the locus of all points 2.25 in. from A.

    Mark and label any points which lie on both loci.

6 X, Y and Z are three observation posts at the vertices of an equilateral triangle of side 20 miles.

Observers at X and Y simultaneously record a UFO equidistant from them (over the mid-point of XY) and moving along their perpendicular bisector towards Z.

Ten seconds later it is recorded as being the same distance from all three observation posts.

a Draw the locus accurately and find the distance the UFO has moved.

b Calculate:

  i the speed of the UFO in mph,

  ii how long it will take, flying at its present speed and course, to appear directly over Z.

7 a Draw a circle of radius 5 cm.

b Draw a number of chords of this circle each 8 cm long and mark their mid-points.

c Deduce the locus of the mid-points of all such chords. Explain your answer.

14.9 SUMMARY

Vectors

Vectors are quantities that have both a size *and* a direction.

Displacement means distance in a particular direction.

Transformations

The word *transformation* means *change*.

All transformations change a diagram – by altering its position, size or shape.

We have to know about four types of transformation:

▸ translation

▸ reflection

▸ rotation

▸ enlargement

We call the original position of a shape the *object* and the final position the *image*.

Transformations are often called *mappings* and the object is said to be *mapped onto* the image.

Translation

Translation is the simplest of the four transformations.

In a translation every point on a shape is moved by the same displacement.

We can think of a translation as sliding the shape from its object position to its image position.

A translation is written as a column vector $\begin{pmatrix} x \\ y \end{pmatrix}$.

The number in the top row is the translation in the x-direction and the number in the bottom row is the translation in the y-direction.

Translation does not affect the size or shape of the object. It only changes the position.

All the lines drawn between any pair of corresponding object and image points are equal and parallel.

Any image point is found by adding the translation vector to the corresponding object point.

Reflection

Reflection occurs when a shape has a line of symmetry – one half of the shape can be *reflected* or *folded* along a mirror line on to the other half.

Each half is the *mirror image* of the other.

Reflection does not affect the size and shape of the object. It only changes the position.

The effect on position is that the object is *folded* over a mirror line.

The image of any point is the same distance behind the mirror line that the corresponding object point is in front.

The mirror line is called the perpendicular bisector of the line joining the object and image points.

If an object point lies on the mirror line the image is the same point.

Reflections can easily be shown using tracing paper.

One side of the mirror line is drawn and, when turned over, it can easily be seen to *fit* the other side of the mirror line.

When finding the image of object shapes on graph paper the mirror line is often written as an equation.

Rotation

An angle is a rotation of one line onto another.

Every point on the object shape turns through the same angle about a fixed point.

Rotation does not affect the size and shape of the object. It only changes the position.

Every point on the shape is turned through the same angle about a certain fixed point.

This amount of turning is called the *angle of rotation*.

The fixed point is called the *centre of rotation*.

It is the only point that does not change in the rotation.

It can be either inside or outside the object shape.

The direction of rotation must be specified.
Anticlockwise is taken as positive and clockwise as negative.
The object and image are congruent shapes.
Rotations can easily be shown using tracing paper. The object is drawn, together with the axes and fixed point. The tracing paper can then easily be turned through the required angle and the image drawn in the correct position.

To find the angle of rotation

If the positions of the object and image are known the angle of rotation can be found.

Method one

Produce two corresponding lines on the diagrams back until they cross.
The angle between them is the angle of rotation.
This method is very useful if we do not know the centre of rotation.

Method two

Draw lines from any two corresponding points on the object and image back to the centre of rotation.
The angle between them is the angle of rotation.

To find the centre of rotation

  i Draw a line between any pair of corresponding points.
 ii Draw the perpendicular bisector of this line.
iii Repeat **i** and **ii** for another pair of corresponding points.
 iv The centre of rotation is the point where these two lines intersect.

Enlargement

The word *enlargement* is used when the size of an object is changed.
Enlargement affects both the position and the size of the object.
Enlargement has no effect on shape – the image is exactly the same shape as the object.
Any pair of corresponding lengths on the object and image are *in the same ratio*.
This ratio is called the *scale factor* of the enlargement.
If the scale factor is numerically greater than one, the image is larger than the object.
If the scale factor is numerically less than one, it is smaller than the object.

Constructing enlargements

Enlargements are constructed from a particular point.
This point is called the *centre of enlargement*.
It can be either inside or outside the shape.
The method is:

  i draw straight lines from the centre of enlargement (O) through each vertex of the object,
  ii measure the distance from O to each vertex,
  iii multiply each of these distances by the scale factor for the enlargement,
  iv mark off these new distances from O through each vertex,
  v join up these points to form the image.

If O is inside the object the diagram is called a *spider diagram*.
If O is outside the object the diagram is called a *ray diagram*.

Maps and scales

A practical use of enlargement is in map drawing.
A map is a scale drawing of a geographical area.
The *scale factor* is the ratio between a given length on the map and the corresponding length on the ground.
The map scale is shown in one of two ways:

  i A ratio, for example, 1 : 25 000.
    This means that one unit on the map represents 25 000 equal units on the ground.
    1 cm : 25 000 cm works out at 1 cm : $\frac{1}{4}$ km.
    1 in. : 25 000 in. works out at 1 in. : 0.4 mile approx.
  ii A map scale, for example, 5 in. = 1 mile.
    This means that 1 inch on the map represents 0.2 mile or 352 yd.

Combined transformations

A combined transformation happens when one transformation is followed by another.
Repeated transformations can often lead to interesting patterns.
Often, two transformations which follow one another can be replaced by a single transformation.

Tessellations

A *tessellation* is a tiling pattern.
It is the arrangement of one or more shapes to completely fill a space.
There must be no gaps between the tiles.
No shape must overlap another shape.
At any vertex (point where shapes touch), all the angles must add up to 360°.

Constructions and loci

To bisect a line AB:

Open a pair of compasses to more than half AB.
With centre at A draw an arc P.
With the compasses at the same setting and with centre B draw an arc Q to intersect arc P.
Draw the line joining the points where the two arcs intersect.
This line bisects AB at right angles.
It is called the *perpendicular bisector* of AB.

To bisect an angle ABC:

With centre at B and any suitable radius, draw an arc intersecting the arms of the angle at P and Q.
With centres P and Q and a radius more than half PQ, draw two arcs to intersect at R.
Join RB.
This line bisects ∠ABC.

To construct the perpendicular at a point on a line:

This is the same as above where ∠ABC is 180°.
We bisect it to get 90°.

To construct the perpendicular from a point, P, to a line XY:

With centre P draw an arc to cut (intersect) the line XY in two places, A and C.
With centres A and C, draw two arcs to cut (intersect) at Q.
Join PQ and mark point B where this line cuts AC.
The perpendicular from P meets the line XY at point B.

Locus

The word *locus* means path.
A locus is the path traced out by a point when it moves to obey a given law or laws.
The plural of locus is *loci*.
When drawing a locus we sometimes have to experiment by marking some points on a diagram that obey the given law.
When we can see what the locus looks like we can complete the diagram.
A locus can sometimes be an area.

Some common loci

The locus of a point which moves such that it is a fixed distance from a given point is the circumference of a circle.

The locus of a point which moves such that it is a fixed distance from a given line is a pair of lines parallel to the given line and the fixed distance from it.

The locus of a point which moves such that it is always the same distance from two fixed points A and B is the perpendicular bisector of AB.

The locus of a point which moves such that it is always the same distance from two fixed straight lines is the angle bisector of the lines.

The bisectors of the interior and exterior angles formed by two straight lines are perpendicular.

CHAPTER 15

Measures

In this chapter you will need to:

▸ be able to use appropriate measuring and drawing instruments – including ruler, protractor, compasses, etc.

▸ know common equivalents i.e.

1 ounce is approximately 30 grams

1 pound is approximately 450 grams

1 kilogram is approximately 2.2 pounds

1 inch is approximately 2.5 centimetres

1 foot is approximately 30 centimetres

1 mile is approximately 1600 metres

5 miles is approximately 8 kilometres

1 pint is approximately 550 millilitres

1 gallon is approximately 4.5 litres

1 litre is approximately 1.75 pints

1 metre is approximately 39 inches or 1.1 yards

▸ understand the differences between discrete and continuous data (see Topic 1.1)

▸ understand decimal calculations (see Topic 4.4)

▸ understand the best accuracy to use in a problem (see Topic 7.7) and understand that no answer is more accurate than the data it uses or is possible

Worked Examples

1   Tricia has a rolling pin 40 cm long. What is the approximate length of the rolling pin in inches?

   2.5 cm is approximately 1 inch, so 40 cm is approximately

   $\frac{40}{2.5} = 16$ inches.

2   Ruth buys 4 oz of jelly babies. How many grams is this approximately?

   1 oz is approximately 28 g, thus 4 oz is approximately 112 g.

PRACTICE 15.1.1   Try these questions with a calculator

1   Hugo runs for 4 km. Approximately how many miles is this?

2   Margaret buys potatoes in a 55 lb bag. Approximately how many kg is this?

3 Bill drinks 3 litres of lager. Approximately how many pints does he drink?

4 Debbie has a 5 foot tape measure. Approximately how many cm is this?

5 Tony buys 150 grams of pipe tobacco. Approximately how many ounces is this?

6 Joan is 5 ft 6 in tall. Approximately how many cm is this?

7 Alan buys $2\frac{1}{2}$ litres of paint. Approximately how many pints is this?

8 Rebecca runs a 3 mile race. Approximately how many metres is this?

9 At the supermarket Dave converts the price per kilo (kg) into the price per pound (lb) as follows:
   i Note the price per kg, say £3.60
   ii Half that value, i.e. £1.80
   iii Subtract $\frac{1}{10}$ of this new value, i.e. £1.80 − 18 pence = £1.62
   iv This is Dave's estimated price per lb.

Use Dave's method on the following prices, to find the cost, to the nearest penny, of:
   a 1 lb of bacon priced at £2.80 per kg.
   b 1 lb of carrots priced at 60 pence per kg.
   c 1 lb of beef priced at £5.40 per kg.
   d 1 lb of strawberry jam priced at £1.90 per kg.
   e A 10 lb turkey priced at £1.20 per kg.
   f A 55 lb sack of potatoes priced at 44 pence per kg.
   g A 3 lb bag of self raising flour priced at 56 pence per kg.

15.2 PERIMETER

For instance, the perimeter of a square of side x m is $4x$ m.

The perimeter of a circle is usually called the circumference (see Topic 13.2).

Worked Examples

1   Calculate the perimeters of the following shapes:

a 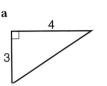   **b** 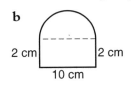   **c**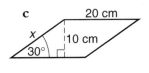

   a By Pythagoras' theorem the hypotenuse squared equals $3^2 + 4^2$
       which is 25. Thus the hypotenuse is 5 and the perimeter
       $= 3 + 4 + 5 = 12$ units.

   b The curved line is half the circumference of a circle of radius 5 cm
       i.e. $3.14 \times 5 = 15.7$. Thus the perimeter $= 15.7 + 10 + 2 + 2$
       $= 29.7$ cm.

   c Using SOHCAHTOA we can see that $\sin 30° = \dfrac{10}{x}$

       i.e. $0.5 = \dfrac{10}{x}$

       Hence $x = \dfrac{10}{0.5} = 20$ cm.

       Thus perimeter $= 4 \times 20 = 80$ cm.

NOTE
You may need to revise
Pythagoras' theorem, circle
circumference and simple
trigonometry to work
these questions out.

PRACTICE 15.2.1a   Try these questions without a calculator

1   Calculate the perimeters of the following shapes:

a 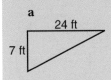   **b**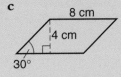

2   A rectangle has a perimeter of 48.6 cm and the longer side of length
    14.5 cm. Find the length of the shorter side.

3   The two shortest sides of a right-angled triangle are 5 mm and 12 mm
    respectively. Find the perimeter of the triangle.

4   A rhombus has diagonals of lengths 12 cm and 16 cm. Find its perimeter.

PRACTICE 15.2.1b   Try these questions with a calculator

1   Calculate the perimeters of the following shapes:

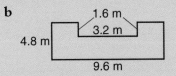

a   **b**   **c**   **d**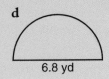

2   A coin is 5 cm in diameter. Calculate its perimeter.

An **area** measures the amount of space inside a flat (or plane) shape. An area is measured in square units, for example:

1 square cm – written 1 cm^2

1 cm

The rectangle 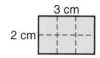 contains an area of 6 cm^2.

Estimating areas

If the figure has curved sides, one way is to divide it up into small squares of known area and simply count them. Where there is less than a half a full square at the edge of the shape, do not count it. Where there is more than half a full square, count it as one full square.

Worked Example

Estimate the area of the given shape.

As we can see, each square more than half filled has been counted as a whole square and each one less than half has not been counted.

The area of the shape is estimated as 8 cm^2.

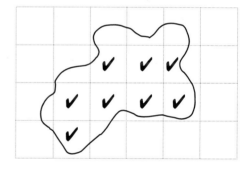

> **NOTE**
> 1 There are other units of area: mm^2, m^2, in.^{2}, ft^2, yd^2, etc.
> 2 In metric measure 1 hectare (1 ha) = 10 000 m^2.
> In imperial measure 1 acre = 4840 yd^2.
> 3 When calculating or measuring areas, we must use the appropriate unit.

PRACTICE 15.3.1

1 This coffee stain is divided into centimetre squares. Estimate its area.

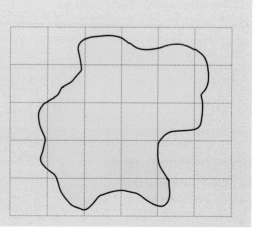

2   The diagram shows a map of Jersey.

Each full square represents 1 square mile.

Estimate the area of Jersey, to the nearest 10 square miles.

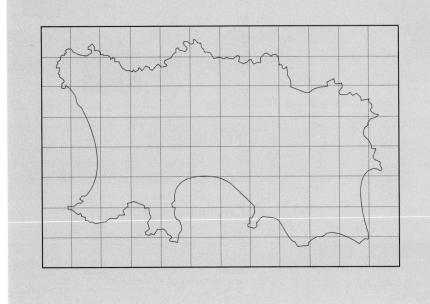

Areas of shapes

1   *The rectangle*

A rectangle is l units long. It divides the rectangle into l vertical strips.

It is w units wide. It divides the rectangle into w horizontal strips.

So the whole rectangle is cut into l lots of w squares $= l \times w$ squares.

Thus the area, A, of a rectangle is given by the formula, $A = lw$.

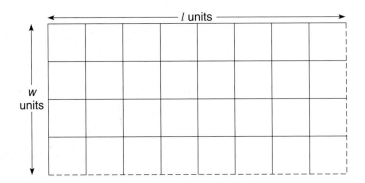

NOTE

You will need to know the formula for the area of a triangle for the examination.

2 *The triangle*

a   Right-angled triangles

We can see that the right angled triangle of base b and height h units is exactly half of a rectangle.

The area of the rectangle is bh so the area of the triangle is $\frac{1}{2}bh$.

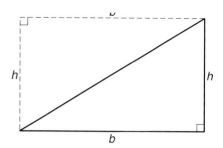

b   Any triangle

Imagine the triangle was enclosed in a rectangle like ACDF.

The width h of the rectangle is the same as the perpendicular height from vertex B to the base of the triangle.

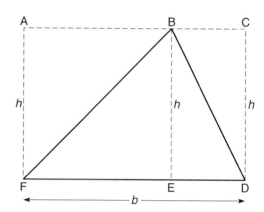

Using the result for right-angled triangles above, we can see that the section BEF of the triangle is exactly half the rectangle ABEF. Similarly, the section BED is exactly half the rectangle CBED. So the whole triangle FBD is exactly half the area of the whole rectangle ACDF.

Hence, the area, A, of triangle FBD is given by $A = \frac{1}{2}bh$.

This is the same formula we obtained for the right-angled triangle. In both cases h was the perpendicular height of the triangle.

Hence:

the area of a triangle $= \frac{1}{2}bh$

where b is the length of the base and h the perpendicular height down on to this base.

Notice that:

i   The base need not necessarily be the *bottom* of the triangle, i.e.

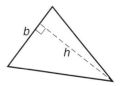

NOTE

Produced means 'extended' here.

ii   If the triangle is obtuse-angled the height is the length of the perpendicular to the base produced.

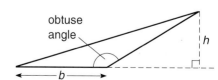

3 *The parallelogram*

The parallelogram ABDF can be made into the rectangle ABCE by translating (see Topic 14.3) the triangle AEF into BCD.

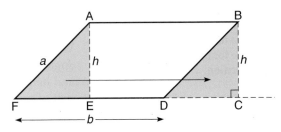

Area of parallelogram ABDF = area of rectangle ABCE
$$= \text{base} \times \text{perpendicular height} = bh.$$

4 *The rhombus*

Make each side *a* units and the vertical height AE *h*.

The result here is the same as for the parallelogram.

The rhombus is a special case of the parallelogram.

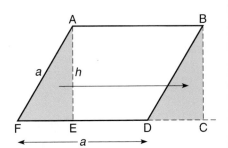

Area of rhombus ABDF = area of rectangle ABCE = *ah*.

5 *The circle*

Imagine a circle divided into a large number of sections – as shown.

If these were cut out and reversed as shown, the area of the circle becomes *almost* the shape of a rectangle.

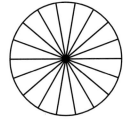

We know the area of a rectangle is length × width.

The length is approximately $\frac{1}{2}$ the circumference on each side, i.e. πr (see Topic 13.2), the width is approximately the radius *r*.

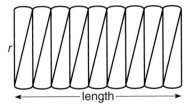

Thus, area is approximately $\pi r \times r = \pi r^2$.

In theory, if an infinite number of sections were taken, we would get a rectangle of exactly length πr and width *r*.

Hence an exact formula is area of circle, $A = \pi r^2$.

When doing a calculation, square *r* first then multiply by π.

6 *The trapezium*

The parallel sides are of length *a* and *b* units. The perpendicular height *h* is the distance between them.

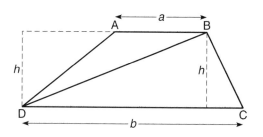

We can see that:

Area of trapezium ABCD
= area of triangle ABD + area of triangle BCD.
= $\frac{1}{2}ah + \frac{1}{2}bh$.

Hence area of trapezium = $\frac{1}{2}(a + b)h$
or (sum of parallel sides) × (perpendicular height divided by 2).

Worked Examples

Find the areas of the following shapes:

1

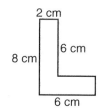

2

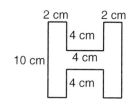

3

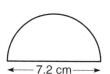

4

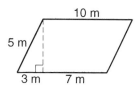

5

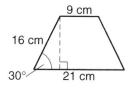

6

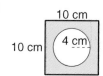

7

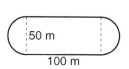

8

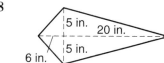

1 We can divide the shape into
   2 rectangles, A and B.

   Area of A = 8 × 2 = 16 cm²
   Area of B = 4 × 2 = 8 cm²
   Total area   = 24 cm²

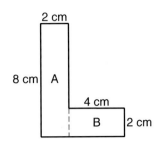

2 Dividing the shape up into
   rectangles, A, B, C,

   Area of A = 10 × 2 = 20 cm²
   Area of B = 10 × 2 = 20 cm²
   Area of C = 4 × 2 = 8 cm²
   Total area   = 48 cm²

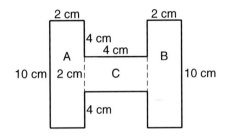

3 This is a semicircle with a diameter of 7.2 cm.

   Hence radius, $r = \dfrac{7.2}{2} = 3.6$ cm

   Area $= \frac{1}{2}$ area of circle $= \frac{1}{2} \times \pi \times 3.6^2$

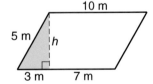

   Using $\pi = 3.14$ we get

   $$A = \frac{3.14 \times 3.6 \times 3.6}{2} \qquad \text{or} \qquad \frac{\pi \times 3.6^2}{2}$$

   $$= 20.35 \text{ cm}^2 \qquad \text{or} \qquad 6.48\pi$$

   Hence $A = 6.48\pi$ or 20.4 cm² (3 sf).

4 We do not know the vertical height
   yet.
   By the triangle shown, and using
   Pythagoras' theorem (see
   Topic 13.5)

   $h^2 + 3^2 = 5^2$
   $h^2 + 9 = 25$
   $\quad\; h^2 = 16$
   i.e. $h = 4$

   Thus perpendicular height = 4 m.

   Hence area of parallelogram = base × height = 10 × 4 = 40 m²

5 Again we do not know the vertical
height.
However, using SOHCAHTOA
from the triangle marked:

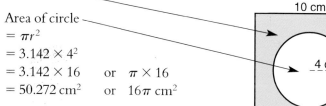

$$\sin 30° = \frac{h}{16} \text{ (see Topic 13.6)}$$

$$0.5 = \frac{h}{16}$$

$$0.5 \times 16 = h$$
$$8 = h$$

i.e. perpendicular height = 8 cm.

Hence, $A = \dfrac{(\text{sum of parallel sides}) \times \text{perpendicular height}}{2}$

$$= \frac{(9 + 21) \times 8}{2} = \frac{30 \times 8}{2} = 120 \text{ cm}^2$$

6 Area of square $= 10^2 = 100 \text{ cm}^2$

Area of circle
$= \pi r^2$
$= 3.142 \times 4^2$
$= 3.142 \times 16$ or $\pi \times 16$
$= 50.272 \text{ cm}^2$ or $16\pi \text{ cm}^2$

Hence required area
$= 100 - 50.272$ or $100 - 16\pi$
$= 49.728$ or $100 - 16\pi \text{ cm}^2$
$= 49.7 \text{ cm}^2$ (3 sf)

7 In this case we have a rectangle
A and the two ends which are
half circles.

Area of A
$= 100 \times 50$
$= 5000 \text{ m}^2$

Radius of circle $= 25$ m

Thus area of half circle
$= \frac{1}{2} \times \pi \times 25^2$

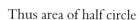

$= \frac{1}{2} \times 3.14 \times 625$
$= 981.25 \text{ m}^2$ or $312.5\pi \text{ m}^2$

Therefore total area $= 5000 + 2 \times 981.25 \text{ m}^2 = 6960 \text{ m}^2$ (3 sf)
              or $5000 + 2 \times 317.5\pi$
                $= 5000 + 625\pi \text{ m}^2$

NOTE
The area of the two half
circles could have been
calculated as the area of a
full circle of radius 25 m.

8   In this case the two left hand
    triangles A can be rearranged to
    form a complete rectangle, as
    shown in the diagrams, as do
    the two triangles B.

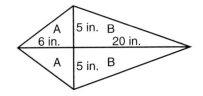

Hence area of 2A
= 5 × 6
= 30 in.²

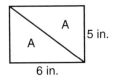

Hence area of 2B
= 5 × 20
= 100 in.²

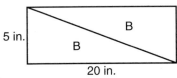

Total area of kite = 130 in.²

PRACTICE 15.3.2   Try these questions with a calculator

Find the areas of the following shapes. Write your answers to questions
17–19, 21 and 22   **i** in terms of π and   **ii** to 3 sf.

1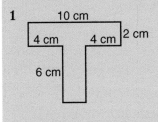

4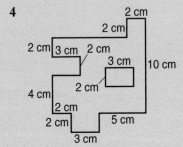

2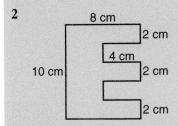

5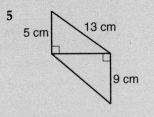

3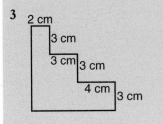

6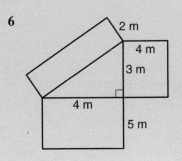

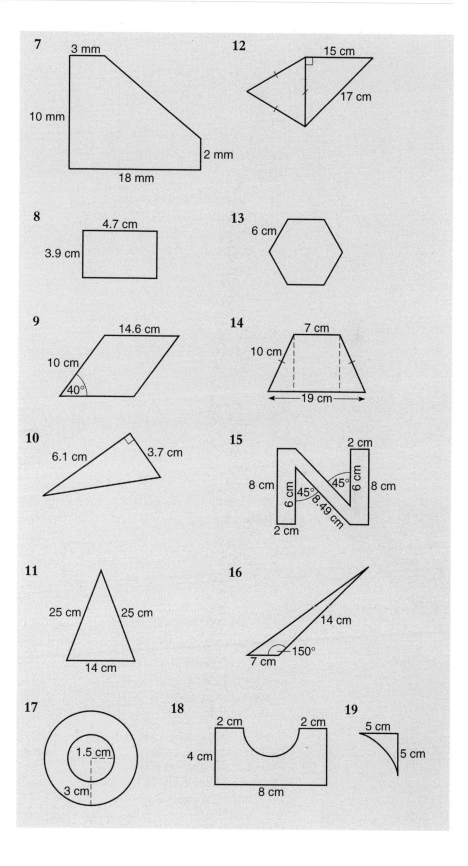

7 3 mm / 10 mm / 18 mm / 2 mm

8 4.7 cm / 3.9 cm

9 14.6 cm / 10 cm / 40°

10 6.1 cm / 3.7 cm

11 25 cm / 25 cm / 14 cm

12 15 cm / 17 cm

13 6 cm

14 7 cm / 10 cm / 19 cm

15 2 cm / 6 cm / 8 cm / 45° / 45° / 8.49 cm / 2 cm / 6 cm / 8 cm

16 14 cm / 7 cm / 150°

17 1.5 cm / 3 cm

18 2 cm / 2 cm / 4 cm / 8 cm

19 5 cm / 5 cm

20 Find the area of the shaded section.

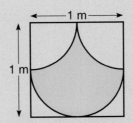

21 The metal head of a garden
implement consists of a sharp
semicircle of diameter 7.5 in.
mounted on the end of a
rectangle 4 in. by 2.5 in.

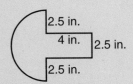

Find the area of the head.

22 The British Kite mark consists of
two semicircles at the top of an
equilateral triangle of side 4 in.
Find the area.

23 Find the area of a regular octagon of side 5 cm.

15.4 VOLUME

Area measures the flat surface inside a plane figure.
Volume measures the total space contained in a three-dimensional figure.

There are several units of volume we often use – all *cubes*:

the cubic centimetre or cm^3
the cubic inch or in^3
the cubic metre or m^3
the cubic foot or ft^3

There are many others, though they are not so common.

Thus, for example, a cuboid,
4 cm by 3 cm by 2 cm will contain
$4 \times 3 \times 2 = 24$ cubes each of side 1 cm.

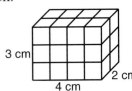

Thus the volume of the cuboid is $24\,cm^3$.

Volumes of figures

Many three-dimensional figures can be put into one of two types:

1 *Shapes with a given cross section*

The general name for any shape with a constant cross section is **prism**. Some prisms have special names:

a The square or rectangular cross section becomes a *cube* (all sides equal) or *cuboid*. The volume of a cuboid is given by $V = lbh$, where l is the length, b the breadth and h the height of the cuboid.
Hence, volume of a cube, $V = l^3$.

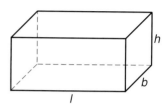

b The circular cross section becomes a cylinder.

If the radius of the circular cross section is r and the height of the cylinder is h, the volume of the cylinder is given by $V = \pi r^2 h$.

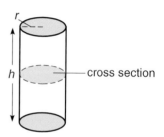

NOTE
You will need to know the formula for the volume of a prism for the examination.

c Other shapes are called prisms, e.g.
triangular prisms

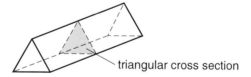

triangular cross section

octagonal prisms

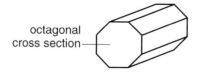

octagonal cross section

and so on …

However, there is an easy way to work out the volume of a prism whatever the shape of the cross section.
  i Work out the area of the cross section,
  ii multiply by the height,
  iii **volume of prism = area of cross section × height**
(We have already seen that this is true for the cuboid and cylinder.)

2 *Shapes which come to a point*

The general name for any shape which comes to a point is **pyramid**. The point is called the **apex**.

There is also a general formula for the volume, i.e.

volume of pyramid $= \frac{1}{3} \times$ base area $\times$ perpendicular height

$$= \frac{1}{3}Ah$$

Again, some pyramids have special names:

a The triangular based pyramid is called a **tetrahedron**.

This comes from a Greek word which means *four faces*.

We can see that the tetrahedron does contain four triangular faces.

b Other shapes are called pyramids e.g. square-based pyramid.

As for the prism, the easy way to work out the volume is:
i work out the area of the base,
ii multiply by the height,
iii divide by 3.

Hence *volume of pyramid* $= \dfrac{\textbf{base area} \times \textbf{perpendicular height}}{\textbf{3}}$

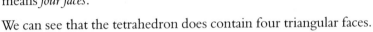

Points to remember:

1 *Perpendicular height* means the distance from the apex vertically down on to the base.

2 *Slant height* means the *slanting distance* up the side of a pyramid (see the cone diagram).

3 In the cone, slant height (l), perpendicular height (h) and base radius (r) are all connected by Pythagoras' theorem.

4 If the apex is vertically above the centre of the base the shape is said to be *right*, i.e. we would have a *right circular cone*, or a *right square pyramid*, etc.

Surface area

The surfaces of most 3-dimensional shapes are usually squares, rectangles, triangles, etc. Therefore the surface area can be found by calculating each face using the formulae from Topic 15.3 and adding them together. However, we do need to be able to calculate the surface area of a cylinder.

Surface area of a cylinder

If the curved surface of a
cylinder is *cut* and opened
up, we get a rectangle. One
side of the rectangle is the
same as the height, h, of the
cylinder.
The other side is the
circumference of the circular
base $2\pi r$. Hence

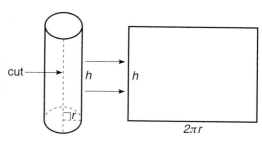

area of the curved surface = area of rectangle
$$= 2\pi rh$$

When calculating the *total* surface of a cylinder, we have to include a circular
base if the cylinder is open, or two circular ends if it is closed.
Hence the total surface area $= 2\pi rh + \pi r^2$ (if one end open) or $2\pi rh + 2\pi r^2$.

Worked Example

A cylindrical water butt, open at the top, is 1.5 m high and has a base of
radius 30 cm. Calculate the area of wood used to make it.
$$A = 2\pi rh + \pi r^2$$
$$= 2 \times 3.14 \times 30 \times 150 + 3.14 \times 30 \times 30$$
$$= 28\,260 + 2826$$
$$= 31\,086 \text{ cm}^2$$

Density

We have all noticed that the same volume of different substances have
different masses. This is because some materials are *denser* than others.

The **density** of a body is the mass of 1 unit volume.

Density is measured in grams per cubic centimetre (g/cm³)
or kg per cubic metre (kg/m³)
or pounds per cubic inch (lb/in³), etc.

There is an easy formula;
if M is the mass, V is the volume and d is the density, then

$$\boldsymbol{M = V \times d} \quad \text{or} \quad \boldsymbol{V = \frac{M}{d}} \quad \text{or} \quad \boldsymbol{d = \frac{M}{V}}$$

For example, if a $\frac{1}{2}$ kg block of a materials takes up 100 cm³ of space, we can say

$$100 \times d = 500$$
$$\text{i.e.} \quad d = 5$$

the density of the material is 5 g/cm³.

Worked Examples

Find the volumes of the following bodies.
Find the surface areas of questions **1–4**.

1

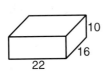

4

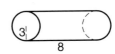

2

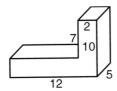

5

3

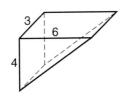

6

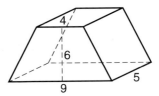

1 For a cuboid $V = 22 \times 16 \times 10$
$$= 3520 \text{ unit}^3$$

Surface area
There are 2 faces each 10×16 giving total area $2 \times 10 \times 16 =$ 320
There are 2 faces each 10×22 giving total area $2 \times 10 \times 22 =$ 440
There are 2 faces each 22×16 giving total area $2 \times 22 \times 16 =$ 704
i.e. total surface area $= \overline{1464}$

2 The shape can be divided into 2 cuboids

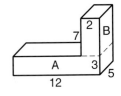

A: $3 \times 12 \times 5 = 180$
B: $7 \times 2 \times 5\ \ = 70$
Total volume $\ \ = 250 \text{ unit}^3$

Surface area
There are 8 rectangular faces altogether:
The front face is made up of 2 rectangles area $10 \times 3 + 10 \times 2 =$ 50
The back face is made up of 2 rectangles area $10 \times 3 + 10 \times 2 =$ 50
The right hand end is a rectangle of area $10 \times 5 =$ 50
The left hand end is a rectangle of area $3 \times 5 =$ 15
The top is a rectangle of area $2 \times 5 =$ 10
The bottom is a rectangle of area $12 \times 5 =$ 60
The horizontal left hand face is a rectangle of area $10 \times 5 =$ 50
The vertical left hand face is a rectangle of area $7 \times 5 = \ \ \underline{35}$
i.e. total surface area $= \overline{320}$

3 For a prism

the cross section is a right-angled triangle

therefore area of cross section $= \frac{1}{2} \times$ base $\times$ height

$$= \frac{1}{2} \times 4 \times 6 = 12$$

volume = cross section $\times$ *height*

$$= 12 \times 3$$

$$= 36 \text{ unit}^3$$

Surface area

There are two rectangular and three triangular faces:

To find the large sloping rectangle we have to use Pythagoras to find the hypotenuse of the large triangle:

Thus (hypotenuse)^2	$6^2 + 4^2 = 36 + 16 = 52$
i.e hypotenuse	$\sqrt{52} = 7.211$
Thus Area of large sloping rectangle	$3 \times 7.211 = 21.63$
Area of small left side rectangle	$3 \times 4 = 12$
Area of top rectangle	$3 \times 6 = 18$
There are 2 triangular faces each of area	$\frac{1}{2} \times 6 = 4 = 12$
(other face)	$= \underline{12}$

i.e. total surface area $= 75.63$

$$= 75.6 \text{ to } 3 \text{ sf}$$

4 For a cylinder,
$$\begin{aligned} \text{volume} &= \text{base area} \times \text{height} \\ &= \pi r^2 h \\ &= 3.14 \times 3^2 \times 8 \\ &= 3.14 \times 9 \times 8 \\ &= 226 \text{ unit}^3 \end{aligned}$$

Surface area

The circular ends each have area $\quad \pi \times 3^2 = 9\pi$ (or 28.28)

The curved surface area $= 2 \times \pi \times 3 \times 8 = 48\pi$ (or 150.8)

Thus, the total surface area $= 2 \times 9\pi + 48\pi = 66\pi$ (or 207 (3 sf))

5 For a rectangular based pyramid, the base area is a rectangle

$$\begin{aligned} \text{area} &= l \times w = 4 \times 6 \\ &= 24 \text{ unit}^2 \\ \text{volume} &= \frac{1}{3} \times \text{base area} \times \text{height} \\ &= \frac{1}{3} \times 24 \times 5 \\ &= 40 \text{ unit}^3 \end{aligned}$$

6 For a prism, with the cross section of a trapezium

$$\text{area of cross section} = \frac{h(a + b)}{2}$$

$$= \frac{6(4 + 9)}{2}$$

$$= \frac{6 \times 13}{2} = 39 \text{ unit}^2$$

$$\text{volume} = \text{cross-sectional area} \times \text{length}$$
$$= 39 \times 5$$
$$= 195 \text{ unit}^3$$

PRACTICE 15.4.1   Try these questions with a calculator

(Take $\pi = 3.14$ or use the π button on your calculator.)

Find the volumes of the following shapes. All dimensions are in cm.

1

4

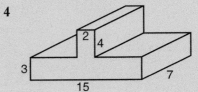

2

5

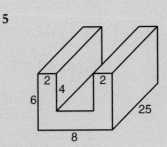

3

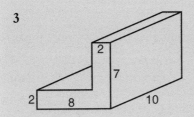

6

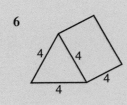

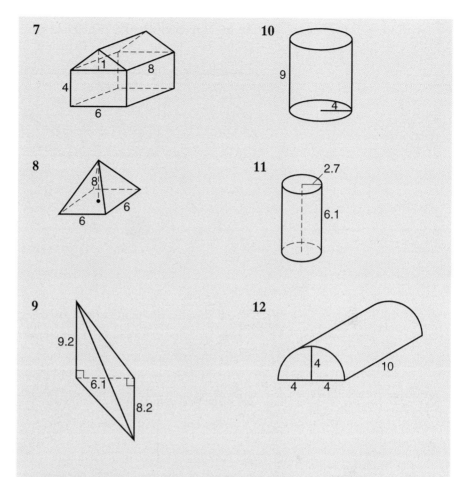

13 A lead cylinder, height 5 cm and base radius 1.5 cm is melted down and recast into a number of lead cubes of side length 1 cm. How many cubes can be made?

14 An iron pipe is 50 cm long and has an outer radius of 1 cm with a central hole of radius 0.5 cm.

    a Find the volume of iron in the pipe.
    b Find the mass of the pipe if the density of iron is 7.86 g/cm^3.

15 Assume the earth is a sphere of radius 3960 miles with mean density 5.53 lb/in^3.

    a Calculate the volume of the earth.
    b Calculate the approximate mass of the earth.
    c The surface area of a sphere is given by the formula $A = 4\pi r^2$. Calculate the surface area of the earth.
    d A rampant virus kills every living thing in its tracks. It can infect 5000 miles^2 of the earth in 1 day. How long will life survive on earth?

16   An unsharpened wooden pencil takes the form of a hexagonal prism.
Each side of the hexagon is 0.15 in. and the pencil is 6 in. long.

The graphite core is a cylinder of radius 0.04 in.

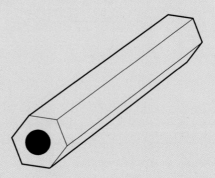

  a   Calculate:
  i   the area of the hexagonal cross section,
  ii   the total volume of the pencil and core,
  iii   the volume of the graphite core,
  iv   the volume of wood used in the pencil.

  b   What percentage of the whole pencil is taken up by the core?

The pencil has a mean density of 0.5 oz/in.^{3}.

  c   Find the mass of the pencil.

  d   How many pencils would there be in a mass of 1 lb?

17   Pam takes a slice out of a slab of butter, as shown in the diagram.

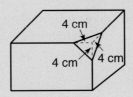

  a   Calculate the volume of the slice removed.

  b   Calculate the volume of butter remaining.

  c   How many *slices* of the same volume could Pam remove before the
butter is used?

Areas and volumes of similar figures

1

2

3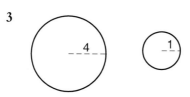

Consider all these pairs of similar figures.

1   Ratio of corresponding lengths in rectangles $= 3 : 1$
2   Ratio of corresponding lengths in triangles $= 6 : 3 = 2 : 1$
3   Ratio of corresponding lengths in circles $= 4 : 1$

Now consider areas:

1   Area of small rectangle $= 1 \times 2 = 2$ unit^2
    Area of large rectangle $= 3 \times 6 = 18$ unit^2
    Ratio of areas $= 18 : 2 = 9 : 1$

2   Area of small triangle $= \frac{1}{2} \times 5 \times 3 = 7.5$ unit^2
    Area of large triangle $= \frac{1}{2} \times 10 \times 6 = 30$ unit^2
    Ratio of areas $= 30 : 7.5 = 4 : 1$

3   Area of small circle $= \pi \times 1^2 = \pi$ unit^2
    Area of large circle $= \pi \times 4^2 = 16\pi$ unit^2
    Ratio of areas $= 16\pi : \pi = 16 : 1$

Hence:

Shape	Ratio of sides	Ratio of area
1 rectangle	3	9
2 triangle	2	4
3 circle	4	16

These results show a general rule for any similar figure:

ratio of areas = (ratio of corresponding sides)^2

A similar result is also true for three-dimensional shapes:

ratio of volumes = (ratio of corresponding sides)^3

Worked Examples

1 The scale drawing of a shape has an area of 126 cm². If the drawing is on a scale of 1 : 50, find the area of the actual shape.

$$\text{Ratio of corresponding lengths} = \frac{50}{1}$$

$$\text{Therefore ratio of areas} \left(\frac{50}{1}\right)^2 = \frac{2500}{1}$$

$$\begin{aligned}\text{Hence actual area} &= 2500 \times 126 \\ &= 315\,000 \text{ cm}^2\end{aligned}$$

2 A metal tray weighs $\frac{1}{2}$ lb. How heavy will a similar tray be, with dimensions twice that of the original?

$$\text{Ratio of corresponding lengths} = \frac{2}{1}$$

$$\text{Therefore ratio of volumes} = \frac{2^3}{1} = \frac{8}{1}$$

$$\text{Hence the weight of the larger tray} = 8 \times \tfrac{1}{2} = 4 \text{ lb}$$

3 A cylindrical container is 10 cm high and contains 400 ml of liquid. How much liquid will a similar container hold 15 cm high?

$$\text{Ratio of corresponding lengths} = \frac{15}{10} = \frac{3}{2}$$

$$\text{Therefore ratio of volumes} \left(\frac{3}{2}\right)^3 = \frac{27}{8}$$

$$\text{Hence larger container will hold } \frac{27}{8} \times 400 = 1350 \text{ ml}$$

4 A rectangular slab 20 cm long weighs 48 kg. How much would a similar slab weigh if it was 15 cm long but was the same thickness?

$$\text{Ratio of corresponding lengths} = \frac{15}{20} = \frac{3}{4}$$

Since the thickness of both slabs is the same the ratio of weights is the same as the ratio of the areas.

$$\text{The ratio of areas} \left(\frac{3}{4}\right)^2 = \frac{9}{16}$$

$$\text{Therefore the weight of the second slab} = \frac{9}{16} \times 48 = 27 \text{ kg}$$

PRACTICE 15.4.2 Try these questions with a calculator

1 On a photograph Hannah height is 9.6 cm and her arm measures 4 cm. Hannah is actually 144 cm tall. How long is her arm?

2 An exact model is made of the same material as a statue. The model is 1 m high and weighs 2.5 kg. The statue is 10 m high. What is its weight?

3 A small jug, 10 cm high, holds 0.3 litre. How much would a similar jug hold if it was 17 cm high?

4 A bar of chocolate costs 95 p. How much would a similar bar cost with dimensions $\frac{3}{4}$ of the original?

5 On a map the scale is 1:10 000. A lake has an area of 2.5 cm^2 on the map. What is the real area of the lake?

6 A cone is 8 in. high and is made of thin metal weighing 10 oz. A similar cone **of the same thickness** weighs 27.44 oz. What is the height of this cone?

7 The area of the base of the smaller cone in question **6** is 4.4 in.^{2}. What is the area of the base of the larger cone?

8 Ruth blows up a balloon until it is spherical with a radius of 12 cm. She continues to blow until it has a radius of 48 cm. What fraction of the original thickness of the rubber is the new thickness?

9 The traffic police notice that it takes a motorist 3 seconds to completely fill a breathalyser bag. How long would it take the same motorist, blowing at the same rate, to fill a similar bag twice as big?

15.5 DIMENSIONS

All the formulae for perimeters, areas and volumes have **dimensions**. The dimension of a formula is the *power* to which the unit of length is raised.

1 All **perimeters** are of the *first dimension,* i.e. the power is 1.

For example, the perimeter of an equilateral triangle of side x units is $3x$ units, i.e. 3 times x to the *power 1.*

For a rectangle of length x units and width y units, it is $2x + 2y$ units, *both* terms are raised to the *power 1.*

Thus *all formulae for lengths must be of the first dimension.*

2 All **areas** are of the *second dimension*, i.e. the power is 2.

For example, $A = x^2$, for a square of side x units (x to the *power 2*)

$A = \pi r^2$, for a circle (r to the *power 2*)

A = lw, for a rectangle (*lw* means $l \times w$ which is
(a length) $\times$ (a length) so has a *total power 2*)

Thus *all formulae for areas must be of the second dimension.*

3 All **volumes** are of the *third dimension*, i.e. the power is 3.

For example, $V = x^3$, for a cube of side x units (x to the *power 3*)

$V = \frac{4}{3}\pi r^3$, for a sphere (r to the *power 3*)

$V = \pi r^2 h$, for a cylinder ($r^2 h$ means $r^2 \times h$ which is
(a length)$^2 \times$ (a length) so has a *total power 3*)

$V = lwh$, for a cuboid (i.e. (a length) $\times$ (a length) $\times$ (a length)
so has a *total power 3*)

Thus *all formulae for volumes must be of the third dimension.*

The constants in the formulae, like 2, $\frac{4}{3}$, etc. have no dimensions. They are said to be *dimensionless*.

Worked Examples

a, b and c are different lengths.
State whether the following formulae could represent lengths, areas or volumes.

1 $3ab$ **2** $4a + 3b + 2c$ **3** $5a + 4a^2$ **4** $6a^2 b$ **5** $\dfrac{6a^2 b}{c}$

1 This is of dimension 2. The formula could represent an area.

2 This is of dimension 1. The formula could represent a length.

3 The first term is dimension 1, the second is dimension 2. This formula has mixed dimensions so could not represent any physical quantity.

4 $a^2 b$ is of dimension 3. The formula could represent a volume.

5 $a^2 b$ is of dimension 3. c is of dimension 1. We can **cancel** dimensions like fractions, so $\dfrac{(\text{length})^3}{\text{length}} = (\text{length})^2$. Thus $\dfrac{6a^2 b}{c}$ could represent an area.

PRACTICE 15.5.1

a, b and c are different lengths.
State whether each of the following formulae could represent a length, an area, a volume, or none of these.

1 $2ab$

2 $3a + 2b + 4c$

3 $4a + b^2$

4 abc

5 $5a^2c$

6 $b^2 + c^3$

7 $2a(b + c)$

8 $3a + 4$

9 $a - b$

10 $\frac{1}{2}b^2c + \frac{1}{4}a^3$

11 $8c(2a^2 + bc)$

12 $\frac{1}{3}\pi a^2c$

13 $\frac{4}{3}\pi b^3$

14 $2(ab + bc + ca)$

15 $2(a + b)$

16 $\dfrac{4a}{b}$

17 $\dfrac{4ab}{c}$

18 $\dfrac{2a(b + 3c)}{c}$

19 $\dfrac{2a(b + 3)}{c}$

20 Sian thinks that $\frac{4}{3}\pi r^2$ is the volume of a sphere. Explain why she could not possibly be right.

21 State whether the following measurements are of dimensions 1, 2 or 3.
   a The distance from Birmingham to Bilbao
   b The volume of the Channel Tunnel
   c The area of the Oval Cricket Ground
   d The radius of a circle
   e A pint of beer
   f A hectare
   g The number of people watching Manchester United last Saturday
   h A DVD
   i The perimeter of a parallelogram
   j The surface of a photograph
   k The number of books in the British Museum

22 Find the numbers that the $\star$ represents in each of the following formulas:

   a Length $= 4r\star$
   b Volume $= 7ab\star$
   c Area $= 125d\star$
   d Area $= 3(x\star + yz)$
   e Volume $= 2(a + b + c)\star$

   f Length $= \dfrac{5abc}{d\star}$
   g Volume $= 8(e\star + f\star g)$
   h Area $= 2(p\star - qr\star)$
   i Area $= \dfrac{2(p\star - qr\star)}{s}$

Perimeter

The *perimeter* is the distance around the edge of a shape.
The perimeter of a circle is called the circumference.

Area

An *area* measures the amount of space inside a plane shape.
An area is measured in square units.
1 square cm is written $1\,\text{cm}^2$.
There are other units of area: mm^2, m^2, in.^2, ft^2, yd^2, etc.
In metric measure 1 hectare (1 ha) $= 10\,000\,\text{m}^2$.
In imperial measure 1 acre $= 4840\,\text{yd}^2$.
When calculating or measuring areas, we must use the appropriate unit.

Estimating areas

If a figure has curved sides, divide it up into small squares of known area and count them.
Where there is less than a half a full square at the edge of the shape, do not count it. Where there is more than half a full square, count it as one full square.

The rectangle

The area, A, of a rectangle is given by the formula, $A = lw$.
A square is a special case where all sides are of length l. Hence $A = l^2$.

The triangle

Area of a triangle $= \frac{1}{2}bh$, where b is the length of the base and h the perpendicular height down on to this base.
The base need not necessarily be the *bottom* of the triangle.
If the triangle is obtuse-angled the height is the length of the perpendicular to the base produced.

The parallelogram

Area of a parallelogram $=$ base $\times$ perpendicular height $= bh$.

The rhombus

Area of a rhombus $= ah$, where $a =$ the length of a side and $h =$ the perpendicular height.

The circle

Area of a circle $= \pi r^2$, where r is the radius.
When doing a calculation, square r first, then multiply by π.

The trapezium

Area of a trapezium $= \frac{1}{2}(a + b)h$
or (sum of parallel sides) $\times$ (perpendicular height divided by 2).

Volume

Volume measures the total space contained in a 3-dimensional figure.
There are several basic units of volume:

- the cubic centimetre or cm^3,

- the cubic inch or in.^{3},

- the cubic metre or m^3,

- the cubic foot or ft^3.

Volumes of figures

Many three-dimensional figures can be put into one of two types:

1 *Shapes with given cross section*

The general name for any shape with a constant cross section is *prism*.

Some prisms have special names:

The square or rectangular cross section becomes a *cube* (all sides equal) or
cuboid.
The volume of a cuboid is $V = lwh$
(l is the length, w the width, h the height).
$V = l^3$ for a cube of side l.
The circular cross section becomes a *cylinder*.
The volume of a cylinder is $V = \pi r^2 h$.
There is an easy way to work out the volume of a prism , whatever the
shape of the cross section:

a work out the area of the cross section,

b multiply by the height,

c volume of prism $=$ area of cross section $\times$ length.

2 *Shapes which come to a point*

The general name for any shape which comes to a point is *pyramid*.
The point is called the *apex*.
There is a general formula for the volume:

volume of a pyramid $= \frac{1}{3} \times$ base area $\times$ perpendicular height

$$= \frac{1}{3}Ah$$

Some pyramids have special names:

The circular based pyramid is called a *cone*,
hence, volume of a cone, $V = \frac{1}{3}\pi r^2 h$.

The triangular based pyramid is called a *tetrahedron*.
Other shapes are just called *pyramids* e.g. square, or rectangular, based pyramid.

There is an easy way to work out the volume:

a work out the area of the base,
b multiply by the height,
c divide by 3.

Volume of pyramid = base area × perpendicular height ÷ 3.

Perpendicular height is the distance from the apex vertically down on to the base.
Slant height is the slanting distance up the side of a pyramid.
In the cone, slant height (*l*), perpendicular height (*h*) and base radius (*r*) are all connected by Pythagoras' theorem.
If the apex is vertically above the centre of the base the shape is said to be *right*, i.e. we would have a *right circular cone*, or a *right square pyramid*, etc.

Surface area of a cylinder

Area of the curved surface $= 2\pi rh$.
When calculating the *total surface* area of a cylinder, we have to include a circular base if the cylinder is open, or two circular ends if it is closed.
Total surface area of a cylinder $= 2\pi rh + \pi r^2$ (if one end open) or $2\pi rh + 2\pi r^2$.

Density

The *density* of a body is the mass of 1 unit volume.
Density is measured in grams per cubic centimetre (g/cm^3) or kg per cubic metre (kg/m^3) or pounds per cubic inch (lb/in.^{3}), etc.
If M is the mass, V is the volume and d is the density, then

$$M = V \times d \quad \text{or} \quad V = \frac{M}{d} \quad \text{or} \quad d = \frac{M}{V}$$

Areas and volumes of similar figures

Ratio of areas = (ratio of corresponding sides)^2.
Ratio of volumes = (ratio of corresponding sides)^3.

Dimensions

All the formulae for perimeters, areas and volumes have *dimensions*.
The dimension of a formula is the power to which the unit of length is raised.
All formulae for lengths are of the first dimension i.e. the power is 1.
All formulae for areas are of the second dimension i.e. the power is 2.
All formulae for volumes are of the third dimension i.e. the power is 3.

NOTE

More past papers can be found at www.aqa.org.uk.

The final module (module 5) is assessed through two 75 minute papers comprising Paper 1 – without a calculator and Paper 2 – with a calculator. The following (Intermediate tier) sample papers should be tackled under timed examination-type conditions. Allow 45 minutes per paper for your first attempt. Answer as many questions as you can in the time available and check your answers with those given at the back of the book – no cheating!

When you have marked your work you can revisit those topics where you have not done so well and practise further questions from the specimen papers or else from past papers available from your tutor or the examination board.

Good luck.

CHAPTER 16
Sample exam papers

16.1
WITHOUT A CALCULATOR

Module 5 – Terminal

You may need to use the following formulae.

Area of trapezium $= \frac{1}{2}(a + b)h$

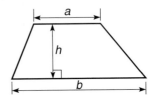

Volume of prism = area of cross section × length

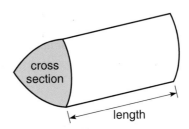

1 Janine says to her friends

'Think of a number, add 7, then divide by 2.
Tell me your answer.'

a Terry thinks of the number 5.
What is his answer?   *(1 mark)*

b Amanda says her answer is 12.
What number did she start with?   *(2 marks)*

2 a Complete the table of values and use it to draw the graph of $y = 8 - 2x$.

x	-1	0	1	2	3
y					

(3 marks)

The graph of $y = 3x - 4$ has been drawn for you.

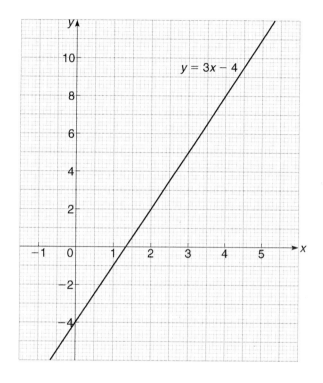

b Write down the coordinates of the point of intersection of $y = 8 - 2x$ and $y = 3x - 4$.   *(1 mark)*

3 The diagram shows triangle ABC with AB = BC.

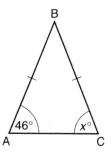

Work out the value of x. Give a reason for your answer.   *(2 marks)*

4 Two-fifths of the area of this shape is shaded. Calculate the area of the
shaded part.

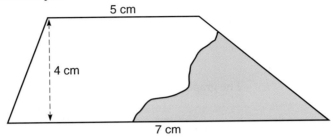

(3 marks)

5 A sequence of numbers begins

        2,   5,   8,   11,   …

   a Write down the next number in this sequence.   (1 mark)
   b Work out the 10th number in this sequence.   (1 mark)
   c Find the *n*th number of this sequence.   (2 marks)

6 A stopwatch records times to the nearest 0.1 second.
   The time taken for Duncan to swim 100 metres is recorded as 88.5
   seconds.
   What are the maximum and minimum times that Duncan could
   have taken?   (2 marks)

7 Calculate the circumference of a circle with radius 7 cm.
   Give your answer in terms of π.   (2 marks)

8 The diagram shows three triangles P, Q and R.

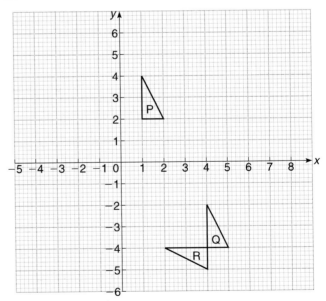

   a Describe fully the single transformation which maps triangle
       P onto triangle Q.   (2 marks)
   b Describe fully the single transformation which maps triangle
       Q onto triangle R.   (2 marks)

9 Solve these equations.

  a $\frac{1}{3}x + 2 = 9$ *(2 marks)*

  b $3(x - 3) = 2(x - 3)$ *(2 marks)*

  c $x^2 - 2x = 8$ *(3 marks)*

10 Tony is writing down some formulae for some shapes.
  The letters a, b and c represent lengths.

$$a + b + c, \quad \tfrac{1}{3}\pi a^2 b, \quad \pi a(b + c), \quad \sqrt{b^2 + c^2}, \quad 2\pi ab, \quad \pi(2a + b^2), \quad \pi c\sqrt{a^2 + b^2}$$

  Which of these formulae could represent area?   *(2 marks)*

11 In the diagram below, the chords PQ and RS are perpendicular.
  Angle QPS = 40°.

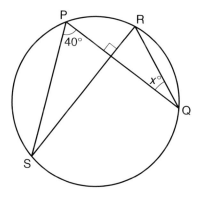

  Calculate the value of x.

  You must give a reason for your answer.   *(3 marks)*

12 a The sum of two numbers is 5.

   The product of these numbers is 9.

   If one of the numbers is x, show that

$$x^2 - 5x + 9 = 0$$ *(3 marks)*

  b Solve the equation

$$(x - 3)(x + 2) = 0$$ *(1 mark)*

16.2 WITH A CALCULATOR

Module 5 – Terminal

You may need to use the following formulae.

Area of trapezium $= \frac{1}{2}(a + b)h$

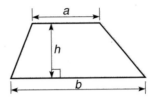

Volume of prism = area of cross section $\times$ length

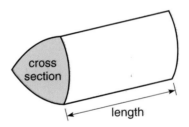

1 ABCD is a quadrilateral.

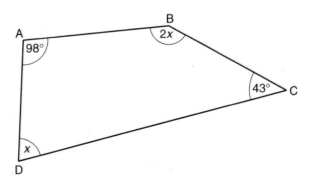

Work out the value of x.   *(4 marks)*

2 The diagram shows a solid.

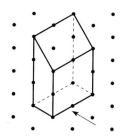

On the grid below, draw the elevation of this solid from the direction shown by the arrow.

(2 marks)

3 Rachael receives two boxes.

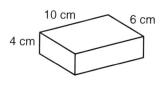 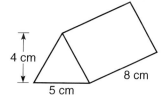

Calculate the difference between the volumes of the two boxes. State your units.

(5 marks)

4 a Work out the value of $\dfrac{1}{(0.5)^2}$.   *(2 marks)*

   b If $x = 12$ and $y = -5$ find the value of

     i $5x - y$,   *(2 marks)*

     ii xy,   *(2 marks)*

     iii $\dfrac{x}{x + 3y}$.   *(2 marks)*

5 The grid shows the numbers from 1 to 50.

1	2	3	4	5	6	7	8	9	10
11	12	13	14	15	16	17	18	19	20
21	22	23	24	25	26	27	28	29	30
31	32	33	34	35	36	37	38	39	40
41	42	43	44	45	46	47	48	49	50

A **T** shape has been drawn on the grid. It is called T_{13} because the first number is 13. The sum of the numbers in T_{13} is $13 + 14 + 15 + 24 = 66$.

a The diagram shows T_n with three numbers missing.
   Complete the **T** shape in terms of n.   *(2 marks)*

b Find the sum of the numbers in T_n in terms of n.
   Give your answers in its simplest form.   *(2 marks)*

c Explain why you cannot find a value for n in which $T_n = 115$.   *(2 marks)*

6 Paresh is using trial and improvement to find a solution to the equation,

$$x^3 - x = 39$$

This table shows his first two trials.

x	$x^3 - x$	**Comment**
3	24	Too small
4	60	Too large

Continue the table to find a solution to the equation.

Give your answer correct to **1 decimal place**.   *(3 marks)*

7 a Solve this inequality

$$3x - 7 \leqslant 14$$

(2 marks)

b Multiply out and simplify

$$(x - 9)^2 - 9$$

(2 marks)

c Simplify

$$3x^4 \times 4x^5$$

(2 marks)

8 In the diagram PQR and TS are parallel.
TOQ is a diameter of the circle, centre O.
Angle OTS = 36°.

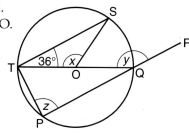

a Find the size of

   i angle x, *(2 marks)*

   ii angle y. *(2 marks)*

b Write down the size of angle z.
Give a reason for your answer. *(2 marks)*

ANSWERS

Chapter 1

Practice 1.1.1 – p. 3

1 a quantitative **d** quantitative **g** qualitative
b qualitative **e** quantitative **h** quantitative
c qualitative **f** quantitative **i** qualitative

2 a continuous **d** continuous **g** discrete
b continuous **e** discrete **h** continuous
c discrete **f** discrete

Practice 1.2.1 – p. 9

1 a give each student a unique number and choose numbers randomly using random number tables or else a computer
b ensure that the sample is representative of the population as a whole by considering such factors as gender, type of course, age of student, etc.

2 depending on the sample size you might choose every nth name from the electoral roll

3 a the sample is restricted to shoppers only or shoppers at that particular store (the question doesn't say which food store)
b the sample is restricted to surnames beginning with M
c the sample is restricted to telephone owners and would not include those without a telephone or those who are ex-directory

4 people using a bus to get to work would probably have left already, the sample size is very small and the sample is restricted to telephone owners and would not include those without a telephone or those who are ex-directory

5 a the sample is restricted to men. Cambridge may not be representative of the country as a whole and 500 is quite a small sample in view of the population size
b include men and women over 18 in the sample, sample a variety of different locations and increase the sample size

6 a the sample is not truly representative of the populations since the population of Marchwoode will be over represented by the chosen sample
b Little Whitton 140; Marchwoode 40; Newtonabbey 120

Practice 1.3.1 – p. 11

1 questions should not be personal or offensive
2 to ascertain likely problems, highlight areas needing further clarification and improve questionnaire design

3 a the question would be very difficult to answer accurately
b the question is not relevant to the survey
c the question is badly composed and doesn't make sense

4 a the question is biased as it expresses a view; alternative question: 'What do you think about our fruit juice?'
b the question is too personal and might not be answered; alternative question:
Tick your annual income:
£0–£4999 ☐ £10 000–£19 999 ☐
£5000–£9999 ☐ £20 000+ ☐
c the question is badly composed and doesn't make sense; alternative question: 'Do you agree with a new bypass?'

d the question is biased as it expresses a view; alternative question: 'How many cigarettes do you smoke a day?'
e the question is badly composed and doesn't make sense; alternative question: 'Do you prefer a non-smoking area? Yes ☐ No ☐'
f the question is too personal and would be difficult to ask in a non-personal way

5 no instructions are given, the period of time is not specified (per week, per month, …?) and not all of the amounts are covered (what about £10.50?)

6 any suitable questionnaire

Practice 1.4.1 – p. 14

1

4	II 2
5	III 3
6	IIII 4
7	ⅢⅠ 6
8	ⅢⅠ 6
9	ⅢⅠ 6
10	I 3
	30

3

blue	ⅢⅢ III	13
green	ⅢⅠ	6
red	ⅢⅢ	10
white	ⅢⅡ	7
yellow	IIII	4
		40

2

cash	ⅢⅢⅢⅢ III	18
cheque	ⅢⅢ II	12
switch	ⅢⅡ	7
storecard	Ⅲ	5
visa	ⅢⅢ	8
		50

4

bus	ⅢⅢ I	11
train	ⅢⅢⅢ	15
walk	ⅢⅢⅢⅢ	20
cycle	ⅢⅢ	9
car	Ⅲ	5
		60

Practice 1.4.2 – p. 17

1

0–4	III	3
5–9	ⅢⅡ	7
10–14	ⅢⅠ	6
15–19	Ⅲ	5
20–24	IIII	4
25–29	II	2
		27

2

3.00 up to but not including 3.05	I	1
3.05 up to but not including 3.10	Ⅲ	5
3.10 up to but not including 3.15	Ⅲ III	8
3.15 up to but not including 3.20	ⅢⅠ	6
3.20 up to but not including 3.25	II	2
		22

The group frequencies may alter if 3.05, 3.10, 3.15, … etc. are included in the previous intervals

3

wages	tally	freq.
£25 000–29 999	ⅢⅡ	7
£30 000–34 999	ⅢⅢ	10
£35 000–39 999	ⅢⅢ IIII	14
£40 000–44 999	ⅢⅢ	8
£45 000–49 999	ⅢⅠ	6
£50 000–54 999	IIII	4
£55 000–59 999	I	1
		50

4

time (mins)	tally	freq.
$10 \leqslant t < 15$	II	2
$15 \leqslant t < 20$	III	3
$20 \leqslant t < 25$	ⅢⅢ	10
$25 \leqslant t < 30$	ⅢⅢ	8
$30 \leqslant t < 35$	IIII	4
$35 \leqslant t < 40$	ⅢⅡ	7
$40 \leqslant t < 45$	IIII	4
$45 \leqslant t < 50$	II	2
		40

Practice 1.5.1 – p. 20

1

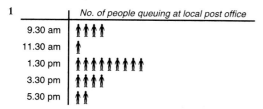

No. of people queuing at local post office

| 9.30 am |
| 11.30 am |
| 1.30 pm |
| 3.30 pm |
| 5.30 pm |

2

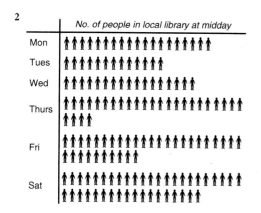

No. of people in local library at midday

Mon, Tues, Wed, Thurs, Fri, Sat

3

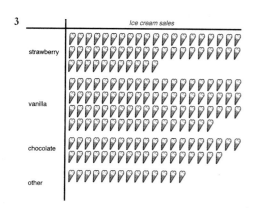

Ice cream sales

strawberry, vanilla, chocolate, other

4

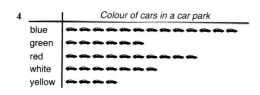

Colour of cars in a car park

blue, green, red, white, yellow

5

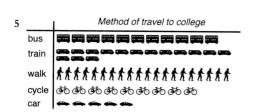

Method of travel to college

bus, train, walk, cycle, car

Practice 1.5.2 – p. 25

1

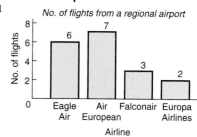

No. of flights from a regional airport

2

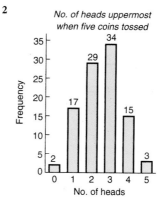

No. of heads uppermost when five coins tossed

3

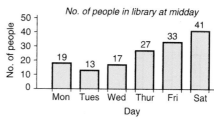

No. of people in library at midday

4

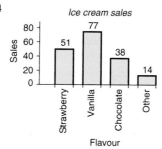

Ice cream sales

5

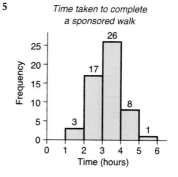

Time taken to complete a sponsored walk

6

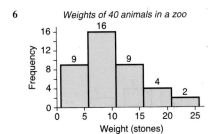

Weights of 40 animals in a zoo

7

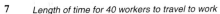
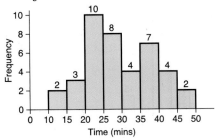

Length of time for 40 workers to travel to work

8

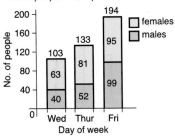

No. of people in a department store

9 a

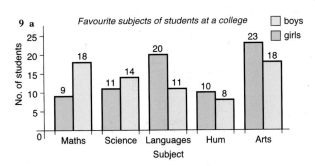

Favourite subjects of students at a college

b

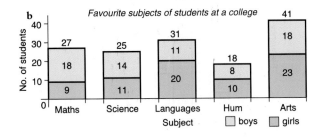

Favourite subjects of students at a college

10 a

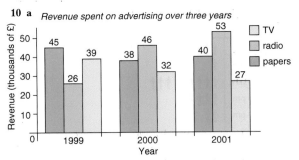

Revenue spent on advertising over three years

b

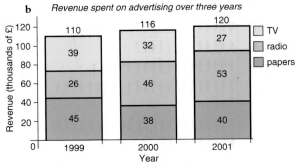

Revenue spent on advertising over three years

11 a day 1 = 83 vehicles, day 2 = 94 vehicles
 b 14 lorries   **c** 16 buses

Practice 1.5.3 – p. 30

1 Average hours of sunshine   5 | 6 means 5.6

8	1
7	2 2 2 5 6 8 9
6	1 6 6 7 7 8 8 8 8
5	0 1 4
4	2 3 6 7 8
3	3 5 5 6 9
2	4 5 9 9 9

2 Number of accidents   2 | 3 means 23

2	2 2 3 4 7 9
1	3 3 5 6 9 9

3 Gestation times   5 | 6 means 56

7	9
6	1 1 3 3 3
5	5
4	2 2 4
3	0 0
2	2 9
1	2 3 4 6 9

4 CD track times   3.1 | 6 means 3 min 16 secs

3.5	0 5
3.4	3
3.3	0 0 3 4 4 5
3.2	1 2
3.1	9 9
3.0	0 7
2.5	4 4 4 5 7 7
2.4	3 4 4 5 9
2.3	
2.2	2 2 4 5 5 5 9
2.1	0 0
2.0	8

Practice 1.5.4 – p. 33

1

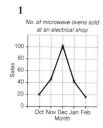

2

3

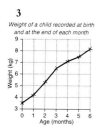

4

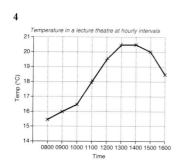

  a approx. 1230

  b approx. 20.25 °C

    (the answers are estimates as the line graph presumes that the temperature rises and falls uniformly between each hourly reading)

5 a 10

  b 38

  c 16

  d the answer is only an approximation as we are presuming that the graph continues uniformly between the hourly intervals

  e 38

Practice 1.5.5a – p. 37

1 Survey of favourite pets: Cat 100°, Dog 130°, Rabbit 60°, Bird 30°, Fish 40°.

2 Types of ticket sold on the Eurostar service to Paris: Business 184°, Pass holder 24°, Senior 48°, Child 34°, Leisure First 70°.

3 Ice cream sales: Strawberry 102°, Vanilla 154°, Choc 76°, Other 28°.

4 No. of flights from regional airport: Europa 40°, Falconair 60°, Air European 140°, Eagle Air 120°.

5 No. of heads uppermost when 5 coins are tossed: none 7°, one 61°, two 104°, three 122°, four 54°, five 11°.

Practice 1.5.5b – p. 38

1 Types of properties advertised in an estate agent's window: Semi-detached 76.5°, Flat 90°, Terraced 81°, Detached 63°, Bungalow 49.5°.

2 How 50 people paid for their goods: Visa 58°, Cash 130°, Cheque 86°, Switch 50°, Storecard 36°.

3 Number of people in local library at midday: Mon 46°, Tues 31°, Wed 41°, Thurs 65°, Fri 79°, Sat 98°.

4 a 12

  b 84°

  c Lost 84°, Won 144°, Drawn 132°

5 a car

  b 30%

  c 30% of 200 = 60

  d cycling

  e 180

  f 70

Practice 1.5.6 – p. 41

1

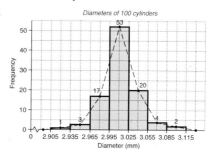

2

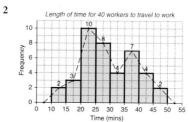

3

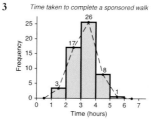

4

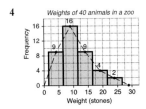

Weights of 40 animals in a zoo

2

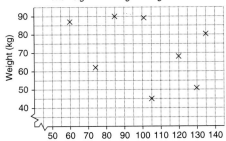

The height and weight of eight students

No correlation, so no line of best fit

Practice 1.5.7 – p. 43

1

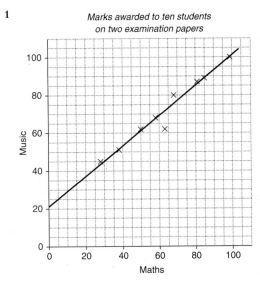

Marks awarded to ten students on two examination papers

3

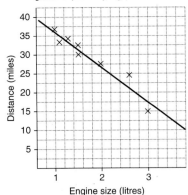

Engine size and distance travelled on one gallon of petrol by eight different cars

a   24 miles (accept 23 and 25)   **b** $12\frac{1}{2}$ miles
the estimate in **b** is not so reliable as the estimate in **a** because we are making presumptions about the relationship between engine size and distance travelled outside the scope of the information given in the question

Chapter 2

Practice 2.2.1 – p. 52

1 a   6   **c**   33 and 35   **e**   −1
   b   2   **d**   12.3 and 13.5
2 white
3 a   4 items   **b**   7   **c**   0 credit cards
4 21
5 7
6 2.5–3.5

Practice 2.2.2 – p. 55

1 a   6   **d** $101\frac{1}{2}$ **g**   −2
   b   5   **e**   6
   c $5\frac{1}{2}$ **f** $6\left(\dfrac{5+7}{2}\right)$
2 $5\frac{1}{2}$
3 19

Practice 2.2.3 – p. 57

1 a   7   **d** $10\frac{1}{2}$ **g**   3.05
   b   6   **e** $20\frac{1}{2}$ **h**   305
   c   10   **f** $30\frac{1}{2}$ **i**   −305

Practice 2.2.4 – p. 58

1 $\Sigma fx = 102$; $\Sigma f = 24$; mean = 4.25
2 mean = 240 ÷ 15 = 16 p
3 $\Sigma fx = 1414$; $\Sigma f = 80$; mean = 17.7 (3sf)
4 $\Sigma fx = 530$; $\Sigma f = 30$; mean = 17.7 (3sf)

Practice 2.2.5 – p. 61

1 $\Sigma fx = 730$; $\Sigma f = 32$; mean = 22.8 mm (3sf)
2 $\Sigma fx = 2235$; $\Sigma f = 75$; mean = £29.80
3 $\Sigma fx = 703.5$; $\Sigma f = 337$; mean = 2.09 mins (3sf)
4 $\Sigma fx = 4680$; mean = 62 kg (to an appropriate degree of accuracy)
5 $\Sigma fx = 2217$; $\Sigma f = 58$; mean = 38.2 mins

Practice 2.2.6 – p. 62

		mode	median	mean
1	**a**	4	3	3
	b	6	$5\frac{1}{2}$	5
	c	7	4	4.5
	d	2	$3\frac{1}{2}$	4
	e	no mode	$5\frac{1}{2}$	$5\frac{1}{2}$
	f	no mode	$15\frac{1}{2}$	$15\frac{1}{2}$
	g	−1	$-\frac{1}{2}$	−0.125

2 a 16 **b** 12 **c** 11 **d** 46 **e** 1

f using

brothers	0	1	2	3	4	5
freq.	15	12	11	6	3	1

mean = $\frac{69}{46} = \frac{3}{2}$ = 1.5 (3sf)

3 a i 25.9 **ii** 27.5 **iii** 28

b i the mean increases to 26.2

ii the median is not affected

iii the modal mark is not affected

4 the median gives the best measure as the mean will be affected by extreme values (£119 500) and the mode is inappropriate for such small numbers

Practice 2.3.1 – p. 66

1 a

Value	Average
2	
4	3.67
5	3.67
2	3.33
3	3.67
6	5.67
8	6

b

Value	Average
203	
215	
	203.5
206	
	201.5
190	
	200.25
195	
	199.25
210	
	197.25
202	
	196
182	
	193.5
190	
200	

c

Value	Average
55	
57	
62	58.4
60	58.8
58	59.4
57	61
60	62.2
70	63.2
66	63.8
63	64.6
60	64.8
64	65.2
71	65.6
68	
65	

2

Value	Average
55	
52	54.33
56	52.33
49	49.67
44	46.67
47	45.67
46	47
48	48.33
51	49.33
49	50
50	51.33
55	

3

		Value	6 pt avge	12 pt avge			Value	6 pt avge	12 pt avge
Year 1	Jan	210.00			Year 2	Jan	200.00	176.83	147.00
	Feb	204.00				Feb	190.00	168.83	149.08
	Mar	165.00	157.50			Mar	158.00	154.67	148.83
	Apr	144.00	134.50			Apr	140.00	138.67	149.42
	May	126.00	109.00			May	130.00	119.67	149.83
	Jun	96.00	107.00	145.75		Jun	110.00	118.33	150.17
	Jul	72.00	108.83	144.92		Jul	104.00	122.00	
	Aug	51.00	117.50	143.75		Aug	76.00	130.83	
	Sep	153.00	134.00	143.17		Sep	150.00	145.67	
	Oct	155.00	155.33	142.83		Oct	162.00		
	Nov	178.00	178.50	143.17		Nov	183.00		
	Dec	195.00	179.33	144.33		Dec	199.00		

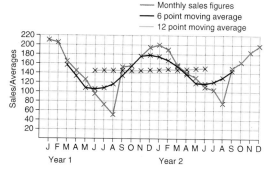

— Monthly sales figures
— 6 point moving average
— 12 point moving average

i The sales are in steady decrease; the 6 point moving average (half yearly trend) shows a steady decrease; the 12 point moving average (yearly trend) shows a fairly steady increase.

ii The sales are in steady decrease; the 6 point moving average (half yearly trend) shows a steady increase; the 12 point moving average (yearly trend) cannot be viewed until two more months are completed.

4

		Value	6 pt avge			Value	6 pt avge
Week 1	Mon	248		Week 3	Mon	225	288
	Tues	253			Tues	247	291
	Wed	305	304		Wed	298	293
	Thu	241	298		Thu	234	300
	Fri	356	294		Fri	342	305
	Sat	422	290		Sat	412	309
Week 2	Mon	209	286	Week 4	Mon	266	318
	Tues	233	281		Tues	278	326
	Wed	277	277		Wed	321	330
	Thu	220	280		Thu	288	
	Fri	326	282		Fri	389	
	Sat	397	286		Sat	440	

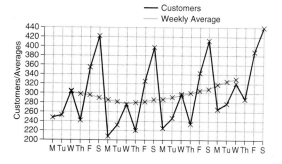

— Customers
— Weekly Average

The most suitable moving average is the weekly (6 point) one. It shows a gradual decrease in attendances over the first week and a half and then a steadily rising one after that.

Practice 2.4.1 – p. 68

1 a   16
   b   16
   c   11 cm
   d   6.9 km

   e   16
   f   8.9
   g $\frac{62}{80} = \frac{31}{40}$

Practice 2.4.2 – p. 74

1

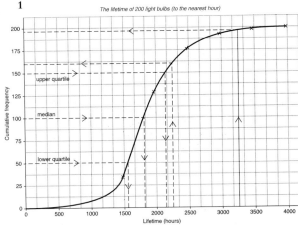

The lifetime of 200 light bulbs (to the nearest hour)

   a   161
   b   34
   c   5
   d   median = 1800 hours
   e   interquartile range = 2133 − 1550 = 583 hours

2

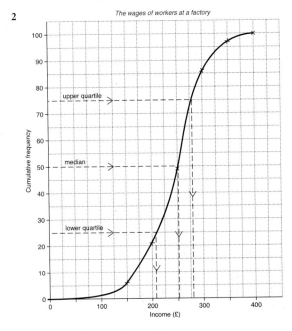

The wages of workers at a factory

   a   £253
   b   £280 − £208 = £72

3

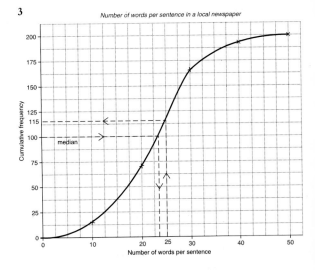

Number of words per sentence in a local newspaper

   a   23.5

   b $\frac{200 - 115}{200} \times 100\% = 42.5\%$

4

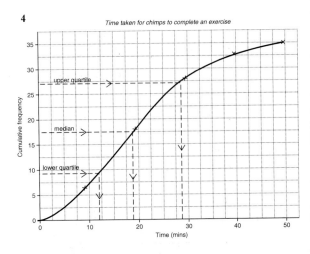

Time taken for chimps to complete an exercise

   a   median = 19 mins; interquartile range = 29 − 12 = 17 mins
   b   as the interquartile range for this class is bigger than in **a**, then the spread of the time taken to complete the exercise is bigger

5

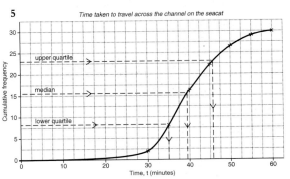

Time taken to travel across the channel on the seacat

median = 39.5 mins; interquartile range = 46 − 35 = 11 mins

Practice 2.4.3 – p. 77

1 a i Ordering the data we obtain:

$$4 \quad 6 \quad 6 \quad 8 \quad 11 \quad 13 \quad 15$$

Hence the range = $15 - 4 = 11$

$$Q_1 = \frac{(7+1)\text{th observation}}{4} \quad \text{i.e. 2nd observation} = 6$$

$$Q_2 = \frac{(7+1)\text{th observation}}{2} \quad \text{i.e. 4th observation} = 8$$

$$Q_3 = \frac{3(7+1)\text{th observation}}{4} \quad \text{i.e. 6th observation} = 13$$

The interquartile range is $Q_3 - Q_1 = 13 - 6 = 7$

The box plot is as shown below:

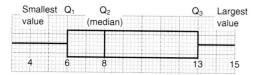

ii Ordering the data we obtain:

$$-2.4 \quad -0.6 \quad 0.8 \quad 2.1 \quad 3.4 \quad 5.7 \quad 6.5$$

Hence the range = $6.5 - (-2.4) = 8.9$

$$Q_1 = \frac{(7+1)\text{th observation}}{4} \quad \text{i.e. 2nd observation} = -0.6$$

$$Q_2 = \frac{(7+1)\text{th observation}}{2} \quad \text{i.e. 4th observation} = 2.1$$

$$Q_3 = \frac{3(7+1)\text{th observation}}{4} \quad \text{i.e. 6th observation} = 5.7$$

The interquartile range is $Q_3 - Q_1 = 5.7 - (-0.6) = 6.3$

The box plot is as shown below:

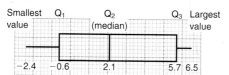

b The range and interquartile ranges have already been calculated on page 73. The box plots are shown below:

Ex. 1

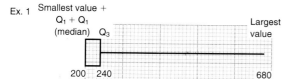

Ex. 2

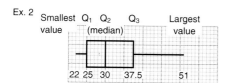

2 Range = $3750 - 1250 = 2500$
Interquartile range = $2133 - 1550 = 583$

The box plot is as follows:

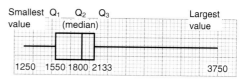

3 Range = $375 - 125 = 250$
Interquartile range = $280 - 208 = 72$

The box plot is as follows:

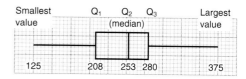

4 Range = $45.5 - 5.5 = 40$
Interquartile range = $28 - 18 = 10$ (read from graph)

The box plot is as follows:

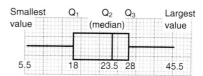

5 Range = $44.5 - 4.75 = 39.75$
Interquartile range = $29 - 12 = 17$

The box plot is as follows:

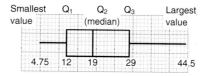

6 Range = $57.5 - 27.5 = 30$
Interquartile range = $46 - 35 = 11$

The box plot is as follows:

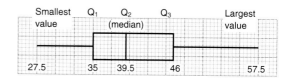

Practice 2.5.1 – p. 78

1 a no correlation
  b moderate negative correlation
  c moderate positive correlation
  d no correlation/moderate negative correlation
  e moderate positive correlation

2 a

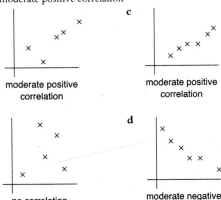

moderate positive correlation

moderate positive correlation

no correlation

moderate negative correlation

Practice 2.5.2 – p. 81

Lines of best may vary. Accept sensible answers to either side of those given here.

1

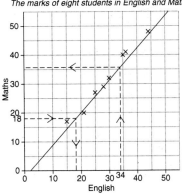

The marks of eight students in English and Maths

a there is a moderate positive correlation between English and Maths
b **i** 36   **ii** 18

2

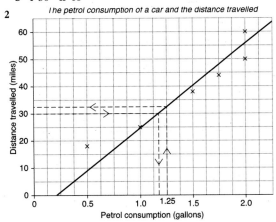

The petrol consumption of a car and the distance travelled

a there is a moderate positive correlation between the petrol consumption of a car and the distance travelled
b **i** 1.175 gallons   **ii** 32.5 miles

3

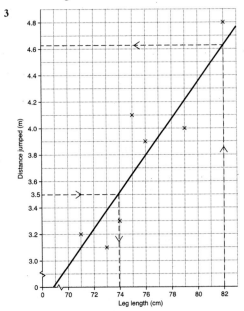

a **i** 73.6 cm   **ii** 4.64 m
b the estimate in **a i** is more reliable because it is more within the scope of the data collected.

Practice 2.6.1a – p. 89

1 a mean = 4; s.d. = 2
  b mean = 4; s.d. = 2.45 (3sf)
  c mean = 1; s.d. = 3.16 (3sf)
  d mean = 5; s.d. = 1.71 (3sf)
2 mean = 35 min; s.d. = 8.12 (3sf)
3 $\Sigma \bar{x} = 960\,000$; $\Sigma(x - \bar{x})^2 = 744\,000$; $\bar{x} = 96\,000$; s.d. = 8.63 (3sf)
4 $\Sigma x^2 = 92\,904\,000\,000$; s.d. = 8.63 (3sf)
(note that it may be better to work with the figures in thousands, i.e. 84, 94, 96, 90, …, etc.)

Practice 2.6.1b – p. 89

1 mean 1; s.d. = 4

a	mean = 2; s.d. = 4	add 1 to each original number
b	mean = 6; s.d. = 4	add 5 to each original number
c	mean = 0; s.d. = 4	subtract 1 from each original number
d	mean = 2; s.d. = 2 × 4 = 8	multiply each original number by 2
e	mean = $\frac{1}{2}$; s.d. = $\frac{1}{2}$ × 4 = 2	divide each original number by 2
f	mean = 3; s.d. = $\frac{1}{2}$ × 4 = 2	divide each original number by 2 and add $2\frac{1}{2}$
g	mn = $\frac{1}{100}$; s.d. = $\frac{1}{100}$ × 4 = $\frac{1}{25}$	divide each original number by 100

Chapter 3

Practice 3.1.1 – p. 93

1 a

Practice 3.2.1 – p. 94

1 a $\frac{1}{2}$ c $\frac{13}{52} = \frac{1}{4}$

  b $\frac{3}{6} = \frac{1}{2}$ d $\frac{1}{52}$

2 a $\frac{1}{11}$ c $\frac{2}{11}$

  b $\frac{4}{11}$ d $\frac{0}{11}$ or 0

3 a $\frac{1}{8}$ b $\frac{4}{8} = \frac{1}{2}$ c $\frac{2}{8} = \frac{1}{4}$

4 a $\frac{13}{26} = \frac{1}{2}$ b $\frac{6}{26} = \frac{3}{13}$ c $\frac{9}{26}$

5 a $\frac{10}{20} = \frac{1}{2}$ c $\frac{8}{20} = \frac{2}{5}$ e $\frac{7}{20}$

  b $\frac{6}{20} = \frac{3}{10}$ d $\frac{8}{20} = \frac{2}{5}$ f $\frac{6}{20} = \frac{3}{10}$

6 a $\frac{5}{20} = \frac{1}{4}$ c $\frac{0}{20} = 0$ e $\frac{5}{20} = \frac{1}{4}$

  b $\frac{6}{20} = \frac{3}{10}$ d $\frac{10}{20} = \frac{1}{2}$

7 $\frac{465}{500} = \frac{93}{100}$

8 a $\frac{10}{25} = \frac{2}{5}$ c $\frac{18}{25}$ e $\frac{25}{25} = 1$

  b $\frac{8}{25}$ d $\frac{0}{25} = 0$

9 a 4   c 12

  b 16   d 8

10 a 17   b 3

Practice 3.2.2 – p. 96

1 $\frac{2}{3}$ 4 65%

2 0.996   5 0.4

3 0.998

Practice 3.2.3a – p. 99

1 30

2 5

3 a 30   b 9   c 5

4 4

5 a $\frac{30}{200} = \frac{3}{20}$ c $\frac{1}{2}$

  b $\frac{36}{200} = \frac{9}{50}$ d 5

6 a experimental probability   c experimental probability

  b equally likely outcomes

Practice 3.2.3b – p. 100

1 24

2 9 times

3 a 250   b 125   c 38   d 10

4 187

5 a $\frac{350}{1000} = \frac{7}{20}$ or 0.35   b 20 300 000

6 You should play 50 times to 'expect' to win once, on average. This would cost you $50 \times 20p = £10$ in order to win £5. You are NOT likely to win more than you spend.

Practice 3.3.1 – p. 102

1 a mutually exclusive   e not mutually exclusive

  b not mutually exclusive   f not mutually exclusive

  c mutually exclusive   g mutually exclusive

  d mutually exclusive

2 $\frac{5}{52}$

3 0.74

4 a $\frac{1}{12}$ c $\frac{5}{12}$

  b $\frac{6}{12} = \frac{1}{2}$ d $\frac{2}{12} = \frac{1}{6}$

5 a $\frac{1}{3} + \frac{2}{5} = \frac{11}{15}$

  b $\frac{2}{5} + \frac{1}{10} = \frac{5}{10} = \frac{1}{2}$

  c $\frac{1}{3} + \frac{2}{5} + \frac{1}{10} = \frac{25}{30} = \frac{5}{6}$

6 the two events are not mutually exclusive as someone can be left-handed and wear glasses

Practice 3.4.1 – p. 103

1

	1	2	3	4	5	6
H	H1	H2	H3	H4	H5	H6
T	T1	T2	T3	T4	T5	T6

a $\frac{1}{12}$ b $\frac{3}{12} = \frac{1}{4}$

2

	1	2	3	4	5	6
R	R1	R2	R3	R4	R5	R6
R	R1	R2	R3	R4	R5	R6
R	R1	R2	R3	R4	R5	R6
R	R1	R2	R3	R4	R5	R6
G	G1	G2	G3	G4	G5	G6
G	G1	G2	G3	G4	G5	G6
G	G1	G2	G3	G4	G5	G6

a $\frac{4}{42} = \frac{2}{21}$ b $\frac{3}{42} = \frac{1}{14}$ c $\frac{12}{42} = \frac{2}{7}$

3 drawing a table to show the total score …

	1	2	3	4
1	2	3	4	5
2	3	4	5	6
3	4	5	6	7
4	5	6	7	8
5	6	7	8	9
6	7	8	9	10

a $\frac{2}{24} = \frac{1}{12}$ b $\frac{4}{24} = \frac{1}{6}$ c $\frac{1}{24}$

4 drawing a table to show the total score …

	1	2	3	4	5
1	2	3	4	5	6
2	3	4	5	6	7
3	4	5	6	7	8
4	5	6	7	8	9
5	6	7	8	9	10

a $\frac{1}{25}$ b $\frac{5}{25} = \frac{1}{5}$ c $\frac{2}{25}$

5

	1	2	3	4	5	6
HH	2	4	6	8	10	12
HT	1	2	3	4	5	6
TH	1	2	3	4	5	6
TT	0	0	0	0	0	0

a $\frac{3}{24} = \frac{1}{8}$ b $\frac{8}{24} = \frac{1}{3}$

6 a i $\frac{1}{10}$
   ii $\frac{1}{5} + \frac{1}{20} + \frac{1}{10} + \frac{1}{20} = \frac{8}{20} = \frac{2}{5}$
   iii $\frac{1}{5} + \frac{1}{20} + \frac{1}{10} = \frac{7}{20}$
   iv $\frac{1}{10} + 0 + \frac{1}{20} + \frac{1}{10} + 0 + \frac{1}{20} = \frac{6}{20} = \frac{3}{10}$
   (remember not to count blue and 4 twice)
 b i 40 counters
   ii 10 blue counters

Practice 3.4.2 – p. 106

1

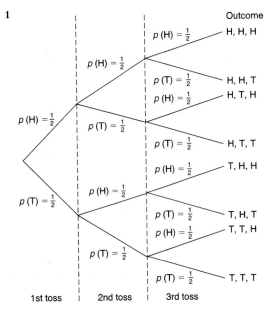

2

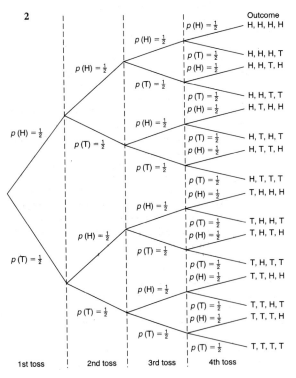

3

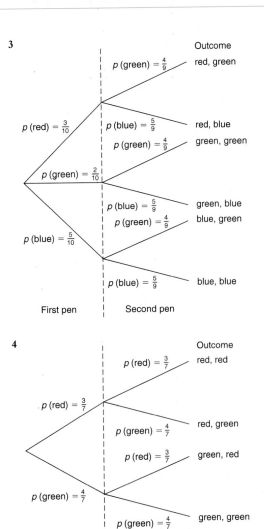

4

5

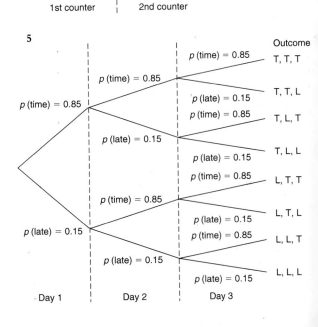

Practice 3.5.1a – p. 109

1 a $\frac{1}{2} \times \frac{1}{4} = \frac{1}{8}$ **c** $\frac{1}{2} \times \frac{1}{52} = \frac{1}{104}$
    b $\frac{1}{2} \times \frac{4}{52} = \frac{1}{26}$ **d** $\frac{1}{2} \times \frac{1}{52} = \frac{1}{104}$

2 a $\frac{3}{7} \times \frac{3}{7} = \frac{9}{49}$ **b** $\frac{4}{7} \times \frac{4}{7} = \frac{16}{49}$ **c** $\frac{3}{7} \times \frac{4}{7} = \frac{12}{49}$
    d p (one red and one green) = p (first red and second green **or** first green and second red) = $\frac{3}{7} \times \frac{4}{7} + \frac{4}{7} \times \frac{3}{7} = \frac{24}{29}$

3

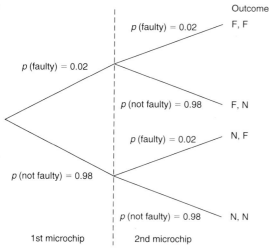

a $0.02 \times 0.02 = 0.0004$
b $0.0196 + 0.0196 = 0.0392$

4 a 0.4
    b $0.6 \times 0.6 = 0.36$
    c $0.24 + 0.24 = 0.48$

5 $\frac{1}{2^5} = \frac{1}{32}$

Practice 3.5.1b – p. 109

1 0.925 (the probability here is not affected by previous performance)

2 a $\frac{5}{8} \times \frac{5}{8} = \frac{25}{64}$
    b $\frac{5}{8} \times \frac{5}{8} \times \frac{5}{8} = \frac{125}{512}$
    c $\frac{485}{512}$

3 $\frac{1}{2^6} = \frac{1}{64}$

4 a $0.2 + 0.4 = 0.6$
    b $0.4 \times 0.4 = 0.16$
    c $0.24 + 0.24 = 0.48$

Chapter 6

Practice 6.1.1a – p. 123

1 a 256   **b** 400   **c** 625   **d** 900   **e** 1024
2 a 27   **b** 343   **c** 0   **d** 1728   **e** 27 000

Practice 6.1.1b – p. 123

1 B $69 = \sqrt{13}$ **E** $\sqrt{10\,000} = 100$
2 a   **i** ± 7
     ii ± 8.8
     iii ± 9.49 (3 sf)
     iv ± 30
     v ± 35.12
   b All are exact except **iii**
3 a 2025   **b** 20.25   **c** 174.24   **d** 772.84   **e** 10.5625
4 a 8   **c** 32   **e** 2.5
   b 20   **d** 1.2   **f** 32.6

Practice 6.1.2 – p. 124

1 a 5 to the power 2 or 5 squared
   b 9 to the power 2 or 9 squared
   c 15 to the power 2 or 15 squared
   d 4 to the power 3 or 4 cubed
   e 11 to the power 3 or 11 cubed
   f 6 to the power 4
   g 3 to the power 7
   h 2 to the power 10
2 a 25   **c** 225   **e** 1331   **g** 2187
   b 81   **d** 64   **f** 1296   **h** 1024
3 a 5^4 **b** 4^7 **c** 8^3 **d** 16^{10} **e** 3^6

4 $A = 625$
5 $C = 343$
6 a $9 + 125 = 134$ **b** $25 + 64 = 89$
7 a $3^2 = 9, 2^3 = 8$, so 3^2 is greater
   b $5^2 = 25, 2^5 = 32$, so 2^5 is greater
   c $3^4 = 81, 4^3 = 64$, so 3^4 is greater
   d $2^4 = 16, 4^2 = 16$, so both are the same
8 If he cuts it once the height is $0.01 \times 2 = 0.02$
If he cuts it twice the height is $0.01 \times 2 \times 2 = 0.01 \times 2^2 = 0.04$
If he cuts it three times the height is
$$0.01 \times 2 \times 2 \times 2 = 0.01 \times 2^3 = 0.08$$
If he cuts it four times the height is
$$0.01 \times 2 \times 2 \times 2 \times 2 = 0.01 \times 2^4 = 0.16$$
If he cuts it five times the height is
$$0.01 \times 2 \times 2 \times 2 \times 2 \times 2 = 0.01 \times 2^5 = 0.32$$
So, if he cuts it 50 times the height will be
$$0.01 \times 2^{50} = 1.125\,899\,907 \times 10^{13} \text{ inches;}$$
which is $1.125\,899\,907 \times 10^{13} \div 12 = 9.382\,499\,224 \times 10^{13}$ feet;
which is $9.382\,499\,224 \times 10^{11} \div 5280 = 177\,698\,848.9$ miles;
i.e. the resulting column will be almost 180 million miles high!!

Practice 6.1.3 – p. 126

1 a $23 - 2 + 5 = 26$ $23 - (2 + 5) = 16$
   b $17 - 2 \times 3 = 11$ $(17 - 2) \times 3 = 45$
   c $8 \times 5 - 1 = 39$ $8 \times (5 - 1) = 32$
   d $12 - 6 \div 3 = 10$ $(12 - 6) \div 3 = 2$
2 a 6   **c** 9   **e** 18
   b -4 **d** 9   **f** 13
3 a $4 \times (3 - 1) = 8$ **c** $(9 + 6) \div 3 = 5$
   b $(4 + 5) \times 2 = 18$ **d** $10 \div (5 \times 2) = 1$

4 a 28, 28, 26   26 is the odd one out
  b 27, 25, 27   25 is the odd one out
  c 29, 39, 39   29 is the odd one out
  d 27, 27, 30   30 is the odd one out
  e 44, 45, 44   45 is the odd one out
  f 24, 25, 24   25 is the odd one out
  g 34, 30, 30   34 is the odd one out
  h 7, 10, 10   7 is the odd one out
  i 4, 4, 5   5 is the odd one out
  j 5, 6, 5   6 is the odd one out
  k 18, 16, 18   16 is the odd one out
  l 16, 18, 18   16 is the odd one out

Practice 6.2.1 – p. 128

1 $12°$ 2 $5°$ 3 $24°$

4 a $^+14$ d $^+14$ g $^+1$ j $^+6$
  b $^-5$ e 0 h $^-9$ k $^+2$
  c $^+21$ f $^-10$ i $^-18$ l $^-5$

Practice 6.2.2 – p. 129

1 a $^-21$ f $^-6$ k $^+121$
  b $^-21$ g $^+1$ l $^-27$
  c $^+45$ h $^+6$ m $^+72$
  d $^+56$ i $^+2\frac{1}{2}$
  e $^-15$ j $^+25$

Practice 6.3.1 – p. 130

1 a 1, 3, 5, 15
  b 1, 2, 3, 4, 6, 8, 12, 24
  c 1, 37
  d 1, 7, 49
  e 1, 2, 3, 4, 5, 6, 10, 12, 15, 20, 30, 60

2 a 1, 2   c 1, 2, 4   e 1, 3
  b 1, 2, 3, 6   d 1, 3, 5, 15

3 a 4   d 8   g 4
  b 5   e 24   h 15
  c 6   f 7

Practice 6.3.2 – p. 130

1 a 3, 6, 9, 12, 15, 18   d 12, 24, 36, 48, 60, 72
  b 5, 10, 15, 20, 25, 30   e 13, 26, 39, 52, 65, 78
  c 8, 16, 24, 32, 40, 48

2 9, 18, 27, 36, 45, 54
3 60, 72, 84, 96
4 14, 28, 42, 56, 70, … (any five)
5 15, 30, 45, 60, 75, … (any three)
6 28, 56, 84, 112, 140, … (any three)
7 a 10   b 18   c 20   d 36   e 28   f 60

Practice 6.3.3 – p. 131

1 23, 29, 31, 37, 41
2 53
3 71, 73, 79, 83, 89

Practice 6.3.4 – p. 133

1 a 18   b 140   c 90   d 2079
2 a $2^3 \times 3$ e $2^2 \times 5^2 \times 7$ i $3 \times 7^2 \times 13$
  b $2^2 \times 3^2$ f $2^3 \times 3^3 \times 5$ j $3^2 \times 5^3 \times 7$
  c $3^2 \times 5^2$ g $2^4 \times 3 \times 5^2$ k $3^2 \times 5 \times 7 \times 11^2$
  d $2^3 \times 5 \times 11$ h $2 \times 5 \times 13^2$
3 a HCF = 21; LCM = 735   c HCF = 48; LCM = 576
  b HCF = 12; LCM = 1188   d HCF = 18; LCM = 5544

Practice 6.4.1 – p. 134

1 a $\frac{2}{4} = \frac{3}{6} = \frac{4}{8} = \ldots$(any three)
  b $\frac{2}{5} = \frac{4}{10} = \frac{6}{15} = \frac{8}{20} = \frac{10}{25} = \frac{12}{30} = \ldots$(any three)
  c $\frac{1}{3} = \frac{2}{6} = \frac{4}{12} = \frac{5}{15} = \frac{6}{18} = \ldots$(any three)
  d $\frac{26}{200} = \frac{39}{300} = \frac{52}{400} = \ldots$(any three)

2 a $\frac{4}{7}$ and $\frac{12}{21}$ c $\frac{6}{7}$ and $\frac{12}{14}$
  b $\frac{4}{9}$ and $\frac{24}{54}$ d $\frac{4}{100}$ and $\frac{12}{300}$

3 a $\frac{1}{2}$ d $\frac{2}{5}$ g $\frac{4}{7}$ (already in its lowest terms)
  b $\frac{3}{4}$ e $\frac{4}{5}$ h $\frac{4}{9}$
  c $\frac{4}{5}$ f $\frac{1}{4}$

4 a $\frac{1}{2}, \frac{1}{2}, \frac{12}{25}$ $\frac{12}{25}$ is the odd one out
  b $\frac{1}{3}, \frac{3}{11}, \frac{1}{3}$ $\frac{3}{11}$ is the odd one out
  c $\frac{3}{8}, \frac{2}{5}, \frac{2}{5}$ $\frac{3}{8}$ is the odd one out
  d $\frac{5}{6}, \frac{4}{5}, \frac{5}{6}$ $\frac{4}{5}$ is the odd one out
  e $\frac{2}{5}, \frac{3}{8}, \frac{3}{8}$ $\frac{2}{5}$ is the odd one out
  f $\frac{7}{12}, \frac{7}{12}, \frac{14}{25}$ $\frac{14}{25}$ is the odd one out

5 a $\frac{1}{4} = \frac{3}{12}$ h $\frac{1}{6} = \frac{7}{42}$ o $\frac{88}{96} = \frac{11}{12}$
  b $\frac{2}{3} = \frac{10}{15}$ i $\frac{5}{8} = \frac{30}{48}$ p $\frac{4}{20} = \frac{1}{5}$
  c $\frac{3}{5} = \frac{18}{30}$ j $\frac{7}{12} = \frac{28}{48}$ q $\frac{15}{35} = \frac{3}{7}$
  d $\frac{5}{6} = \frac{50}{60}$ k $\frac{3}{9} = \frac{1}{3}$ r $\frac{42}{48} = \frac{7}{8}$
  e $\frac{2}{8} = \frac{8}{28}$ l $\frac{8}{20} = \frac{2}{5}$ s $\frac{32}{72} = \frac{4}{9}$
  f $\frac{3}{4} = \frac{15}{20}$ m $\frac{24}{42} = \frac{4}{7}$ t $\frac{55}{132} = \frac{5}{12}$
  g $\frac{4}{5} = \frac{12}{15}$ n $\frac{45}{120} = \frac{3}{8}$

6 a $\frac{2}{5}$ $\frac{3}{5}$ $\frac{1}{5}$ $\frac{4}{5}$ i.e. $\frac{7}{35}$ $\frac{6}{15}$ $\frac{12}{20}$ $\frac{8}{10}$
  b $\frac{4}{12}$ $\frac{10}{12}$ $\frac{2}{12}$ $\frac{6}{12}$ $\frac{8}{12}$ i.e. $\frac{5}{30}$ $\frac{4}{12}$ $\frac{21}{42}$ $\frac{24}{36}$ $\frac{15}{18}$
  c $\frac{7}{8}$ $\frac{5}{8}$ $\frac{3}{8}$ $\frac{1}{8}$ $\frac{2}{8}$ i.e. $\frac{6}{48}$ $\frac{6}{24}$ $\frac{21}{56}$ $\frac{25}{40}$ $\frac{28}{32}$

Practice 6.4.2 – p. 136

1 $\frac{30}{50} = \frac{3}{5}$ 2 $\frac{25}{60} = \frac{5}{12}$ 3 $\frac{12}{15} = \frac{4}{5}$
4 $\frac{40}{200} = \frac{1}{5}$ (remember to convert to same units)
5 $\frac{3}{8}$ (there are 8 pints in a gallon)
6 $\frac{3}{5}$ (there are 100 cm in a metre)
7 $\frac{3}{10}$ (there are 1000 m in a kilometre)
8 $\frac{1}{200}$ (there are 1000 ml in a litre)
9 $\frac{1}{5000}$ (there are 1000 mg in a gram and 1000 g in a kilogram)
10 $\frac{360}{480} = \frac{3}{4}$ 12 $\frac{30}{150} = \frac{1}{5}$ 14 $\frac{140}{240} = \frac{7}{12}$
11 $\frac{36}{162} = \frac{2}{9}$ 13 $\frac{22}{30} = \frac{11}{15}$

Practice 6.4.3 – p. 137

1 a $\frac{2}{3}$ h $\frac{1}{5}$ o $-\frac{1}{10}$
  b $\frac{5}{7}$ i $\frac{1}{7}$ p $-\frac{1}{21}$
  c $\frac{7}{11}$ j $\frac{9}{40}$ q $\frac{11}{12}$
  d $\frac{6}{9} = \frac{2}{3}$ k $\frac{9}{36} = \frac{3}{12} = \frac{1}{4}$ r $\frac{19}{24}$
  e $\frac{3}{6} = \frac{1}{2}$ l $\frac{11}{56}$ s $\frac{1}{24}$
  f $\frac{24}{35}$ m $-\frac{1}{5}$ t $\frac{13}{60}$
  g $\frac{31}{44}$ n $-\frac{3}{9} = -\frac{1}{3}$

2 $\frac{1}{3} + \frac{1}{4} = \frac{7}{12}$ $\frac{5}{12}$ are cattle
3 $\frac{3}{10} + \frac{8}{15} = \frac{5}{6}$ $\frac{1}{6}$ are notes
4 $\frac{1}{5} + \frac{7}{30} + \frac{3}{10} = \frac{11}{15}$ The fourth member took $\frac{4}{15}$ of the time
  i Fastest leg was run by the first runner
  ii Slowest leg was run by the last runner

Practice 6.4.4 – p. 139

1 a $1\frac{5}{7}$ e $7\frac{11}{12}$ i $1\frac{1}{8}$
   b $12\frac{7}{12}$ f $6\frac{11}{20}$ j $1\frac{2}{5}$
   c $2\frac{1}{4}$ g $1\frac{4}{8} = 1\frac{1}{2}$ k $5\frac{8}{15}$
   d $3\frac{5}{10} = 3\frac{1}{2}$ h $1\frac{3}{8}$ l $\frac{1}{36}$

Practice 6.4.5 – p. 140

1 a $7\frac{3}{7}$ e $15\frac{47}{40} = 16\frac{7}{40}$ i $1\frac{3}{5}$
   b $10\frac{9}{20}$ f $18\frac{59}{42} = 19\frac{17}{42}$ j $3\frac{5}{8}$
   c $3\frac{37}{40}$ g $1\frac{2}{5}$ k $5\frac{21}{40}$
   d $9\frac{9}{7} = 10\frac{2}{7}$ h $4\frac{3}{8}$ l $4\frac{17}{35}$

2 $5\frac{7}{12}$ kg   4 $28\frac{5}{24}$ yards   6 $2\frac{5}{6}$ miles

3 $9\frac{3}{4}$ in.   5 $1\frac{28}{45}$ litres   7 $\frac{51}{56}$ metres

Practice 6.4.6 – p. 141

1 a $\frac{2}{15}$ f $\frac{3}{9} = \frac{1}{3}$ k $\frac{51}{5} = 10\frac{1}{5}$
   b $\frac{6}{35}$ g $\frac{7}{5} = 1\frac{2}{5}$ l $\frac{18}{1} = 18$
   c $\frac{8}{27}$ h $\frac{7}{5} = 1\frac{2}{5}$ m $\frac{4}{5}$
   d $\frac{12}{20} = \frac{3}{5}$ i $\frac{6}{4} = \frac{3}{2} = 1\frac{1}{2}$
   e $\frac{6}{15} = \frac{2}{5}$ j $\frac{1}{1} = 1$
   n $\frac{16}{25}$ (remember that $(\frac{4}{5})^2 = \frac{4}{5} \times \frac{4}{5}$)
   o $\frac{25}{16} = 1\frac{9}{16}$ (remember that $(1\frac{1}{4})^2 = 1\frac{1}{4} \times 1\frac{1}{4}$)
   p $\frac{1000}{27} = 37\frac{1}{27}$ (remember that $(3\frac{1}{3})^3 = 3\frac{1}{3} \times 3\frac{1}{3} \times 3\frac{1}{3}$)

Practice 6.4.7 – p. 141

1 a 30   b 6   c 8   d $\frac{32}{7} = 4\frac{4}{7}$

2 9 metres

3 30 millilitres

4 a 8   b 15

5 450   6 $\frac{1}{2}$ 7 $\frac{1}{3}$ hr   8 $55\frac{5}{9}$ cm

Practice 6.4.8 – p. 143

1 a $\frac{5}{6}$ e $\frac{1}{3}$ i $\frac{5}{3} = 1\frac{2}{3}$
   b $\frac{11}{7} = 1\frac{4}{7}$ f 2   j 3
   c $\frac{1}{2}$ g $\frac{5}{3} = 1\frac{2}{3}$ k 2
   d $\frac{2}{7}$ h $\frac{2}{3}$ l $\frac{1}{2}$

2 6 bottles ($\frac{2}{3}$ litre remaining)   6 40 minutes

3 $\frac{4}{15}$ 7 40

4 1600 m or 1.6 km   8 £28

5 105 seconds

Practice 6.5.1 – p. 144

1 a 6   c 6000   e $\frac{6}{100\,000}$
   b 600   d $\frac{6}{10}$

2 a 30   b 200   c $\frac{7}{10}$ d $\frac{8}{100}$

3 25.15; 0.009; 3417.6; 384.07; 1010.101

4 a 0.5   e 1.02   i 21.27
   b 0.02   f 9.005   j 258.904
   c 0.009   g 3.27
   d 4.7   h 5.908

5 a 8.3   c 9.062   e 23.406
   b 4.76   d 41.7   f 0.962

Practice 6.5.2 – p. 145

1 a $\frac{2}{5}$ c $\frac{14}{25}$ e $\frac{11}{40}$ g $\frac{111}{500}$
   b $\frac{11}{20}$ d $\frac{23}{50}$ f $\frac{17}{40}$ h $\frac{469}{2000}$

2 a $4\frac{1}{2}$ c $10\frac{3}{25}$ e $70\frac{18}{25}$ g $2\frac{1}{8}$
   b $7\frac{7}{20}$ d $20\frac{19}{20}$ f $12\frac{3}{25}$ h $17\frac{31}{200}$

Practice 6.5.3 – p. 146

1 a 0.6   f 1.3   k $0.\dot{3}$
   b 0.7   g 15.2   l $0.\dot{5}$
   c 0.04   h 22.12   m $0.5\dot{4}$
   d 0.35   i 1.45
   e 0.325   j 6.06

Practice 6.5.4 – p. 148

1 a 0.5   e 1.95   i 105.01
   b 1.01   f 0.603   j 0.49
   c 1.64   g 3.7   k 30.2
   d 0.988   h 9.3

2 a 0.5   d 0.837   g 7.6
   b 0.25   e 3.99   h 4.8
   c 0.36   f 0.09   i 14.999

3 £83.24   6 $16 - 12.88 = 3.12$ km

4 11.325 m   7 $15 - (4.805 + 4.756) = 5.439$ km

5 14.95 cm

Practice 6.5.5 – p. 149

1 a 0.18   d 0.56   g 4.8
   b 14.4   e 0.000 225   h 0.000 015
   c 12   f 36

2 £7

3 53.4 m

4 236.88 miles

5 101.68 cm^2

6 7.36 sq. ft

7 33.8 lbs = 33 lbs 13 oz (to the nearest ounce)

8 $5 \times 46 \times 19.4 = 4462$ kg

Practice 6.5.6 – p. 151

1 a 0.53   d 120 000   g 50
   b 0.12   e 130   h 4000
   c 4400   f 0.02

2 5.2 m/s

3 900

4 21

5 26 150 (nearest 10)

6 41; 1.6 m left

7 a 14.3 lb   b 40.71 lb   c 72.1 lb

Practice 6.6.1 – p. 153

1 a 50%   e 70%
   b 25%   f 15%
   c 40%   g 17%
   d 37.5%   h 16.666… or 16.7% (3sf)

2 a $\frac{3}{5}$ d $\frac{9}{10}$
   b $\frac{9}{20}$ e $\frac{5}{8}$
   c $\frac{13}{20}$ f $\frac{33}{100}$ (note that 33% is not equal to $\frac{1}{3}$)

Practice 6.6.2 – p. 153

1 a 50%   c 60%   e 37.5%
   b 20%   d 35%   f 41.25%

2 a 0.25   d 0.225   g 0.002
   b 0.45   e 0.05   h 0.0001
   c 0.9   f 0.025

A n s w e r s

Practice 6.6.3 – p. 154

1

Decimal	Fraction	Percentage
0.3	$\frac{3}{10}$	30
0.55	$\frac{11}{20}$	55
0.875	$\frac{7}{8}$	87.5
0.333̇	$\frac{1}{3}$	$33\frac{1}{3}$
0.75	$\frac{3}{4}$	75
0.8	$\frac{4}{5}$	80
0.01	$\frac{1}{100}$	1
0.025	$\frac{1}{40}$	$2\frac{1}{2}$
0.48	$\frac{12}{25}$	48
1.25	$1\frac{1}{4}$	125
2.66666̇	$2\frac{2}{3}$	$266\frac{2}{3}$
3.2	$3\frac{1}{5}$	320

2 $\frac{1}{2} = 50\%$, $\frac{26}{50} = 52\%$, $\frac{48}{100} = 48\%$, $\frac{505}{1000} = 50.5\%$, $0.46 = 46\%$,
$0.488 = 48.8\%$, so the order is 0.46, 47.9%, $\frac{48}{100}$, 0.488, $\frac{1}{2}$, $\frac{505}{1000}$,
51.0%, $\frac{26}{50}$

3 a $0.76 = \frac{19}{25}$ **b** $\frac{3}{8} = 0.375$ **c** $57\% = 0.57$

4 The one labelled '$\frac{1}{4}$ off' since this is 25%

5 $\frac{3}{8} = 37.5$ which is bigger than 35%. The first will rebound higher.

6 $\frac{11}{25} \times 100 = 44\%$

Practice 6.6.4 – p. 156

1 50%
2 20%
3 10%
4 14.285… = 14.3% (3sf)
5 4%
6 5%
7 20% (3 feet = 1 yard)
8 20.8%
9 75%
10 56%

Practice 6.6.5a – p. 158

1 a £4
  b 270 metres
  c 18 apples
  d 700 g
2 £210
3 19 cars (rounded to nearest whole number)
4 12 minutes
5 130 CDs
6 12 matches
7 96

Practice 6.6.5b – p. 158

1 a £93.60
  b 174 m
  c 218.4 litres
  d 46 inches or 3 feet 10 inches
2 £368
3 £11.25
4 104
5 222 houses; 25 sales
6 96.6 m² (3 sf); 100 m²

Practice 6.6.6a – p. 161

1 £625
2 £390
3 £51
4 a £5500   **b** £6050
5 51.25 kg
6 84 cm
7 1.2 kg
8 2%

Practice 6.6.6b – p. 161

1 £259.60
2 £30.75
3 £32
4 a £3852   **b** £4121.64
5 a £5590   **b** £4807.40
6 46.2 litres
7 £47.20
8 between 4th and 5th year

Practice 6.6.7a – p. 163

1 10%
2 6.25%
3 20%
4 35%
5 16%
6 44%
7 £460
8 £3416

Practice 6.6.7b – p. 164

1 6.67% (3sf)
2 2.37% (3sf)
3 18.2% (3sf)
4 $\frac{12}{168} = 7.14\%$ (3sf) (in minutes)
5 5%
6 3.34%
7 3.94% (3sf)
8 7.89% (3sf)
9 11.8% (3sf)
10 44.1% (3sf)

Practice 6.6.8a – p. 165

1 200 m
2 75 acres
3 £600
4 £800

Practice 6.6.8b – p. 165

1 70 m
2 £12 800
3 350
4 50 square metres

Practice 6.6.9a – p. 165

1 18 225
2 400
3 a 30 360   **b** 34 914
4 £9000

Practice 6.6.9b – p. 166

1 £26 000
2 £4800
3 44%
4 £25 000

Practice 6.7.1 – p. 167

1 a 3 : 4
  b 1 : 5
  c 1 : 3
  d 3 : 7 (already in its simplest form)
  e 1 : 4
  f 1 : 3
  g 10 : 1
  h 8 : 1
  i 3 : 10
  j 1 : 8
  k 8 : 5
  l 3 : 2
2 2 : 3
3 4 : 10 = 2 : 5
4 8 : 3 (1 m = 100 cm)
5 1 : 4 (16 ounces = 1 pound)
6 a 350 : 560 = 5 : 8   **b** 560 : 350 = 8 : 5

Practice 6.7.2 – p. 169

1 £800 and £1000
2 £500, £750 and £1750
3 £450 and £150 (ratio = 3 : 1)
4 £11 000, £7000 and £4000   £10 560, £7040 and £4400 (a year later)
5 Amy £5250, Brian £9000 and Catrina £3750
6 A got 600; B got 720; C got 1080 votes
7 21 almonds
8 15 eggs
9 86.4 cm²
10 £2401

Chapter 7

Practice 7.2.1 – p. 174

1 a 4^8 b 3^7 c 11^8 d 7^6 e 5^6 f 6^9

2 a 3^{14} b 4^9 c 9^9 d 8^{14} e 6^{25} f 7^{14} g 16^9

Practice 7.2.2 – p. 175

1 a 5^5 b 6^4 c 8^6 d 14^4 e 21^3 f 3^1 or 3

2 a 10^2 b 8^4 c 17^5 d 16^1 or 16 e 9^7 f 4^5

3 a 5^6 b 4^{18} c 6^7 d 18^{13} e 6^3 f 25^1 or 25 g 16^2 h 2^3

4 a 3^5 b 2^{11} c same

5 a 36 b 64 c 64 d 64 e 17 f 18 g 9 h 22

6 a 3^6 b 4^{18} c 6^{13} d 11^{11} e 6^6 f 4^{14} g 6^{10} h 3^{14} i 4^{15} j 4^3 k 9^1 or 9 l 5^5 m 16^4 n 6^4 o $10^0 = 1$ p $7^0 = 1$ q $6^0 = 1$ r 4^{-1} s 5^{-3} t 4^{-9}

Practice 7.2.3 – p. 176

1 a $\frac{1}{4^5}$ b $\frac{1}{6^5}$ c $\frac{1}{2^2}$ d $\frac{1}{12^4}$ e $\frac{1}{7^{19}}$ f $\frac{1}{6^3}$ g $\frac{1}{4^5}$ h $\frac{1}{11^3}$

2 a $\frac{1}{5}$ b $\frac{1}{9}$ c 1 d 1 e $\frac{1}{12}$ f $\frac{1}{4}$ g 1 h 1 i 1 j 100

Practice 7.3.1 – p. 178

1 a 1.4×10^4 b 9×10^6 c 1.3×10^8 d 1.58×10^{11} e 4.5×10^9 f 3.75×10^{11} g 2.006×10^8 h 2.1005×10^{13}

2 a 1 300 000 b 1 430 000 000 c 175 000 000 d 1040 e 889 800 000 f 98 650 000 g 399 580 h 399 i 496.31

3 a 43 000 000 b 197 000 000 c 28 880 000 d 17 483 000 000 e 55 870 000 f 2 980 200 000

4 c, a, e, b, f, d

5 a 14 000 000 b 2 500 000 c 82 360 000 d 1 544 000 e 165 242 000

6 e, c, a, b, d

7 a 9.78×10^2, 4.2835×10^3, 1.26×10^4
b 9.89×10^4, 99 000, 1×10^5

8 a 2.21×10^4 b 3.25×10^7 c 1.1×10^8

9 a $n = 5$ b $n = 4$ c $n = 7$ d $n = 2$ e $n = 1$ f $n = 5$

Practice 7.3.2 – p. 180

1 a 3×10^{-3} b 7.5×10^{-5} c 7×10^{-4} d 1×10^{-1} e 6.25×10^{-7} f 8×10^{-12} g 6.55×10^{-6} h 9.225×10^{-7}

2 a 0.000 000 001 b 0.000 000 000 08 c 0.000 65 d 0.000 004 22 e 0.000 040 05 f 0.000 039 958

3 a 2.46×10^{-2}, 1.3×10^{-2}, 8.79×10^{-5}
b 4.3×10^{-2}, 4.29×10^{-3}, 0.004 28

4 a 1.25×10^{-6} b 1.46×10^{-5} c 0.000 99

Practice 7.3.3 – p. 182

1 7×10^3
2 8.6×10^5
3 8.6×10^8
4 1.157×10^4
5 1.1081×10^8
6 9.85×10^{-3}
7 1.372×10^{-6}
8 1.1×10^2
9 1.6×10^7
10 1.51×10^{10}
11 1×10^4
12 1.068×10^{-4}
13 9.5×10^{-17}
14 $6.535\,36 \times 10^8$
15 6.76×10^7
16 $1.150\,16 \times 10^3$
17 1.866×10^{-2}
18 2.835×10^3

Practice 7.3.4a – p. 183

1 6×10^9
2 4×10^{11}
3 9×10^{16}
4 2.4×10^8
5 7×10^{-1} or $\frac{1}{7}$
6 1.44×10^{-8}
7 2×10^1 or 20
8 3.5×10^2
9 7.5×10^3
10 1.25×10^{-8}

Practice 7.3.4b – p. 183

1 7.119×10^7
2 $8.411\,85 \times 10^9$
3 1.9975×10^8
4 $1.770\,18 \times 10^{20}$
5 1.7664×10^{32}
6 7.744×10^1
7 7.7112×10^5
8 $8.5 \times 10^1 = 85$
9 7.6×10^9
10 2.21×10^{-2}
11 134 kilowatt hours
12 4.25×10^{-2} g

Practice 7.4.1 – p. 185

see answers to Practice 6.4.3, 6.4.4, 6.4.5 and 6.4.8

Practice 7.4.2 – p. 186

1 81
2 64
3 5
4 1
5 1
6 0.25
7 0.01
8 0.0025 or 2.5×10^{-3}
9 0.25
10 0.0256
11 0.03
12 7
13 3
14 2
15 0.0625

Practice 7.4.3 – p. 187

see answers to Practice 7.3.3 and 7.3.4

Practice 7.4.4 – p. 188

1 288.7218
2 3.861 139 9
3 5.751 284 8
4 108.9951
5 0.9274
6 0.305 518 4
7 0.956 036 2
8 9.651 282 8

Practice 7.5.1 – p. 188

1 2150
2 4884
3 13 694
4 12 545
5 17 608
6 37 715

Practice 7.5.2 – p. 189

1 32		**3** 89		**5** 28		**7** 68		**9** 77	
2 45		**4** 46		**6** 59		**8** 78		**10** 93	

Practice 7.6.1 – p. 191

1 $7 \times 10 = 70$

2 $2 \times 48 = 96$

3 $103 \times 1000 = 103\,000$

4 $400 \div 10 = 40$

5 $72 \div 2 = 36$

6 $70 \div 2 = 35$

7 $100 \div 1 = 100$

8 $4 \div 40 = \frac{1}{10}$

9 $610 \div 10 = 61$

10 $10 \div 2 = 5$

11 $12 \times 90 = 1080$

12 $25 \times 4 \div 2 = 50$

13 $12 \times 8 \div \frac{1}{8} = 12 \times 64 \approx 640$

14 $\dfrac{10 + 5}{10 \times 15} = \dfrac{15}{150} = 0.1$

15 $\dfrac{5 \times 100}{4 \times 0.5} = 250$

16 $\dfrac{10^2 - 4^2}{2 \times 10} = 4.2$

17 $6 + \dfrac{2}{5 + 5} = 6.2$

18 $25 \times 4 + \dfrac{5(100 - 30 \times 2)}{11 + 9} = 110$

19 $\dfrac{5 + 5}{\sqrt{4} + 2^2} = \dfrac{10}{6} = \dfrac{5}{3}$

20 $\dfrac{30 + \sqrt{1}}{(16 - 6)^2} = \dfrac{31}{100}$

21 $\dfrac{4^2 - 1^2}{\sqrt{25} + 7} = \dfrac{15}{12}$

22 $10 + \dfrac{\sqrt{1}}{3^2 + 12 \times 1} = 10\frac{1}{21}$

23 Take a beat as each 1 second, then $60 \times 60 \times 24 = 86\,400$

24 Take the orbit as a circle; circumference is $2 \times \pi \times 240\,000$ approx $= 6 \times 250\,000 = 1\,500\,000$ miles

25 Say an average sized car has a wheel of radius 16 in. Its circumference is then approx $2\pi \times 16 = 6 \times 16 = 96$ in. – say 8 ft.
10 miles is 10×5280 ft $= 50\,000$ feet approximately.
Therefore it turns approximately $50\,000 \div 8 = 6250$ times.

Practice 7.7.1 – p. 192

	4dp	3dp	2dp	1dp
1	4.2716	4.272	4.27	4.3
2	2.1606	2.161	2.16	2.2
3	11.7524	11.752	11.75	11.8
4	9.2295	9.229	9.23	9.2
5	13.8980	13.898	13.90	13.9

Practice 7.7.2 – p. 194

	4sf	3sf	2sf	1sf
1	437.8	438	440	400
2	2195	2190	2200	2000
3	0.8966	0.897	0.90	0.9
4	18.69	18.7	19	20
5	505.1	505	510	500

6 a Adam 55   Eve 45   **b** Adam 50   Eve 50

7 a i $39.9\,\text{cm}^2$ **ii** $40\,\text{cm}^2$ **iii** $40\,\text{cm}^2$

b i 25.3 cm

c i 12   **ii** 12.0   **iii** 12.0

d i 3.14   **ii** 3.14   **iii** 3.1416

e i 0.7   **ii** 0.7   **iii** 0.6667

f i 0.4   **ii** 0.4   **iii** 0.429

g i 1.0 m   **ii** 1.00 m   **iii** 1.00 m

h i 0.01 m   **ii** 0.0 m   **iii** 0.010 m

Practice 7.8.1 – p. 195

1
4.1^2	$= 16.81$
4.2^2	$= 17.64$
4.15^2	$= 17.2225$
4.125^2	$= 17.015\,625$
4.1225^2	$= 16.995\,006$
4.1235^2	$= 17.003\,252$
4.1230^2	$= 16.999\,129$

$\sqrt{17} = 4.123$ (3dp) as answer lies between 4.1230 and 4.1235

2
$2.6 \times 2.6 \times 2.6$	$= 17.576$
$2.7 \times 2.7 \times 2.7$	$= 19.683$
$2.65 \times 2.65 \times 2.65$	$= 18.609\,625$
$2.67 \times 2.67 \times 2.67$	$= 19.034\,163$
$2.66 \times 2.66 \times 2.66$	$= 18.821\,096$
$2.665 \times 2.665 \times 2.665$	$= 18.927\,43$

$\sqrt[3]{19} = 2.67$ (2dp) as answer lies between 2.665 and 2.67

3
$2.5 \times 2.5 \times 2.5$	$= 15.625$
$2.6 \times 2.6 \times 2.6$	$= 17.576$
$2.55 \times 2.55 \times 2.55$	$= 16.581\,375$
$2.58 \times 2.58 \times 2.58$	$= 17.173\,512$
$2.57 \times 2.57 \times 2.57$	$= 16.974\,593$
$2.575 \times 2.575 \times 2.575$	$= 17.073\,859$
$2.573 \times 2.573 \times 2.573$	$= 17.034\,107$

$\sqrt[3]{17} = 2.57$ (2dp) as answer lies between 2.57 and 2.573

Chapter 8

Practice 8.2.1 – p. 200

1 a 0300   **d** 1245   **g** 1015

b 1520   **e** 0530   **h** 2359

c 2005   **f** 1955

2 a 10.00 am   **d** 3.05 pm   **g** 10.01 pm

b 11.30 am   **e** 11.59 am   **h** 12.01 am

c 12.50 pm   **f** 11.50 pm

3 85 mins

4 1 h 55 mins

5 1 h 50 mins

6 2025

7 9 h 35 mins

8 a 5.25 pm

b 105 mins

9 0225 (next day)

Practice 8.3.1a – p. 202

1 11 880 ft

2 100 fl oz

3 4750 mm

4 32 m

5 4.57 g

6 0.000 765 km

7 2.5 feet

8 £2.93 (or approx. £3)

Practice 8.3.1b – p. 203

1 250 lb

2 0.0046 t

3 0.005 m

4 18 inches

5 7.0 oz

6 79 fl oz

7 9.1 m

8 £1.92 (nearest penny)

9 £1.64 (nearest penny)

10 80 km/h

Practice 8.4.1 – p. 203

1 a 2 h 25 min   **c** 1 h 40 min
   b 1 h 15 min   **d** 45 min
2 a 10 min   **c** 17 min   **e** 0059 or 12.59 am
   b 27 min   **d** 34 min   **f** 0255 or 2.55 am
3 a 0840   **d** 1 h 8 min   **g** 1755
   b 27 min   **e** 46 min
   c 1 h 13 min   **f** 0926 (catch the 0819 train)
4 a £70   **c** £84
   b £8   **d** £4
5 a £798 (£399 each)
   b £128 (£64 each)
   c £1412 (£353 each)
   d £1823 (reduction of £25 for 8 year old)
   e £276
   f £1290 (reduction of £50 for both children)
   g £375 (4 nights)
6 a £22   **c** £36   **e** £48
   b £22   **d** £3   **f** £112
7 a i £66 **ii** £48   **d** £62 (no concessions)
   b £2.50   **e** £84 (concession for 2 children)
   c £57 (see concessions)
8 a i 1550 miles **ii** 210 miles **iii** 5940 miles
   b i 1540 miles **ii** 6030 miles
   c 4600 miles   **e** Rome
   d 180 miles   **f** London & Paris
9 a 77 miles   **e** Dover & Edinburgh
   b 240 miles   **f** 189 miles
   c 448 miles   **g** 347 miles
   d Portsmouth & Southampton

Practice 8.5.1a – p. 211

1 £9.80   **5** £264
2 £8.40   **6 a** £168   **b** £328
3 £267   **7 a** £162.60   **b** £175.88
4 a £7.04   **b** £10.76   **8** £318.50

Practice 8.5.1b – p. 212

1 £191.25
2 Mon £3.20, Tue £3.00, Wed £3.68, Thu £3.36, Fri £2.60
3 Mon £45.00, Tue £52.50, Wed £63.00, Thu £59.25, Fri £45.00
4 Mon £29.82, Tue £23.10, Thu £36.39, Fri £23.33 (nearest penny)
5 £249.60
6 £163.40
7 £166.43 (nearest penny)

Practice 8.5.2 – p. 215

1 £2115
2 £2476.72
3 £360
4 no tax paid
5 £30.13 per week (nearest penny)
6 taxable income £3105; tax £621 per year
7 taxable income £22 305; tax £5001.15 per year
8 tax £4351.88 (nearest penny)
9 taxable income = £22 600 − £5635 = £16 965
   tax paid = 10% × £1520 + 22% × £15 445 = £3549.90
10 taxable income = 12 × £855.25 − £6050 = £4213
   tax paid = 10% × £1520 + 22% × £2963 = £744.46

Practice 8.6.1a – p. 217

1 a £693.25   **d** £2191.38 (nearest penny)
   b £540.50   **e** £11 614.88 (nearest penny)
   c £276.13 (nearest penny)
2 £108.10

Practice 8.6.1b – p. 217

1 a £693.25   **d** £2191.38 (nearest penny)
   b £540.50   **e** £11 614.88 (nearest penny)
   c £276.13 (nearest penny)
2 £108.10   **3** £320   **4** £2800   **5** £490

Practice 8.6.2 – p. 218

Answers are given to the nearest penny
1 £66.89
2 a £56.18   **b** £137.87   **c** £116.94   **d** £55.24
3 £93.39
4 500 × 7p = £35. Total cost = £35 + £10.33 = £45.33.
   Cost = 1.08 × £45.33 = £48.96
5 a 600 × 7.2p = £43.20.
   Total cost = £43.20 + £10.33 = £53.53.
   Bill = 1.08 × £53.53 = £57.81
   b 1685 × 7.2p = £121.32.
   Total cost = £121.32 + £10.33 = £131.65.
   Bill = 1.08 × £131.65 = £142.18
   c 450 × 7.2p = £32.40.
   Total cost = £32.40 + £10.33 = £42.73.
   Bill = 1.08 × £42.73 = £46.15
   d 172 × 7.2p = £12.38.
   Total cost = £12.38 + £10.33 = £22.71.
   Bill = 1.08 × £22.71 = £24.53
6 a 8444 × 1.4p = £118.22.
   Total cost = £118.22 + 92 × 9.5p = £126.96.
   Bill = £126.96 × 1.08 = £137.12
   b 14 250 × 1.4p = £199.5.
   Total cost = £199.5 + 90 × 9.5p = £208.05.
   Bill = £208.05 × 1.08 = £224.69
   c 18 240 × 1.4p = £255.36.
   Total cost = £255.36 + 92 × 9.5p = £272.65.
   Bill = £272.65 × 1.08 = £294.46

Practice 8.7.1a – p. 221

1 a £581.60   **b** £101.60
2 a £526   **b** £61
3 £160

Practice 8.7.1b – p. 222

1 a £336   **b** £3399.60   **c** £599.60
2 a £22   **b** £257.20   **c** £37.20
3 10 months
4 a £10.74   **c** £5.00   **e** £5.00
   b £20.22   **d** £30.66
5 £132.24
6 amount = £1106.64; interest = 10.7% (3sf)
7 a £587.40   **c** £2348.16
   b £1171.20   **d** £10.56 over 24 months
8 a £410   **b** £35
9 a £25.20   **b** £142.40   **c** £16.40

Practice 8.7.2a – p. 224

1 $44   **3** £1000
2 316 €   **4** £200

Practice 8.7.2b – p. 224

1 £1265.82 (nearest penny)   4 $436.71
2 £1.91 (nearest penny)   5 366.16 €
3 117 F

Practice 8.7.3a – p. 227

1 £392   2 a £500   b £1125   3 2 years

Practice 8.7.3b – p. 227

Answers are given to the nearest penny where appropriate

1	simple interest	amount
a	£52.50	£302.50
b	£121.50	£571.50
c	£362.50	£1612.50
d	£59.38	£534.38
e	£18.40	£708.40 (use $T = \frac{2}{3}$ years)
f	£533.85	£3033.85 (use $T = \frac{41}{12}$ years)

2 $T = 3$ years
3 $R = 3.5\%$
4 $R = 4.5\%$

Practice 8.7.4 – p. 229

1 £562.43 (nearest penny)
2 amount = £2119.87 (nearest penny); interest = £369.87
3 a $A = $ £306.26; $I = $ £56.26   c $A = $ £1480.36; $I = $ £230.36
   b $A = $ £491.41; $I = $ £41.41
4 a £3024.00   b £3028.48
5 £5253.13 (nearest penny)
6 £3552.76 (nearest penny)

Practice 8.8.1a – p. 232

1 43 mph   5 1350 miles
2 $7\frac{1}{3}$ km/h or 7.33 km/h (3sf)   6 2.75 h or $2\frac{3}{4}$ h or 2 h 45 min
3 70 mph   7 $\frac{2}{3}$ g/cm^3
4 8 km/h   8 450 000 g or 450 kg

Practice 8.8.1b – p. 232

1 135 mph   5 28 min
2 75 km/h   6 2.7 g/cm^3
3 $18\frac{2}{3}$ km or 18.7 km (3sf)   7 9×10^{-4} kg/cm^3 or 0.9 g/cm^3
4 $2\frac{1}{2}$ h or 2.5 h   8 1.30 cm^3 (3sf)

Chapter 11

Practice 11.2.1 – p. 247

1 a $6xy$ h f^{10} o $9p^2$
  b $20xy$ i j^{-1} p $-27p^3$
  c $-15cd$ j k^{-3} q $-64p^3$
  d $-24cd$ k $3w^4$ r $-32p^5$
  e e^8 l $\frac{1}{3}v^{-4}$ s $10qr$
  f e^{12} m $8m^3$ t $30qr$
  g f^6 n $81m^4$

2 a $4st$ g $-24wxy$ m $24d^3$
  b $15st$ h $-120wxy$ n $90e^4$
  c $\frac{2}{9}uv$ i $40xyz$ o $24def$
  d $10uv$ j $90xyz$ p $24def^2$
  e $24wxy$ k $140xyz$
  f $120wxy$ l $-90abc$

3 a $6g^2h^2$ h $5f^3g$ o $-9cd^3$
  b g^7h^{10} i $\frac{1}{3}$ p $12w^6v^{-2}$
  c $30m^7n^6$ j $\frac{1}{3}q$ q x^6
  d $56j^{12}k^7$ k $\frac{7}{q^3}$ r m^{28}
  e 3 l $7rs^{-2}$ s $27h^9$
  f $3p^4$ m $-4u$ t $16k^{20}$
  g $4g$ n $5u^{-1}$

4 a 3   g 1   m $\frac{1}{2}$
  b 4   h $3s = 6, s = 2$ n $\frac{1}{2}$
  c 5   i 5   o $2t + 1 = 3, t = 1$
  d 4   j 3   p $2^{8b} = 2^8, b = 1$
  e 3   k 6
  f 3   l $2z = 3, z = 1.5$

Practice 11.3.1 – p. 248

1 a $5x + 4y$ c $\frac{2p}{q^2}$ e $x^3 + \frac{x}{4}$
  b $3c - 2$ d $4a + 2b$ f $x^2 + \frac{1}{4}x$
2 $4a + 2b$ 3 £$(2c + 3d)$
4 a $4y$ c $4y - 7$ e $2y$
  b $y + 6$ d $\frac{7y}{2}$

Practice 11.3.2 – p. 250

1 a $20a$ k no simpler form (NSF)
  b $2b$ l $2w^2 - w - 8$
  c $-2c$ m $6x^2$
  d $12d + 15e$ n $\frac{8}{y}$
  e $3f + 3g$ o $\frac{4}{z^2} - \frac{1}{z}$
  f $-3h - 12k - 5l$ p $11x^3 + x - 3$
  g $7x + 3y - 7m - 1$ q $\frac{3b}{c}$
  h $p - 13q + 3$ r NSF
  i $1\frac{1}{2}r + 2\frac{3}{4}s$ s $12x^3y + 7x^2y^2 - 5xy^3$
  j $7t - t^2 + 3u$ t $13z^3 + 4z^2$

Practice 11.3.3 – p. 252

1 a $2a + 6$ f $-12x - 8y$ k $3wx + 6wy - 9wz$
  b $6a - 2$ g $-12y + 9z$ l $-12w^2 + 15wx - 9w$
  c $6b - 21$ h $21a - 14b$ m $15x^2 + 10x + 35$
  d $8b + 12c$ i $24c + 18d$ n $28y^3 - 4y^2 + 12y$
  e $30f - 15g$ j $6e - 10f$

2 a $5z + 15$ g $d - 6e + 9f$ m $3mn - 15m - 8n$
  b $-z - 15$ h $-11d - 7f$ n $23p^2 + 9pq$
  c $-z + 15$ i $5x^2 + x - 23$ o $-7p^2 + 15pq$
  d $6a + 2$ j $8y^2 - 9y + 30$ p $35yz + 21$
  e $4b - 18$ k $2x^3 + 18x^2 - 20x + 6$ q $-8t + 16$
  f 13   l $xy - 6x$ r $14x + 18y + 26z$

Practice 11.3.4 – p. 255

1 a $a^2 + 12a + 27$ f $y^2 - 3y + 2$ k $x^2 + 10x + 25$
  b $b^2 + 5b - 14$ g $2x^2 + 17x + 21$ l $y^2 - 14y + 49$
  c $c^2 - 3c - 10$ h $6z^2 + 16z - 32$ m $4z^2 + 4z + 1$
  d $x^2 + x - 12$ i $6x^2 - 21x - 12$ n $9x^2 - 24x + 16$
  e $x^2 - 3x - 40$ j $10y^2 - 19y + 6$
2 a $x^2 + 10x + 21$ b $2y^2 + 11y + 15$ c $8z^2 + 10z + 3$
3 a i x^2 ii $2x$ iii $3x$ iv 6   b $x^2 - 5x + 6$
  c HIFG = ACEG − ACDH − BCEF + BCDI (since BCDI has been subtracted **twice**)

15 b

Number of sides	4	5	6	7	8
Number of diagonals	2	5	9	14	20

   c **i** 27   **ii** 35   **iii** 44   **iv** 54

   d $\dfrac{n(n-3)}{2}$

   e **i** 90   **ii** 170   **iii** 1175   **iv** 4850

Practice 12.2.4 – p. 323

1 a **i** 82 **ii** 154 **iii** 302

   c **i** $4x + 10 = 22, x = 3$ **iii** $4x + 10 = 282, x = 68$

      ii $4x + 10 = 102, x = 23$ **iv** $4x + 10 + 374, x = 91$

   d **no**, it does not fit on the grid

2 a **i** -3 **ii** 35 **iii** 62

   c **i** $x - 20 = -4, x = 16$ **iii** $x - 20 = 77, x = 97$

      ii $x - 20 = 33, x = 53$

   d **no**, it does not fit on the grid

3 a **i** 31 **ii** 1969 **iii** 5101

   c **i** $x^2 - 21x + 99 = -9, x = 9$ or 12, but $x = 9$ does not fit on the grid, thus $x = 12$

      ii $x^2 - 21x + 99 = 451, x = -11$ or 32, but $x = -11$ does not fit on the grid, thus $x = 32$

      iii $x^2 - 21x + 99 = 1179, x = -24$ or 45, but $x = -24$ does not fit on the grid, thus $x = 45$

4 a **i** 20 **ii** 20 **iii** 20

Practice 12.3.1 – p. 327

1 $y = 2 - 3(-1) = 5$, **no**

2 $y = 2 \times 2 - 7 = -3$, **yes**

3 $y = 2x - 6$

4 a $y = -3, y = 3, y = 17$

Practice 12.3.2a – p. 330

1 a

b

c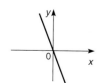

d

e

f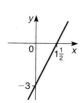

g

h

i

j

k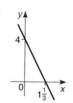

l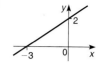

m

n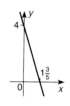

o

p

2 a

5	15	25
75	225	375
95	245	395

   c **i** 140 min   **ii** 290 min   **iii** 365 min

   d 14 lb

Practice 12.3.2b – p. 331

1 a

10 000	25 000	55 000
180	390	810
160	400	880

b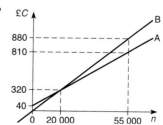

   c (from graph) $n = 20\,000$, £320

   d tariff B is cheaper, a saving of £12

   e tariff A is cheaper, a saving of £60

Practice 12.3.3 – p. 332

1 a

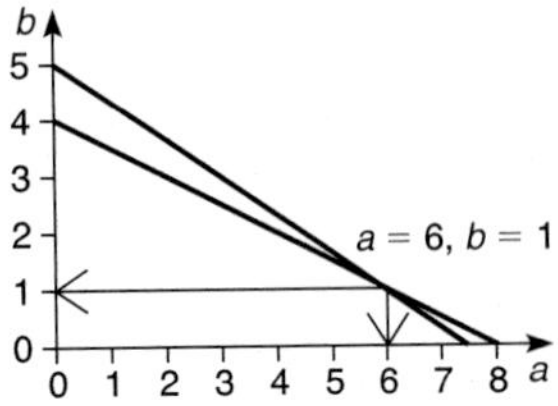

b

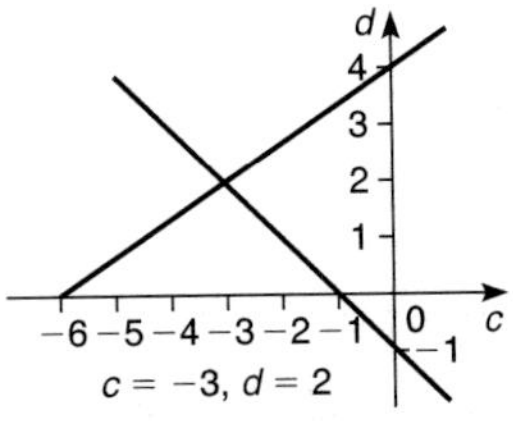

c

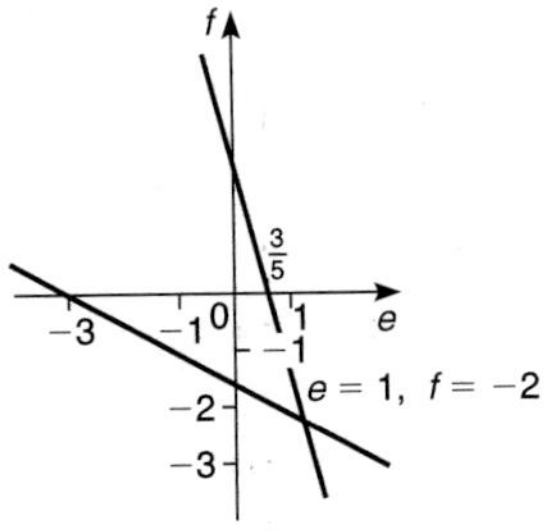

d

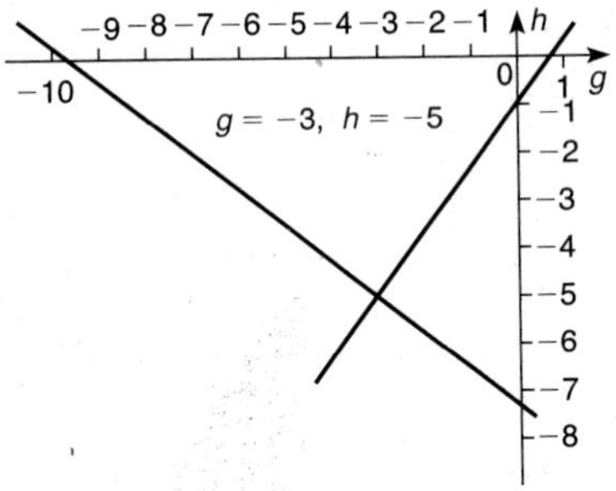

e

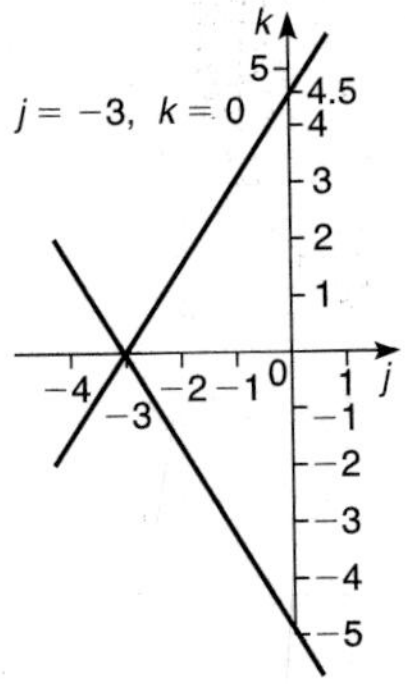

f

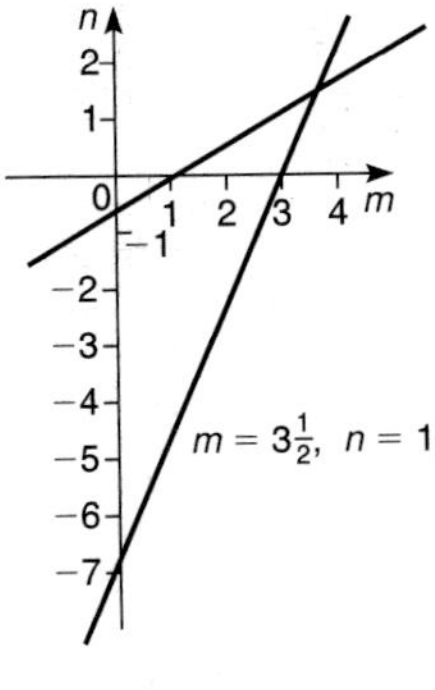

Practice 12.3.4 – p. 335

1 a 7 **c** 1 **e** 7
b −2 **d** $-4\frac{1}{2}$ **f** $2\frac{1}{3}$
2 a 5 **c** 1 **e** $1\frac{1}{2}$
b 7 **d** −2 **f** $1\frac{1}{3}$
3 a $1\frac{2}{3}$ **d** $-\frac{1}{5}$ **g** 1
b $\frac{1}{3}$ **e** $-1\frac{1}{5}$ **h** 0
c $-2\frac{1}{2}$ **f** $\frac{5}{9}$ **i** ∞ (infinity)
4 a 1 **b** 4 **c** −3 **d** $-1\frac{1}{2}$
5 a C **c** A **e** D
b E **d** B
6 a 2 **b** $y = 2x + c$ **c** −2 **d** $y = 2x - 2$
7 $y = -3x$ **8** $y = 4x - 2$ **9** $5y = 12x + 11$

Practice 12.3.5 – p. 339

1 i $y = 3x + 1$ **iii** $y = 3x + 7$ **v** $y = 3x + \frac{2}{3}$
ii $y = 3x - 1$ **iv** $y = 3x - 8$
2 i $y = -2x + 1$ **iii** $y = -2x + 7$ **v** $y = -2x + \frac{2}{3}$
ii $y = -2x - 1$ **iv** $y = -2x - 8$
3 i $y = \frac{2}{3}x + 1$ **iii** $y = \frac{2}{3}x + 7$ **v** $y = \frac{2}{3}x + \frac{2}{3}$
ii $y = \frac{2}{3}x - 1$ **iv** $y = \frac{2}{3}x - 8$
4 i $a = 4, b = -5$ **iii** $a = 1\frac{1}{2}, b = \frac{1}{2}$
ii $a = 3, b = 6$ **iv** $a = 2; b = \frac{3}{4}$
5 a (4, 5); 5.66 (or $\sqrt{32}$)
b $(2\frac{1}{2}, 4)$; 3.61 (or $\sqrt{13}$)
c $(5, 5\frac{1}{2})$; 9.22 (or $\sqrt{85}$)
d (1, 7); 11.66 (or $\sqrt{136}$)
e (−1, 5); 10 (or $\sqrt{100}$)
f (3, 4); 18.87 (or $\sqrt{356}$)
g $(\frac{1}{2}, 1)$; 16.28 (or $\sqrt{265}$)
h $(2\frac{1}{2}, 1)$; 8.54 (or $\sqrt{73}$)
i $(6, -2\frac{1}{2})$; 14.32 (or $\sqrt{205}$)
j $(1\frac{1}{2}, -5\frac{1}{2})$; 9.49 (or $\sqrt{90}$)
k $(-3\frac{1}{2}, -5)$; 15 (or $\sqrt{225}$)
l $(-5, 5\frac{1}{2})$; 9.22 (or $\sqrt{85}$)
m (−5, 5); 8.94 (or $\sqrt{80}$)
n $(2, 2\frac{1}{2})$; 6.40 (or $\sqrt{41}$)
o (0, 0); 18.43 (or $\sqrt{340}$)

Practice 12.4.1 – p. 342

1 a

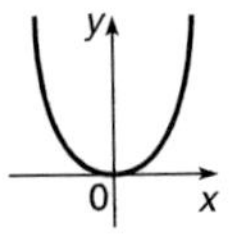

b

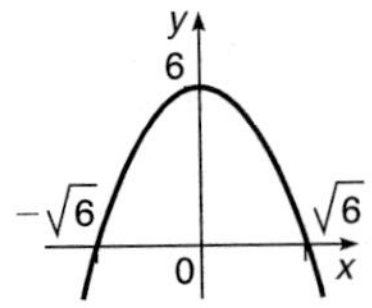

c

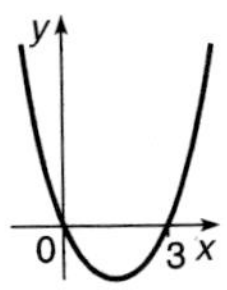

d

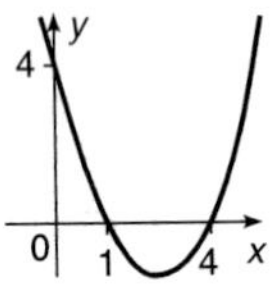

e

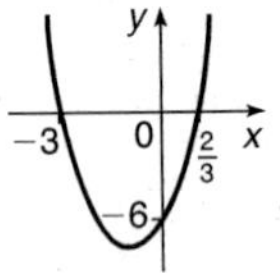

f

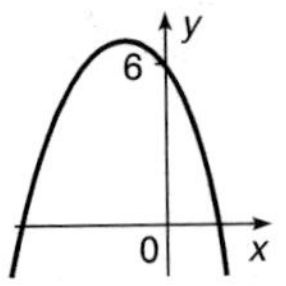

Practice 12.4.2 – p. 343

Answers to 1dp read from graphs

1 a i (0, 0) **ii** $x = 0$ **iii** $x = 0$
b i (0, 6) **ii** $x = 0$ **iii** $x = 2.5, -2.5$
c i (1.5, −2.25) **ii** $x = 1.5$ **iii** $x = 0, 3$
d i (2.5, −2.25) **ii** $x = 2.5$ **iii** $x = 1, 4$
e i (−1.2, −10) **ii** $x = -1.2$ **iii** $x = 0.7, -3$
f i (−1.3, 11.3) **ii** $x = -1.3$ **iii** $x = 0.6, -3.3$

2 a

v	d
0	0
10	5.3
20	14.7
30	28
40	45.3
50	66.7
60	92
70	121.3
80	154.7

b

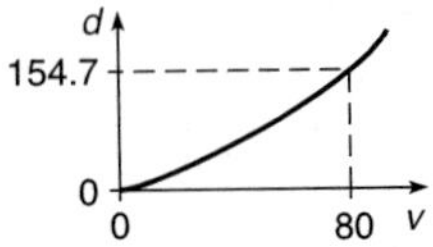

c i 9.5 m **ii** 55.5 m **iii** 137.5 m
d 42.4 mph

3 a $A = x(20 - x) = 20x - x^2$

b

x	A
0	0
4	64
8	96
12	96
16	64
20	0

c i 59 cm² **iii** 100 cm² **v** 10 cm by 10 cm
ii 11.4 cm by 8.6 cm **iv** $x = 10$

4 a

x	h
0	0
10	9.72
20	18.9
30	27.5
40	35.6
50	43.1
60	50

b

c 45.8 m approx.

Practice 12.5.1 – p. 347

1 a 32°F **b** 100°C **c** 37°C **d** 185°F
2 a i 310 m **ii** 520 m **iii** 580 m **iv** 310 m
  b 600 m
  c i 3 min, 37 min **ii** $9\frac{1}{2}$, $11\frac{1}{2}$, $27\frac{1}{2}$ and 30 min
  d 20 min from home
  e 18 min
  f i at 10 min **ii** 8 min **iii** 300 m
  g 1800 m
3 a $45 + 9 = 54$ miles **b** 45 mph **c** 1045 to 1142
4 a 2500 **b** 400 **c** 1500 to 3450
5

6 C
7 A4; B2; C1; D3
8 A

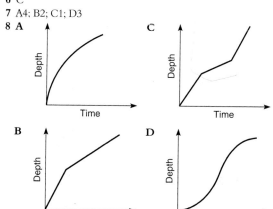

Practice 12.5.2 – p. 352

1 b $m \approx \dfrac{60}{17.6} \approx 3.4$ $c \approx 7$
  c $y \approx 3.4x + 7$ **i** $y \approx 3.4 \times 4 + 7 \approx 20.6$
     ii $y \approx 3.4 \times 10 + 7 \approx 41$

2 b $m \approx \dfrac{-46}{14} \approx -3.3$ $c \approx 46$
  c $y \approx -3.3x + 46$
   i $y \approx -3.3 \times 2.54 + 46 \approx 38$
   ii $y \approx -3.3 \times 11.7 + 46 \approx 7.4$
   iii $y \approx -3.3 \times 14 + 46 \approx 0$

3 b $m \approx \dfrac{15.6}{2} \approx 7.8$; the resistance R
  c i 2.6 A **ii** 11.6 V

4 a and c

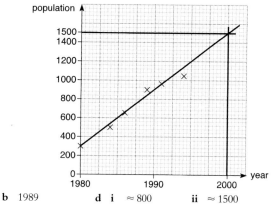

b 1989 **d i** ≈ 800 **ii** ≈ 1500

5 a and b

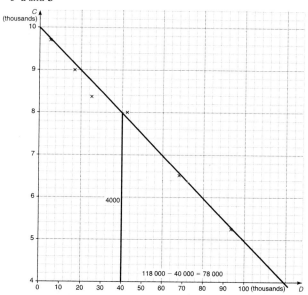

  c i £10 000 **ii** $m \approx \dfrac{-4000}{78\,000} \approx -0.05$
  d $C = 10\,000 - 0.05D$
  e i £9500 approx. **ii** £5000 approx.
  f 50 000 miles approx.

Practice 12.6.1 – p. 357
Answers to 1dp read from graphs

1 a

b

$8\frac{1}{3}$

c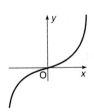

d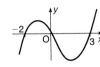

e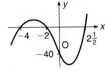

2 a i 3.6
  ii 4.6
 b i 3.6 or 6.8
  ii 10.6
 c (5, 3)

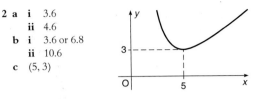

3 a i 1.4
  ii 6.5
 b $y = 3$

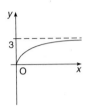

4 a 8.2
 b −4.1
 c i 5.6
  ii −4

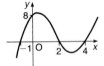

Chapter 13

Practice 13.1.1 – p. 368
1 a 120°   **e** 756°
 b 144°   **f** 60°
 c 540°   **g** 54°
 d 108°   **h** 49.5°

2 6

3 a 60°   **f** 70°
 b 129°   **g** $h° = m° = j° = 35°$, $g° = l° = i° = k° = 145°$
 c 11°   **h** 100°
 d 157°   **i** $p° = 62°$, $q = 46°$
 e 231°   **j** $r° = 87°$, $s = 139°$

4 34°

5 124°

6 a 90°   **d** 160°
 b 120°   **e** 202.5°
 c 105°   **f** 155°

7 65°

8 156°

Practice 13.2.1 – p. 373
1 a 83°   **e** 61°   **i** 70°
 b 36°   **f** 112°   **j** 54°
 c 74°   **g** 36°   **k** 62°
 d 48°   **h** 24°   **l** 65°

2 $53\frac{1}{3}$

3 70°

4 9 cm and 19 cm

5 $(170 − 7x)°$

Practice 13.2.2 – p. 377
1 a 900°   **b** 1620°   **c** 3600°
2 a 5   **b** 9   **c** 15   **d** 16   **e** 32
3 a 3   **b** 5   **c** 12   **d** 24   **e** 30
4 a 144°˙ 36′   **c** 162°; 18°   **e** 170°; 10°
 b 160°; 20°   **d** 165.6°; 14.4°
5 120°   **6** 110°   **7** 3   **8** 9   **9** 10
10 10 sides, 30 sides, exterior angles 36° and 12° and interior
  angles 144° and 168°

Practice 13.2.3 – p. 380
1 a 112°   **f** $m° = 128°$, $n° = 101°$
 b $b° = 50°$, $c° = 40°$ **g** $p° = 128°$
 c $d° = 69°$, $e = 41°$, $f° = 33°$ **h** $q° = 60°$, $r° = 150°$
 d $g° = 47°$, $h° = 90°$,   **i** $s° = 88°$, $t° = 92°$
   $i° = 43°$, $j° = 47°$ **j** $u° = 135°$, $v° = 45°$
 e $e° = 50°$, $k° = 110°$

Practice 13.2.4 – p. 383
Answers to 3sf
1 a i 15.7 cm   **iii** 65.9 cm   **v** 83.8 ft
  ii 37.7 cm   **iv** 27.9 cm
 b i 58.1 in²   **iii** 1810 m²   **v** 2060 ft²
  ii 113 cm²   **iv** 58.1 in²
 c 2 × 14.6 + 3.14 × 14.6 = 75.0 ft or 75.1 ft
2 a 78.5 cm²   **b** 35.7 cm
3 40.2 cm²
4 a i 25 − 6.25π   **ii** 5.37 m²
 b i 76.88 − 19.22π   **ii** 16.5 cm²
 c i 400 − 100π   **ii** 85.8 m²
 d i 14.5π   **ii** 45.5 cm² or 45.6 cm²
5 12.8 cm
6 a 37.7 in.   **b** 1260 in.   **c** 20.9 in/s
7 47.8

Practice 13.2.5 – p. 386

1 a cube **b** BD, KH, AE, LI, FN, GM

2 A and D only

3 a cuboid **c** triangular prism
b square-based pyramid

4 a

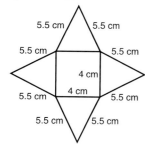

b

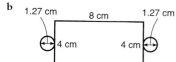

c

d

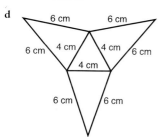

Practice 13.2.6 – p. 388

1 a

c

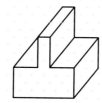

b

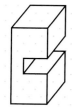

d

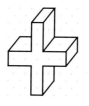

Practice 13.2.7 – p. 389

1 a

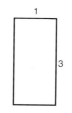

c

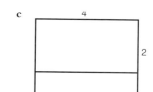

b

d

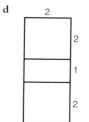

2 a

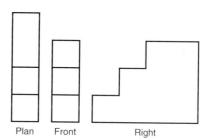

b

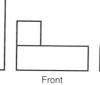

c

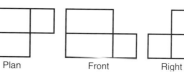

d

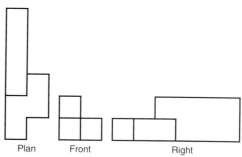

e

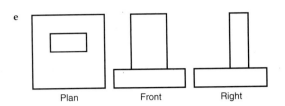

Plan   Front   Right

f

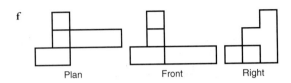

Plan   Front   Right

Practice 13.2.8 – p. 394

1 $\angle A = 72.5°$, $\angle C = 17.5°$

2 $\angle E = 50°$, $\angle F = 50°$

3 $\angle K = 48°$, $\angle I = 42°$

4 $\angle O = 70°$, $\angle N = 35°$, $\angle P = 55°$

5 $\angle S = 80°$

6 $\angle Z = 41°$, $\angle Y = 38°$

7 $\angle K = 24°$

8 $\angle E = 137°$

9 $\angle A = 110°$, $\angle B = 95°$
   $\angle D = 95°$, $\angle O = 140°$

10 $\angle A = 66°$, $\angle B = 66°$
    $\angle D = 66°$, $\angle O = 48°$

11 $\angle P = 90°$, $\angle S = 49°$

Practice 13.3.1 – p. 397

1 a

d

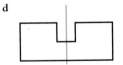

b

e

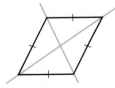

c

f

g

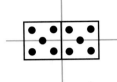

i no axes of symmetry

h

(continued figure)

2 a H, I, X (depending on how it is written)
  b X (depending on how it is written)
  c O
  d H, I, N, S, Z
  e X (depending on how it is written)
  f O
  g N, S, Z

3 a   **c**   **e**

b   **d**

4 a   **c**   **e**

b   **d**

5 a 1 axis   c 4 axes and rotational symmetry of order 4
  b 1 axis   d 1 axis
6 a an infinite number

c

Practice 13.4.1 – p. 401

1 $a = 9$ cm, $b = 4$ cm   5 $d = 7$ cm, $e = 10$ cm, $f = 3\frac{3}{7}$ cm
2 $p = 9$, $q = 6$ m   6 $g = 28.8$ cm, $h = 31.2$ cm
3 $c = 3.2$ cm, $d = 6.5$ cm   7 $m = 2.25$ cm, $n = 6$ cm
4 $r = 4$, $s = 12$ in.   8 68 cm

Practice 13.4.2 – p. 403

1 a yes – sides in ratio 1 : 3
  b no – angles do not match
  c yes – sides and angles match
  d yes – all circles are similar

2 3.75 in.

3 a no   **e** yes   **i** no
  b yes   **f** no   **j** yes
  c yes   **g** yes
  d no   **h** yes

4 10 times

Practice 13.5.1a – p. 407

1 a 17 cm   **b** 25 cm   **c** 48 cm

2 64 m

3 i $\sqrt{23.04}\,\pi$ **ii** 4.8 m

4 a yes $(6^2 + 8^2 = 10^2)$ **d** no $(12^2 + 18^2 \neq 22^2)$
  b no $(10^2 + 15^2 \neq 18^2)$ **e** no $(12^2 + 21^2 \neq 24^2)$
  c yes $(7^2 + 24^2 = 25^2)$

5 8 m

Practice 13.5.1b – p. 408

Answers to 3 sf where needed

1 a $\sqrt{105}$ cm   **b** 6.72 cm   **c** 8.39 cm

2 4.77 m

3 i $\sqrt{29}$ km   **ii** 5.39 km

4 i $\sqrt{65}$ yd   **ii** 8.06 yd

5 11 300 ft

6 10.0 m

7 2.14 in.

8 AM = 9.03 cm, AB = 18.1 cm

9 a 2000 yd   **b** 2010 yd

10 a i $\sqrt{20}$ cm **ii** 4.47 cm   **c i** $\sqrt{113}$ cm **ii** 10.6 cm
   b i $\sqrt{32}$ cm **ii** 5.66 cm   **d i** $\sqrt{80}$ cm **ii** 8.94 cm

11 AB = 13.3 cm, BM = 6.64 cm, MC = 13.2 cm

12 22.8 m

Practice 13.6.1a – p. 414

1 6.76 m

Practice 13.6.1b – p. 415

Answers to 4sf or 3sf where appropriate

1 a 0.4384   **c** 0.9004   **e** 0.9943
  b 0.8387   **d** 0.9468   **f** 36.03

2 a 30°   **c** 72.3°   **e** 0°
  b 30°   **d** 90°   **f** 71.6°

3 a $a = 3$ cm, $b = 5.20$ cm
  b $i = 59.6$ cm, $j = 138$ cm
  c $g = 34.0$ cm, $h = 43.0$ cm
  d $c = 32.5$ cm, $d = 37.1$ cm
  e $p = 5.85$ cm, $q = 13.4$ cm
  f $r = 62.2$ cm, $s = 58.0$ cm
  g $x = 189$ ft, $y = 1018$ ft
  h $u = 10.5$ cm, $v = 11.4$ cm

4 a $a = 20 \div \tan 17 + 20 \div \tan 71 = 72.3$ m
  b $p = 5.87$ cm, $q = 7$ cm
  c $r = 21.2$ m, $s = 3.738$ m
  d $d = 100 \tan 55.7 - 100 \tan 23.1 = 103.9$ in.

5 a $\theta° = 23.6°$
  b $\theta° = 41.7°$
  c $\theta° = 34.1°$
  d $\theta° = \cos^{-1}\left(\frac{12}{13}\right) + \tan^{-1}\left(\frac{15}{12}\right) = 22.62° + 51.34° = 74.0°$

6 AB = 11.8 cm, ON = 4.13 cm

Practice 13.6.2 – p. 419

Answers to 3sf, angles to nearest 0.1°

1 1030 m, 247 m

2 29.6°

3 160 cm

4 8.63°

5 12.3°

6 95.8 ft

7 40.8°

8 QR = 739 yd, PR = 946 yd, course = 2884 yd

9 20.6°

10 11.2 km, 047.6°

11 65 ft

12 23.0 ft

13 a 50 m
  b 10 m

14 BC = 23.5 miles,   OC = 12.5 miles

15 a $CB^2 = 65$, $AB^2 = 52$, $CA^2 = 13$, $65 = 52 + 13$
  b 60.3°

Chapter 14

Practice 14.3.1 – p. 433

1 (4, 8) (1, 6) (−3, −8) (−10, −4)

2 (0, −3), (3, −2), (1, 2)

3 (7, −1), (2, −1), (7, −6), (2, −6)

4 a $\begin{pmatrix} 4 \\ -2 \end{pmatrix}$

  b $\begin{pmatrix} -3 \\ 6 \end{pmatrix}$

  c $\begin{pmatrix} 8 \\ 14 \end{pmatrix}$

  d $\begin{pmatrix} 4 \\ 0 \end{pmatrix}$

5 a it is parallel to the *x*-axis   **b** it is parallel to the *y*-axis

6 a, b

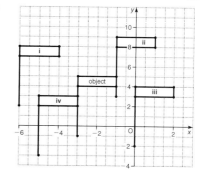

7 $A = \begin{pmatrix} 9 \\ -6 \end{pmatrix}$, $B = \begin{pmatrix} 9 \\ -7 \end{pmatrix}$, $C = \begin{pmatrix} 12 \\ 5 \end{pmatrix}$ **8** (7, −2)

Practice 14.4.1 – p. 436

1

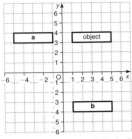

  a $(-1, 3)$ $(-1, 4)$ $(-5, 3)$ $(-5, 4)$
  b $(1, -3)$ $(1, -4)$ $(5, -3)$ $(5, -4)$

2

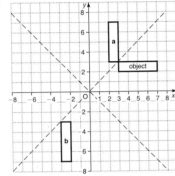

  a $(2, 3)$ $(3, 3)$ $(2, 7)$ $(3, 7)$
  b $(-2, -3)$ $(-3, -3)$ $(-2, -7)$ $(-3, -7)$

3

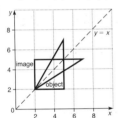

4

  A   B

I_2 is facing the same way as the object but is twice as far from line B as the object is from line A

5

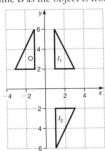

  a $(1, 2)$ $(1, 6)$ $(3, 2)$
  b $(1, -2)$ $(1, -6)$ $(3, -2)$

6

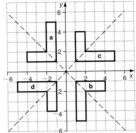

  a $(-1, 1)$ $(-1, 5)$ $(-2, 5)$ $(-2, 2)$ $(-4, 2)$ $(-4, 1)$
  b $(1, -1)$ $(1, -5)$ $(2, -5)$ $(2, -2)$ $(4, -2)$ $(4, -1)$
  c $(1, 1)$ $(1, 4)$ $(2, 4)$ $(2, 2)$ $(5, 2)$ $(5, 1)$
  d $(-1, -1)$ $(-5, -1)$ $(-5, -2)$ $(-2, -2)$ $(-2, -4)$ $(-1, -4)$

7

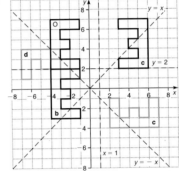

8

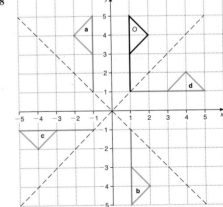

  a $(-1, 3)$ $(-2, 4)$ $(-1, 5)$ $(-1, 1)$
  b $(1, -3)$ $(2, -4)$ $(1, -5)$ $(1, -1)$
  c $(-3, -1)$ $(-4, -2)$ $(-5, -1)$ $(-1, -1)$
  d $(3, 1)$ $(4, 2)$ $(5, 1)$ $(1, 1)$

Practice 14.5.1 – p. 441

  1 i

ii

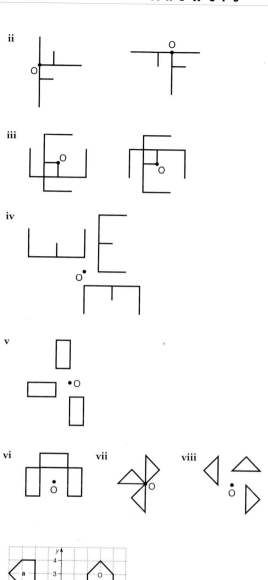

iii

iv

v

vi   vii   viii

2

3

4 a, b

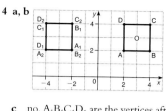

c no, $A_1B_1C_1D_1$ are the vertices after **a**
   and $A_2B_2C_2D_2$ are the vertices after **b**,
   hence the two transformations **a** and **b** are not the same

5 a 90° rotation clockwise about (0, 0)
  b 180° rotation about (0, 0) (clockwise or anticlockwise)

6

Angle is 113°

7 a   d

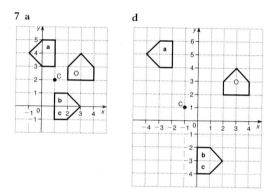

b   e

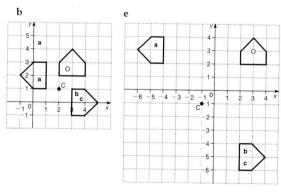

c

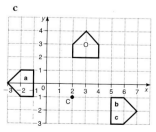

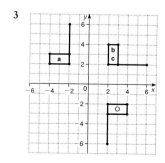

8

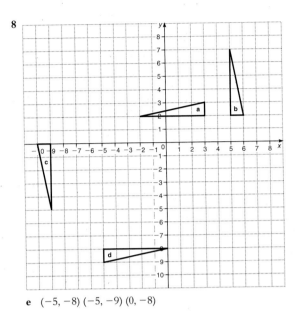

e $(-5, -8)$ $(-5, -9)$ $(0, -8)$

Practice 14.6.1 – p. 445

1 a

3

9

c

12 / 12

8

b

6   6

6

d

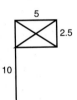

5

2.5

10

2 a sf 5   **b** sf 2.5   **c** sf 2

3 a

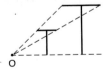

O

b

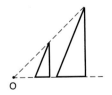

O

c

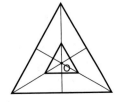

O

4

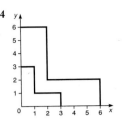

5 a

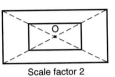

Scale factor 2

b

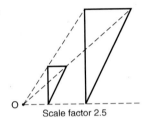

O

Scale factor 2.5

c

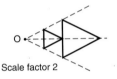

O

Scale factor 2

d

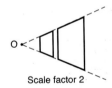

O

Scale factor 2

Practice 14.6.2a – p. 448

1 a 16.8 miles   **b** 8.8 miles
2 a 4 cm   **b** 35.2 cm
3 78 miles

Practice 14.6.2b – p. 448

1 3.28 cm
2 a $1 : \frac{1}{4} \times 1760 \times 3 \times 12 = 1 : 15\,840$, i.e. $1 : 16\,000$ (2sf)
   b 550 yd   **c** 3.41 in.
3 a 1204 m   **b** 17.9 cm

Practice 14.7.1 – p. 450

1

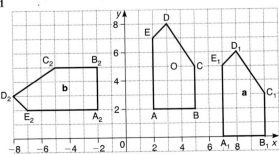

2

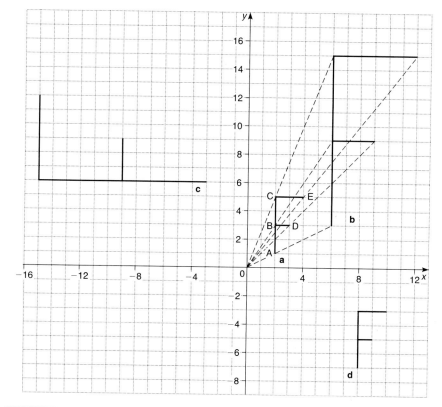

3

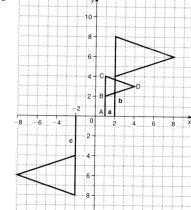

4 a

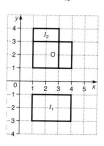

b reflection in the line $y = x$

5 a

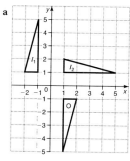

b rotation $+90°$ about $(0, 0)$

6 a

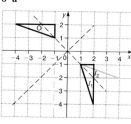

b rotation $180°$ about $(0, 0)$

7 a

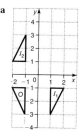

b reflection in the x-axis

8 a

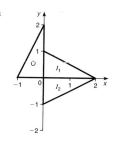

b reflection in the line $y = x$

Practice 14.7.2 – p. 452

1 the equilateral triangle; the square; the hexagon

2 yes   **3** yes

Practice 14.8.1 – p. 453

1 a 9.5 to 10.5 cm
  b 7.75 to 7.85 cm
  c 135.5 to 134.5 mm
  d 6.5 to 7.5 in.
  e 15.15 to 15.25 in.
2 a 24.5° to 25.5°
  b 47.5° to 48.5°
  c 73.5° to 74.5°
  d 122.5° to 123.5°
  e 152.5° to 153.5°
3 a 15.5° to 16.5°
  b 35.5° to 36.5°
  c 68.5° to 69.5°
  d 116.5° to 117.5°
  e 161.5° to 162.5°
4 All angles given to the nearest degree.
  a 23°, 67°, 90°
  b 37°, 53°, 90°
  c 54°, 59°, 67°
  d 48°, 57°, 75°
  e 53°, 18°, 108°
  f 44°, 58°, 78°
5–7 Pupils' own work.
8 You should have ended at the point where you started,
  i.e. constructed a regular pentagon.

9

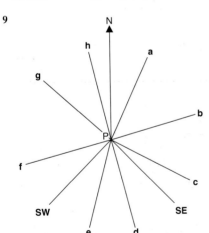

10 a

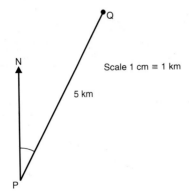

b

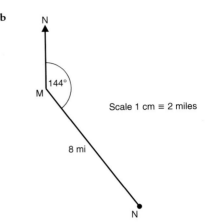

Scale 1 cm ≡ 2 miles

c

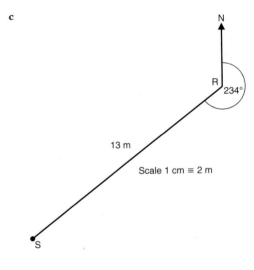

Scale 1 cm ≡ 2 m

d

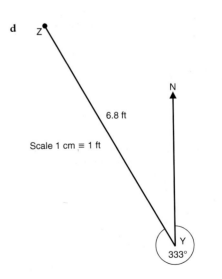

Scale 1 cm ≡ 1 ft

11 a

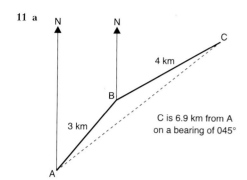

C is 6.9 km from A
on a bearing of 045°

b

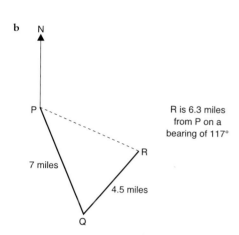

R is 6.3 miles
from P on a
bearing of 117°

c

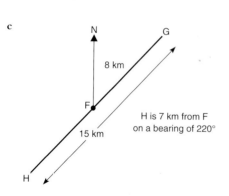

H is 7 km from F
on a bearing of 220°

d

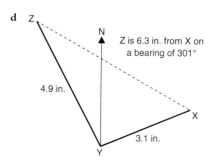

Z is 6.3 in. from X on
a bearing of 301°

Practice 14.8.2 – p. 458

1 left as an exercise for the reader

2

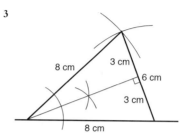

AC = 6.4 cm

3

the base is bisected perpendicularly
4 left as an exercise for the reader
5 left as an exercise for the reader
6 left as an exercise for the reader

Practice 14.8.3 – p. 461

1

BD = 7.1 cm

2 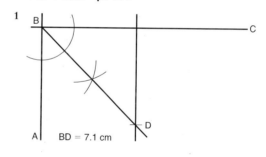 **3**

4

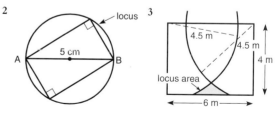

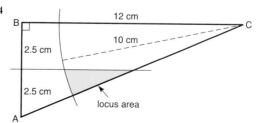

5 a, b

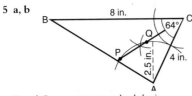

P and Q are common to both loci

6

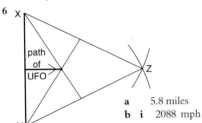

a   5.8 miles
b i   2088 mph   **ii**   30 seconds

7 a
b

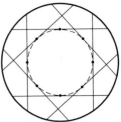

c   locus is another circle of radius 3 cm

Chapter 15

Practice 15.1.1 – p. 468

1   8 km = 5 mi approx; 4 km = 2.6 mi approx
2   55 ÷ 2.2 = 25 kg approx
3   3 × 1.75 = 5 pints approx
4   5 × 30 = 150 cm approx
5   150 ÷ 30 = 5 oz approx
6   66 × 2.5 = 165 cm approx
7   2.5 × 1.75 = 4 pints approx
8   3 × 1600 = 4800 m approx
9 a   £1.26   **b** 27p   **c** £2.43   **d** 85p or 86p
   e   54p per lb; thus 10 × 54 = £5.40
   f   20p approx per lb; thus 55 × 20 = £11
   g   25p approx per lb; thus 3 × 25 = 75p

Practice 15.2.1a – p. 470

1 a   18.2 m   **b** 32 m
2   9.8 cm   **3**   6 cm   **4**   40 cm

Practice 15.2.1b – p. 470

1 a   56 ft   **b** 11.3 in.   **c** 32 cm   **d** 17.5 yds
2   15.7 cm

Practice 15.3.1 – p. 471

1   13 or 14 cm²   **2**   45 miles² (nearest 5 square miles)

Practice 15.3.2 – p. 478

1   32 cm²   9   93.8 cm²
2   64 cm²   10   11.3 cm²
3   48 cm²   11   168 cm²
4   78 cm²   12   87.7 cm²
5   84 cm²   13   93.5 cm²
6   48 cm²   14   104 cm²
7   105 in.²   15   108 cm²
8   18.3 cm²   16   24.5 cm²
17 **i** 6.75π   **ii** 21.2 cm²
18 **i** 32 − 2π   **ii** 25.7 cm²
19 **i** 25 − 6.25π   **ii** 5.37 cm²
20   0.5 m²
21 **i** 10 + 7.031 25π   **ii** 32.1 in.²
22 **i** 6.928 + π   **ii** 10.1 in.²
23   121 cm²

Practice 15.4.1 – p. 486

Answers to 3 sf where appropriate
1   343 cm³
2   48 cm³
3   260 cm³
4   371 cm³
5   800 cm³
6   27.7 cm³
7   216 cm³
8   96 cm³
9   76.7 cm³
10   452 cm³
11   140 cm³
12   251 cm³
13   35
14 **a** 118 cm³
   b 926 g

15 **a** 2.60 × 10¹¹ miles³
   b 3.657 × 10²⁶ lb
   c 1.97 × 10⁸ miles²
   d 39 400 days, i.e. 107.9 years
        approx.

16 **a** **i** 0.0585 in.²
       ii 0.3507 in.³
       iii 0.0301 in.³
       iv 0.321 in.³
   b 8.58%
   c 0.175 oz
   d 91
17 **a** 10.7 cm³
   b 409.3 cm³
   c 39 slices altogether

Practice 15.4.2 – p. 491

1   60 cm
2   2500 kg
3   1.47 litres
4   (0.75)³ × 95 = 40 p
5   25 000 m²
6   $2.744 = \left(\dfrac{h}{8}\right)^2, h = 13.3$ in.
7   2.744 × 4.4 = 12.1 in.²
8   $\left(\dfrac{12}{48}\right)^2 = \dfrac{1}{16}$
9   2³ × 3 = 24 s

Practice 15.5.1 – p. 493

1   area   6   none   11   volume   16   none
2   length   7   area   12   volume   17   length
3   none   8   none   13   volume   18   length
4   volume   9   length   14   area   19   length
5   volume   10   volume   15   length
20   r^2 represents an area, $\frac{4}{3}\pi$ is a constant, thus the whole formula
     can only be an area
21 **a** 1   **c** 2   **e** 3   **g** none   **i** 1   **k** none
   b 3   **d** 1   **f** 2   **h** 3   **j** 2
22 **a** 1   **c** 2   **e** 3   **g** 3; 2   **i** 3; 2
   b 2   **d** 2   **f** 2   **h** 2; 1

4.1 Answers and mark scheme

Q	Part		Answers	Marks	Comments
1	a		Any two valid questions (award 1 mark each)	B1 B1	
	b	i	Any valid method	B1	
		ii	*Telephone directory* Would only question those who are not ex-directory	B1	
			Supermarket Would only question those who shop at this particular supermarket	B1	
2			Jill's mean Because her sample size is bigger	B1 B1	
3	a		Appropriate scale + axes labelled Plots at correct heights within correct classes Plots at mid-points joined to form a polygon	B1 B1 B1	
	b		Modal value = 17	B1	
4	a		Not late = 0.7	B1	
	b		Probability = 0.3×0.1 $\qquad = 0.03$	M1 A1	
5	a		$\dfrac{14 + 20 + 30 + 16}{4} = 20$	B1	
	b		Plots at correct heights in correct order/plots and midway between weeks	B1	± 0.5 small square ± 0.5 small square
	c		Next value about 5.25 $(5.25 \times 40) - (8 + 2 + 9)$ $\qquad = 2$	B1 M1 A1 ft	± 1.0
	d		Valid comment e.g. the sales are not seasonal	B1	

(Total = 20 marks)

4.2 Answers and mark scheme

Q	Part	Answers	Marks	Comments
1		1 | 8 9 2 | 2 3 3 7 3 | 1 6	B2	All correct Correct stem + 1 leaf B1
2	a b	6 Average higher for Team A Median not in middle for Team B Distribution for Team A is symmetrical (or equivalent)	B1 2ans B1 + B1	
3		$\frac{360}{36}$ 150, 120, 70, 20 Pie chart drawn accurately Exactly 4 sectors labelled	M1 A1 A1 A1	Angles calculated correctly ($\pm 2°$)
4	a b c	As rainfall increases the number of deck chair tickets sold decreases (or negative correlation) Line of best fit shown About 250	B1 B1 M1 + A1	reading from graph
5	a b	No.of sixes = $100 \times \frac{1}{4}$ = 25 Probability = $\frac{13}{100}$	M1 A1 B1	
6	a b c	2, 8, 40, 81, 95, 99, 100 7 points at their (increasing) CFs plots at upper class boundaries and joined by curves or lines 100 − 89 = 11	B1 B1 B1 M1	$\pm\frac{1}{2}$ small square For an increasing curve From an increasing CF graph 100 − reading at 3.35 grams

(Total = 20 marks)

9.1 Answers and mark scheme

Q	Part	Answers	Marks	Comments
1		Bill is $79 \times 4 = 316$ Hotel bill is $316 \div 1.58$ $= £200$	B1 M1 A1	
2	a	VAT = 5% of £60 $= \frac{5}{100} \times £60$ $= 3$ $= £3$	M1 A1 B1	£ sign
	b	Total paid is £63	A1	
3	a	2.645 751 3... 2.65	M1 A1	
	b	e.g. $2^2 + 3^2 = 13$ Which is not even	B1	
4		Large: cost £4.60/litre Regular: cost £4.99/litre $\Big\}$ $\therefore$ large is best value	M1 A1 B1 dep	($\div$ same for both)
5		1.883 544 3 1.9	M1 A1	
6		0.000 131 25 or $1.31... \times 10^{-4}$	M1 A1	
7		Interest $= 1.06 \times £4000$ Amount $= £4240$ (1st yr) Amount $= £4494.40$ (2nd yr) Amount $= £4764.064$ (3rd yr) or rounded	M1 M1 A1	$£4000 \times 1.06^3 \Rightarrow$ M2

(Total = 20 marks)

9.2 Answers and mark scheme

Q	Part	Answers	Marks	Comments
1		Train arrives at 17 23 Time is $17\,23 - 15\,49$ $= 1$ hour 34 minutes	B1 M1 A1	
2	a b	£600 $2 \times 35 + 3 \times \frac{1}{2} \times 35$ £122.50	B1 M1 A1	
3	a	$4 \times 2^3 = 32$	B1	
	b	$\dfrac{4.96}{262 + 23.9} \approx \dfrac{5}{50}$ $= 0.1$	B1 B1	
	c	$7^{-2} = \dfrac{1}{7^2} = \dfrac{1}{49}$	B1	
4		$\text{Interest} = 6000 \times \dfrac{4}{100} \times \dfrac{5}{12}$ $= £100$ Vinod withdraws £6100	M1 A1 B1	
5	a	Repeated division by 2 or 3 $2^2 \times 3^3$	M1 A1	or $2 \times 2 \times 3 \times 3 \times 3$
	b	12	B1	
6	a	$ab = 3 \times 10^4 \times 4 \times 10^7$ $= 12 \times 10^{11}$ $= 1.2 \times 10^{12}$	B1 B1	
	b	$\dfrac{a}{b} = \dfrac{3 \times 10^4}{4 \times 10^7}$ $= 0.75 \times 10^{-3}$ $= 7.5 \times 10^{-4}$	 B1 B1	

(Total = 20 marks)

16.1 Answers and mark scheme

Q	Part	Answers	Marks	Comments
1	a	6	B1	
	b	$(12 \times 2) - 7$	M1	
		$= 17$	M1	
2	a	10, 8, 6, 4, 2	B2	3 correct B1
		correct plots, correct line	B1	
	b	(2.4, 3.2)	B1 ft	each value ± 0.1
3		$46°$	B1	
		Base angle of isosceles triangle (oe)	B1	
4		$\frac{1}{2} \times 4 \times (5 + 7) = 24$	M1	
		$\frac{2}{5} \times 24$	M1	
		9.6 (cm^2)	A1	
5	a	14	B1	
	b	29	B1	
	c	nth term $= 3n - 1$ OR $2 + 3(n - 1)$	A1 + M1	
6		Maximum $= 88.55$ seconds	B1	
		Minimum $= 88.45$ seconds	B1	
7		$\pi \times 7^2$	M1	
		$= 49\pi$	A1	
8	a	Translation	M1	
		$\begin{pmatrix} 3 \\ -6 \end{pmatrix}$	A1	
	b	Reflection	M1	
		$y = -x$	A1	
9	a	$\frac{1}{3}x = 7$	M1	
		$x = 21$	A1	
	b	$3x - 9 = 2x - 6$	M1	Expand bracket
		$x = 3$	A1	
	c	$x^2 - 2x - 8 = 0$	M1	
		$(x - 4)(x + 2) = 0$	M1	
		$x = 4 \ or \ -2$	A1	

16.1 Answers and mark scheme – *continued*

Q	Part	Answers	Marks	Comments
10		$\pi a(b + c)$, $2\pi ab$, $\pi c\sqrt{a^2 + b^2}$ all three	B2	3 correct B2 − 1 for each error or omission
11	a b	$\angle SRQ = 40°$ Angles in same segment $x = 50°$	B1 B1 B1	
12	a b	$5 - x$ $x(5 - x) = 9$ $5x - x^2 = 9$ $(x^2 - 5x + 9 = 0)$ $x = 3, x = -2$	B1 B1 B1 B1	

(Total = 40 marks)

16.2 Answers and mark scheme

Q	Part		Answers	Marks	Comments
1			Use of 360° $360 - (98 + 43)$ $3x = 219$ $73°$	B1 M1 M1 A1	or $360 - 141$
2				B2	
3			$6 \times 10 \times 4 = 240$ $\frac{1}{2} \times 5 \times 4 \times 8 = 80$ ('their' 240) $-$ ('their' 80) 160 cm^3	M1 M1 M1 A1 B1	
4	a		4	B2	$\dfrac{1}{0.25}$ gets B1
	b	i	$5 \times 12 - (-5)$ $= 60 + 5 = 65$	M1 A1	
		ii	12×-5 $= -60$	M1 A1	
		iii	$\dfrac{12}{12 + 3 \times -5}$ -4	M1 A1	
5	a		$n + 1, n + 2, n + 11$	B2	
	b		$n + n + 1 + n + 2 + n + 11$ $4n + 14$ **or** $n4 + 14$ **or** $2(2n + 7)$ Penalise further incorrect algebra, e.g. $4n + 14 = 18n \Rightarrow$ M1 A0	M1 A1 ft	
	c		$4n + 14 = 115$ $4n = 101$ and 101 is not a multiple of 4	B1 B1	

16.2 Answers and mark scheme – *continued*

Q	Part		Answers	Marks	Comments
6			Trial for $3.4 \leqslant x < 4$	B1	
			Trials for 3.5 *and* 3.4	B1	
			or trial for 3.45 ($= 37.613 \dots$)		
			Ans = 3.5	B1	
7	a		$3x \leqslant 21$	M1	
			$x \leqslant 7$	A1	
	b		$x^2 - 18x + 81 - 9$	B1	
			$x^2 - 18x + 72$	B1	
	c		$12x^9$	B1	for 12
				B1	for x^9
8	a	i	$180 - (2 \times 36)$	M1	
			$108°$	A1	
		ii	$180 - 36$	M1	
			$144°$	A1	
	b		$90°$	B1	
			Angle in a semicircle	B1	

(Total = 40 marks)

INDEX